Dorothy Austin

948.

D1233082

SPEECH CORRECTION
Principles and Methods

by

C. VAN RIPER

Director of the Speech Clinic
Western Michigan College of
Education

SECOND EDITION

New York
PRENTICE-HALL, INC.
1947

PRINTED IN THE UNITED STATES OF AMERICA

THIS BOOK IS DEDICATED TO
MY WIFE
WHO REFUSES TO ALLOW HER
NAME TO APPEAR AS CO-AUTHOR

Preface to the Second Edition

The author hopes that, by reconsidering and rewriting the text for the most part, he has made a more useful book.

Although, like the poor, the speech defective has always been with us, it is only recently that the general public has come to realize the seriousness of his handicap. This increased awareness of the problem has reflected itself in a rapidly growing demand for an organized body of information concerning the nature of the various speech disorders and the modern methods used in their correction. Educators are recognizing what professional speech pathologists have always known—that the work of the specialist must be supplemented by intelligent classroom and home co-operation if the millions of speech defectives are to have adequate help. Eventually, remedial speech will have the same status in the public schools which remedial reading now enjoys. Every elementary teacher will have some training in speech correction; special speech-correction teachers will be provided for supervision in the larger school systems; and psychoeducational and speech clinics will be available for the more difficult cases. These trends are already being realized in many states. In any society so dependent upon communication, the "teaching of talking" must finally achieve an important place in education.

Unfortunately for those students who desire a basic knowledge of the principles and methods of speech correction, much of our knowledge remains scattered and unsystematized. This condition has been especially apparent in the case of the techniques actually used. When the latter are discussed, they are usually couched in such vague or technical terminology that small help is provided. Much valuable information is contained in scattered periodicals, but good bibliographies are hard to find. These observations merely point to the obvious truth that speech correction is a relatively young profession. The author hopes that this book will aid in the movement toward the systematization and organization which is so urgently needed.

The author is indebted to other writers, past and present, who

have felt a similar demand.   He is indebted to his friends and professional colleagues, to the speech defectives with whom he has
worked, and to his own past experience as a severe stutterer.   He is
especially indebted to Dr. Ernest Henrikson and to Dr. Bryng
Bryngelson.   Finally, as the dedication indicates, this book is the
result of a joint endeavor, and only a feminine reticence prevents
adequate acknowledgment, on the title page, of the debt to my wife.

C. Van Riper

Contents

Illustrations

I

The Handicapped Individual in Society

"Dance today so that others may walk tomorrow!" "Remember the crippled child by buying Easter seals!" "Help the Seeing Eye Society provide dogs for the blind." "Your Tuberculosis Association is financed solely by Christmas seals." "Keep 'Em Hearing!" These are only a few of the appeals which yearly bombard the American public as society awakes to the plight of the handicapped. The day of their isolation is gone. No longer are they denied the right of existence. After many centuries of mistreatment and neglect, we are now beginning to realize our responsibility for our less fortunate brothers.

The physically crippled. Since the disability of the physically handicapped is more obvious and dramatic than that of the speech-handicapped individual, the aid that has been afforded him has always been more adequate and widespread. The election of a president who was crippled by poliomyelitis, and the subsequent institution of the Birthday Balls for those similarly afflicted, have publicized the needs of those crippled by disease. The slogan "Send your dimes to the White House" has not only brought millions of dollars to the infantile paralysis fund but also has benefited every crippled child. Philanthropic associations have flourished in the sunlight of such publicity. Men's luncheon clubs have adopted the cause of the underprivileged. National sororities have turned fairy godmother. Hospitals and schools have been established and supported so that research and treatment may be correlated. State programs of rehabilitation, treatment, education, and job placement are rapidly spreading. Many industries, notably the Ford Motor Corporation, have made a definite attempt to find jobs for the crippled which will enable them to gain that financial security so necessary to happy personal adjustment. The federal government has sponsored a program of free diagnostic service to all crippled children, and, with the end of the war, the future of the crippled individual in our society grows brighter. The

1

legless veteran is a constant reminder to all of us of our responsibility to the handicapped.

The blind. The dark-glassed man with the white cane has been a familiar sight in most communities for many years. Much of the current activity in support of the blind results from the combined sympathy and admiration which such individuals evoke. One of the best recent advances in the treatment of the visually handicapped is the differential treatment provided them according to the degree of visual loss. State aid for teachers trained in Braille or sight conservation has made it possible for all children so handicapped to receive an education especially fitted to their needs. State schools for the blind take care of those whose communities cannot support the special classes provided by most large cities within their school systems. The Seeing Eye Foundation, with its training program for the adult blind and their guide dogs, has helped thousands to attain a maximum of independence. Books and magazines printed in Braille are readily available. Talking books—phonograph records which provide auditory reproduction of most of the best in literature and music—are sent free to the visually handicapped who are confined to their homes. Social organizations enable these people to live fairly satisfactory lives. The trend is constantly toward fitting these individuals into a normal environment. The tin cup and pencil no longer provide the only vocational hope for the blind.

The auditorily handicapped. Of all the signs which point to the fact that the handicapped person will probably receive the recognition he deserves, the newer attitudes toward the deaf or hard of hearing are the most significant. Hearing aids are becoming as common and almost as unnoticeable as glasses. The deaf child is losing the tragic additional label of "and dumb." Classes in speech learning and speech reading (lip reading) are held daily and nightly in almost every city in the country. The manual alphabet, which formerly provided the only type of communication for the deaf person, is yielding to improved methods of normal communication. Electronic hearing aids are being perfected and no longer cost small fortunes. Methods of teaching speech through visual means improve yearly, and some of the newer oscilloscopic devices promise much for the future. The deafened person may be able to hear his own voice by seeing it on a screen.

Great emphasis is now placed on the prevention of hearing loss. Traveling clinics, sponsored by state departments of special education or by universities and colleges, survey large sections of the school population and discover many deaf and hard-of-hearing children who might otherwise be disregarded or severely penalized. There is an American Society for the Hard of Hearing which is very active in promoting the welfare of its members. Government hospitals for deafened veterans have done much to further the cause of the auditorily handicapped. Churches and theaters provide seats equipped with earphones. Special teachers are financed by the states or philanthropic organizations, and all teachers are becoming more aware of the difficult adjustments which the hard-of-hearing child must make. After years of neglect, the deaf have been heard.

The handicapped in speech. Assistance for the speech defective has lagged behind that provided the other types of handicapped, perhaps because the speech cripple cannot speak for himself. Speech defects are unnoticed unless communication is attempted verbally, and many a speech-handicapped person has so encased himself in protective silence that he escapes attention except from his intimates. In spite of this, speech rehabilitation is showing a remarkable development. Colleges and universities have established speech clinics which serve not only as centers to which the speech defective may go to receive help, but also as training centers for special speech-correction teachers who serve their charges in the public schools. In several states, state aid is given to the public schools which employ such teachers. Medical schools are beginning to acquaint their students with the problems of speech pathology, and several of them employ trained speech correctionists. Popular interest in the plight of the speech cripple has increased to such an extent that these "forgotten children," mocked, tormented, and thwarted all their lives, may yet find inclusion within a vocal society. The human race, it seems, may yet become humane to all its children.

Is this aid justified? Against these trends a few sporadic voices have been raised, accusing us of perpetuating the unfit, of coddling the unworthy, of expensively educating those who can return nothing to society. At times, the zeal of those who would help the handicapped has produced negative reactions. Indeed, the emphasis on special education for the handicapped has led some people to feel that it was the normal child who was neglected.

> Johnny Jones has lost a leg
> Fanny's deaf and dumb.
> Marie has epileptic fits;
> Tom's eyes are on the bum.

Sadie stutters when she talks;
Mabel has T.B.
Morris is a splendid case
Of imbecility.
Gwendolin's a millionaire;
Gerald is a fool;
So every one of these darned kids
Goes to a special school.
They've specially nice teachers,
And special things to wear,
And special things to play in,
And a special kind of air.
They've special lunches right in school,
While I—it makes me wild!
I haven't any specialties;
I'm just a normal child.[1]

If such a rhyme brings a wry grin to our faces, it should also remind us that such a condition was not always present and that it is still more rare than commonplace. Centuries of neglect and penalty have perpetrated an unpardonable waste of handicapped human energy. A civilization that does not accept its responsibility for helping the unfortunate scarcely merits the name.

Morally, we cannot deny the right of the handicapped child to his place in the scheme of civilized living. The philosopher and the priest, in every age and country, have generally recognized this moral obligation. Economically, we have wasted a great deal of man and brain power by failing to develop those abilities which the handicapped possess. In times of emergency, as during World War II, the halt and deaf and blind were rushed into service. Their records were admirable. Of all their desires, the desire to support themselves and thereby to free society from their burden has always been a vital one. It is to the everlasting credit of thousands of handicapped persons that, despite prejudice and penalty, they have conquered almost insurmountable obstacles in their struggle to attain self-sufficiency and self-respect.

Modern society needs no justification for removing a few of the obstacles which every handicapped person finds in his path. The illustrious names of those who have given great things to civilization despite their handicaps are proof enough of such a policy. Music?

---

[1] From the *School Board Journal*, quoted by Scheideman, N. V., *The Psychology of Exceptional Children*, Boston, Houghton Mifflin, 1931.

Gounod, Handel, Mozart were crippled; Mendelssohn had a speech defect; Beethoven was deaf; Templeton is blind. Literature? Byron, Poe, Scott, Balzac were physically handicapped; Milton and Homer were blind; Somerset Maugham stutters. Science? Steinmetz, Edison, Darwin are a few of the legion. Philosophy? Socrates, Spinoza, Erasmus, and Schopenhauer left a considerable legacy. If these giants could arise in spite of the penalties of society, the cause of the handicapped is the duty of every civilized human being.

History of the handicapped. No one can understand the problem of the handicapped except in terms of the penalties which their infirmity provokes. Every handicap has an emotional fraction of shame, fear, or frustration, the heritage of centuries of cruelty and neglect. Cultural history demonstrates that the stupid, the blind, the deaf, the crippled, and those who could not talk have been treated progressively as a nuisance, a disgrace, an object of mirth, a problem, and a challenge. These attitudes are still in evidence.

Rejection. Primitive society tolerated no weakness. Tribes struggled hard for survival, and those members who could not aid materially were quickly rejected. The leaders were killed by the younger men after the former had lost their teeth or their energies had abated. The inhabitants of ancient India cast their cripples into the Ganges; the Spartans hurled theirs from a precipice. The Aztecs regularly sacrificed deformed persons in times of famine or when one of their leaders died. The Melanesians had a simple solution for the problem of the handicapped; they buried them alive. Among the earlier Romans, twins were considered so abnormal that one of them was always put to death, and frequently both were killed. They left their malformed children on the highways or in the forests. If the children survived, they were often picked up by those who always prey upon the handicapped and were carried to the market place to be trained as beggars. They were not valuable enough to be slaves.

The Bible clearly reflects these early rejection attitudes. Remember Job? The prevailing belief in Old Testament times was that man's physical state was determined by his good or bad relationship with his deity. Disabilities were regarded as divine punishment for sin. A normal person could invoke similar punishment merely by associating with those who had thus incurred the wrath of God. Consequently, the blind and the crippled wailed with the lepers—outside the city wall.

During the Middle Ages the physically disabled were frequently considered to be possessed of evil spirits. They were confined to their own homes. They dared not walk to the market place lest they be stoned. Even in this century, elimination of the handicapped has been practiced. The Kaffir tribes in South Africa clubbed sickly or deformed children. The Nazis kept only the best of their civilian prisoners for slaves. The others died in the gas chamber, in the crematorium.

In this country we would hang the man who killed his crippled son. We have come far in our journey toward civilization, but perhaps not far enough. Rejection takes many other forms. Spirits, too, can be killed. This is what one handicapped person has to say:

We think the inhabitants of old Sparta cruel for putting to death the weak, those who would be unable to compete, or to contribute much to their society; but were they after all much more inhuman than we, who nurse the weakling, keep it alive, yet as much as possible keep it from normal persons, especially the children, for fear its contact will contaminate them; then throw it out to compete with normal adults? [2]

How many of the students who read this book would unhesitatingly accept an invitation to a dance if it were tendered by a hunchback?

Humor. It did not take the promoters long to discover that the handicapped provided a rewarding source of humor. One history of the subject states that before 1000 B.C. the fool or buffoon became a necessary part of feast making and "won the laughter of the guests by his idiocy or his deformity." In Homer's *Iliad* comic relief from tragedy was illustrated by the vain efforts of the one-eyed Polyphemus to pursue his tormentors after they had blinded him. For a thousand years thereafter every court had its crippled buffoons, its dwarf jesters, its stuttering fools. Attila the Hun held banquets at which "a Moorish and Scythian buffoon successively excited the mirth of the rude spectators by their deformed figures, ridiculous dress, antic gestures, and absurd speech." Cages along the Appian Way held various grotesque human disabilities including "Balbus Blaesus" the stutterer, who would attempt to talk when a coin was flung through the bars. In Shakespeare's *Timon of Athens* Caphis says, "Here comes the fool; let's ha' some sport with 'im." Often this sport consisted of physical abuse or exposure of the twisted limb. These handicapped fools accepted and expected ridicule. At least it provided a means of

---

[2] McKnight, R. V., "A Self-analysis of a Case of Reading, Writing, and Speaking Disability," *Archives of Speech*, 1936, Vol. 1, page 43.

Fig. 1.   The circus side show finds them profitable.

survival, a livelihood, and it represented an advance in civilized living.

Gradually, the use of the handicapped to provoke mirth became less popular in continental Europe, and the more enterprising had to migrate to less culturally advanced areas to make a living. At one time Peter the Great had so many fools that he found it necessary to classify them for different occasions. In this country today we have a much higher regard for the handicapped than Cortez found when he conquered Mexico and discovered deformed creatures of all kinds at the Court of Montezuma. Now you may find them used to provoke laughter only in the circus side shows, in the movies, on the radio, and in every schoolyard.

Pity. Religion is doubtless responsible for the development of true pity as a cultural reaction to the handicapped. James Joyce says that pity is the feeling which arrests the mind in the presence of whatsoever is grave and constant in human suffering and unites it with the human sufferer. It was this spontaneous feeling that prompted religious leaders to give the handicapped shelter and protection. Before 200 B.C. Asoka, a Buddhist, created a ministry for the care of unfortunates and appointed officers to supervise charitable works. Confucius said, "With whom should I associate but with suffering men?" Jesus preached compassion for all the disabled and made all men their brothers' keepers. In the seventh century after Jesus' death the Mohammedan religion proposed a society free from cruelty and social oppression, and insisted on kindliness and consideration for all men. A few hundred years later St. Francis of Assisi devoted his life to the care of the sick and the disabled. Following this, the "Mad Priest of Kent," John Ball, was so aroused by the plight of the crippled and needy left in the wake of the Black Death that he pled publicly for their cause, often at the risk of his own life. With the rise of the middle class, true pity for the handicapped became much more commonplace. The oppression which the merchants and serfs had suffered left them more sympathetic to others who were ill used. The doctrine of the equality of man did much for the handicapped as well as for the economically downtrodden.

However, many crimes have been committed in the name of charity. The halt and the blind began to acquire commercial value as beggars. Legs and backs of little children were broken and twisted by their exploiters. Soon the commercialization of pity became so universal that it became a community nuisance. Alms became a conventional gesture to buy relief from the piteous whining that dominated every public place. True pity was lost in revulsion. Recognizing this unhappy trend, Hyperius of Ypres advocated that beggars should be classified so that work could be provided according to their capacities. His own motives were humanitarian, but he cleverly won support for his cause by pointing out that other citizens "would be freed of clamor, of fear of outrage, of the sight of ugly bodies." His appeal was successful, and asylums and homes for the handicapped began to appear, if only to isolate the occupants so the public need not be reminded of their distress. Another motive which improved the position of the handicapped was the belief that one could purchase his way into heaven or out of hell by charity. The coin thrown to the cripple has been impelled by many motives. The longing for religious security, the heightening of one's own superiority by comparison with the unfortunate, the social prestige of philanthropy, and the desire to be freed from embarrassment have all contributed to the welfare of the handicapped. Pseudo pity has accomplished much, but true compassion would have ended the tragedy.

Use. As the problem of the handicapped kept irritating the consciences of civilized men everywhere, the true solution began to present itself. Somehow the person who is different must be given a specialized type of education to enable him to attain self-sufficiency or at least to contribute to the group welfare. If he cannot be ornamental, at least he can be useful. In the seventeenth century the Sisters of Charity, realizing that the handicapped needed work as well as food, endeavored to find manual jobs commensurate with their individual ability. By 1560 a college for the blind had been established at Bruges where the pupils were taught to play the organ and other musical instruments, to make brooms and baskets, and to manipulate wine presses and hand mills. The implication of this occupational therapy in decreasing the total handicap gradually found acceptance. Much of this first activity was mere busy work to facilitate contentment in their isolation. Then in 1832 a philanthropist in Munich founded the first comprehensive institution for the care and education of cripples. In this country, the Boston Industrial School for the Crippled and Deformed, the first true training school that recognized the handicapped person's need for usefulness, was founded as recently as 1893. Both World Wars have given tremendous impetus to the vocational and social rehabilitation of the handicapped, and the future is bright.

Because our cultural attitudes toward the handicapped have progressed from the cruel to the humane, we must not think that the older reactions have entirely vanished. Children and uneducated adults often react in the old, primitive ways. Every handicapped person has experienced degrees of rejection, mockery, and pity. The old attitudes are there to salt his wounds. They multiply his insecurities, decrease his courage, and destroy his hope. The defective in speech know them well.

Present treatment of the speech handicapped. We have sketched the treatment accorded the handicapped at some length because the speech-defective person is diagnosed immediately as belonging to that unfortunate group. The moment the cleft-palate child or stutterer speaks he joins his brethren, the crippled, the deaf, the spastic, the blind, and, perhaps, the fool. He is different. He possesses an abnormality. A little child hesitates in his speech; his parents diagnose him as a stammerer; he reacts to his hesitations as though they were revoltingly unpleasant; his playmates accept his evaluation, or his parents' evaluation, and reject, laugh at, or pity him; and so he joins the unhappy tribe of the million stammerers who exist in this country today.

It may seem strange to learn that the primitive attitudes of rejection, humor and pity, are still very common reactions to the perception of speech defects today. Listen to these:

They got me inside a circle of them and every time I tried to break out and go home, they pushed me back. "Make a speech. Make a speech." I tried to tell them I had to get my groceries home. My mother had to have them for supper, but the men would just laugh all the harder and push me back. They told me to say different things if I wanted to get out, things like "She sells sea shells" and dirty words. I was crying and I got mad and swore at them and then they let me go but I can hear them yet.

I asked the girl for a dance and had a hard time getting it out. She flushed, then blurted out, "Well, I'm not that hard up yet."

I can take almost anything but that pitying glance. It's sort of as if I have a cup in my hand every time I talk and people feel they ought to put some pennies in it. I can't explain it but when they look away or down at their feet, I feel like something unclean. I can't help it that my operation tore loose, and I talk through my nose, but I can't even explain it to them.

We no longer keep our "Balbus Blaesuses" in cages, but a current radio program features a "comedian" whose main humorous appeal is based upon his substitution of *w* for *l* and *r*. The song about "K-K-K-Katy" is still being sung although "Stuttering in the Starlight" and "You-you-you tell 'em that I-I-I stutter" have been forgotten. Cartoons and comic strips do not fail to exploit the impediments of speech.

Many of these primitive reactions to speech handicaps exist because of a lack of understanding. Abnormal speech has been attributed to everything from feeble-mindedness to a lack of will power. Few people know anything of the causes or development of the various speech disorders. Then, too, the general public is unaware of the great number of speech defectives in our population. All of us meet an occasional person with faulty speech, but few of us realize that there are more speech cripples than there are crippled, deaf, and blind combined. The report of the White House Conference (1931) on Special Education, still the most comprehensive survey of speech defects, cited an average incidence of 5 per cent (9). One of the more intensive surveys of a city school system[3] showed over 10 per cent to have speech defects. At any rate, two or three million persons are handicapped in speech, and they deserve more understanding and better treatment than they have been receiving. Finally, few normally speaking individuals realize that communication is the lifeblood of modern existence and that a person who cannot communicate effectively is severely handicapped. In procuring an education, in winning a mate, in holding a job, effective speech is vital. Without it, the normal activities of a highly communicative society become very difficult. The frustration and anxiety which result from a speech defect often build an additional emotional handicap which doubles the speech defective's burden. Only those normal speakers who have lived in close relationship to some speech cripple understand this. As society comes to understand the problem of the speech handicapped, the old attitudes will be replaced. Meanwhile, there is much work to be done.

The responsibility for speech correction. Some agency of society must accept the responsibility for seeing that these millions of speech-handicapped individuals receive the rehabilitation they so urgently

---

[3] Mills, A. and Streit, H., "Report of a Speech Survey, Holyoke, Massachusetts," *Journal of Speech Disorders*, 1942, Vol. 7, pages 161–169.

need. In this country the medical profession, which in Europe treated or supervised the treatment of speech defects, has seemed uninterested in the problem. Parents do not have the information or the teaching ability that is required. Our public-school system is about the only organization large enough to do the job. It can employ trained teachers and it has the child during those years when speech correction can be most effective. It has already accepted responsibility for training other types of handicapped persons. It has the contact with the colleges and universities whose research and teacher-training facilities are so vital to adequate therapy. The basic philosophy of our public schools is education according to the student's need. The average speech defective is retarded one year in school because of his handicap, and the over-all educational expenditure is, because of the retardation, greater. In terms of dollars and cents alone, it would be economical to provide speech-correction services in the public schools. Many of the larger school systems have recognized this practical economy by hiring speech correctionists. The total annual expenditure for the special education of handicapped children in New York City (6) in 1938 shows that the actual cost of caring for the speech-defective child is surprisingly low. The comparative figures make it seem almost negligible.

SPECIAL EDUCATION COSTS
IN NEW YORK CITY

Type of Handicap	Total Annual Expenditure per Pupil
Blind	$515.26
Deaf	570.67
Crippled	267.86
Speech Defective	5.65

Despite the great expense involved in educating the physically handicapped, the majority of them are receiving this help. The feeble-minded child, however, receives far more special education than does the speech handicapped. We hold no brief for decreasing educational expenditures for the physically handicapped. We only wish to point out that the future economic gain in turning the speech handicapped from economic misfits into productive, self-sufficient individuals far outweighs the trifling expense. We teach our children to read and write. Some day we shall be teaching our children to talk as well. The elementary schoolteacher will be trained in the daily program, and speech-improvement classes will be a part of elementary speech correction. Special speech-correction departments in the teachers colleges and universities will organize programs of parent education and teacher training and provide clinics where adults may receive treatment. When that day comes, and it is fast approaching, the speech-handicapped child will no longer be laughed at, rejected, or pitied. He will be helped.

References

1. Anderson, V. A., "The College and University Speech Clinic," *Quarterly Journal of Speech*, 1940, Vol. 26, pages 80–88.
A description of the services offered the speech handicapped by the principal speech clinics of the country. General descriptions of administrative and clinical procedures are provided.

2. Carlson, A., "Crippled in the Tongue," *Harper's Magazine*, October, 1937, pages 539–546.
A popular description of the handicap of the speech defective, the penalties inflicted upon these individuals by society, the need for speech correction, and some brief accounts of treatment of organic speech defects, and therapy for the spastic and the stutterer.

3. Duckat, Walter, "The Attitude Toward the Handicapped in the Bible," *The Crippled Child*, October, 1942, pages 67–83.
The majority of Biblical references to the handicapped are cited and discussed in terms of their social implications.

4. Martin, L. C., "Shall We Segregate Our Handicapped?" *Journal of Exceptional Children*, March, 1940, Vol. 6, pages 223–237.
The contrast between modern educational theory which rejects the principle of segregation and the actual practice of providing special schools or classes in which no contact with the normal child is possible is made very clear.

5. McKibben, S., "The Spastic Situation," *Journal of Speech Disorders*, 1943, Vol. 8, pages 147–153.
Written by an individual who has spastic paralysis, this article gives a vivid account of the handicapped individual's reaction to the social attitudes toward abnormality.

6. *Physically Handicapped Children in New York City*, New York, Board of Education of the City of New York, 1941, pages 1–155.
The program for the education and rehabilitation of the various types of handicapped children in New York City is described in terms of organization, administration, and costs. The general philosophy underlying the provision of education especially suited to the needs of handicapped children is discussed.

7. Pintner, R., Eisenson, J., and Stanton, M., *The Psychology of the Physically Handicapped*, New York, Crofts, 1941.
The blind, deaf, crippled, and speech-defective child's problem is discussed.

in terms of the following factors: intelligence, educational achievement, personality and special abilities.   Chapters on personality development and mental hygiene of the handicapped will be of interest to the speech correctionist.

8. Shortley, M. J., "Helping the Disabled to Help Themselves," *Journal of Exceptional Children*, November, 1944, pages 34–41.
A discussion of modern attitudes toward the handicapped with especial emphasis on vocational placement.

9. *White House Conference on Child Health and Protection, Special Education*, Chapter on "The Child Defective in Speech," New York, D. Appleton-Century, 1931.
A report from questionnaires issued to cities with populations of over 10,000, showing incidence of speech defectives to range from 1.0 to 21.4 per cent, with an average from the totals of 5 per cent.

10. White, Helen C., *Social Criticism in Popular Religious Literature of the Sixteenth Century*, New York, Macmillan, 1944.
Medieval attitudes toward the handicapped are vividly described with many illustrations from the literature of the time.   The beginnings of modern practices in the treatment of the unfortunate are clearly sketched.

II

The Disorders of Speech

What is a speech defect? The definition of a speech defect is truly important in speech correction. Those who give a child possessing speech within the normal range of variation such labels as "speech defective" or "stutterer" should be sued for criminal libel. Normal speech tolerates many minor differences in rhythm, pronunciation, or voice quality. We need some functional definition to separate normal from abnormal speech.

A successful auctioneer became worried and came to our clinic when a public school dramatics teacher told him his voice was too nasal. After examining his speech we offered our congratulations and sent him home contented with the same timbre he had brought.

A woman brought her two-year-old daughter for examination complaining that she was saying "mamma" for "mother" and "tawberry" for "strawberry." We suggested that the mother attend nursery school for a week.

One week after a student in an introductory college class in speech correction had first listened to the repetitions of a severe stutterer, she came, agitated and aghast, to tell us that she had repeated three times that very day and had discovered that she stuttered too. We reassured her and told her that many students in abnormal psychology classes experienced parallel misgivings as to their sanity.

These *curiosa* indicate that we must be careful in diagnosing a speech defect as such. Many definitions have been used in the attempt to differentiate normal from abnormal speech, but none of them is completely successful for the very good reason that no clearcut distinction can exist. Perhaps the best definition is as follows:

Speech is defective when it deviates so far from the speech of other people that it calls attention to itself, interferes with communication, or causes its possessor to be maladjusted.

All speech deviations are not, of course, speech defects. There are thousands of ways in which the sound of *s* may be produced, and not only do so-called normal speakers differ from one another in their production of the speech sounds, but they are not even consistent in their own speech.   According to research,[1] no two persons make the same tongue-palate contact for a sound such as *k*, and no person makes the same sound in the same way even in the same word on the same day.   If a number of people are asked in turn to produce a prolonged *s*, the differences heard or seen will vividly illustrate the point that deviations in themselves are not defects.   The speech difficulty must be so conspicuous that other people notice it.

When you listen, not to what a stranger says, but to his peculiar voice or hesitations or distorted consonants, communication is broken. If his face suddenly jumps around as he struggles to utter an ordinary word, all communicative content is lost in amusement or amazement. Many stutterers habitually lower their eyes to escape the shock of observing the expression of incredulity and surprise on the faces of their auditors.   Cleft-palate adults have been known to pretend to be deaf and dumb and to beg for a pencil so that their communication could be accomplished without interruption.

The final part of our definition deals with the maladjustment and emotional handicap which the speech defective adds to his disability. Sometimes this maladjustment is the dominant feature of the disorder. We worked with a woman who claimed to have stuttered actually only once in her life—during a high-school graduation speech.   Her speech was certainly not fluent since it was marked by numerous hesitations, pauses, and avoidances of certain words.   She was badly handicapped socially and vocationally.   Her listeners were constantly puzzled and confused by her peculiar speech behavior.   And yet she had actually "stuttered" only once.   This case, of course, is an extreme instance of the importance of maladjustment in producing a speech defect.   Usually, the abnormality of rhythm, voice, or articulation is sufficiently bizarre to provoke so many social penalties that maladjustment is almost inevitable.

Classification of speech disorders.   It should be obvious that before anyone can treat a speech-defective child he must be able to recognize the type of disorder present.   Yet so deep is the ignorance surrounding speech disorders that the following letter is not unusual.

---

[1] Moses, E. R., "Palatography and Speech Improvement," *Journal of Speech Disorders*, 1939, Vol. 4, pages 103–114.

Dear Sir: I am a country schoolteacher in a two-room school. In my room there is a little boy in the third grade with a kind of funny voice. I mean he doesn't talk like other children. He can't say some of the words right that he knows just as well as I do. I have tried to correct him on the word "scissors" which is hard for him but he just can't get it out right. Is this stammering or just baby talk and how can I cure him? Please send me some tongue exercises or something. He is a sweet little child and needs some help.

In terms of our definition, we find that speech defects or speech disorders divide themselves into four large categories: disorders of rhythm, articulation, phonation, and symbolization, according to the types of symptoms shown. Many other classifications, of course, may be used, and many other terminologies are common. However, in our presentation we shall use the most common classification, that of the symptoms.

Under disorders of rhythm we include *stuttering* (stammering) and *cluttering*. It is difficult to define or describe stuttering. The flow of speech is broken by hesitations, stoppages, or repetitions and pro- longations of the speech sounds. Fluency is interrupted by spasms, contortions, tremors, or abnormalities of phonation and respiration. It consists of moments of speech interruption of such frequency and abnormality as to attract attention, interfere with communication, and produce maladjustment. It is the speech behavior that has been labeled by others and accepted by its possessor as "stuttering." This label is usually first bestowed when the child's speech is "marked by effortless repetition of words, phrases, or the first sounds or syllables of words" without any awareness on his part "either that he was re- peating or that the repetitions constituted a difficulty or abnormal- ity." [2] This phase of the disorder is termed *primary stuttering*. The child does not struggle or consciously withdraw from speaking. He just bubbles along, doing his best to communicate. An excerpt from a parent's letter may illustrate this primary stuttering.

I would appreciate some advice about my daughter. She is almost three years old, and has always been precocious in speech. Four weeks ago she recovered from a severe attack of whooping cough and it was immediately after that when she began to show some trouble with her speech. One morning she came downstairs and asked for orange juice, and it sounded like this: "Wh-wh-wh-wh-where's my orange juice?" Since

---

[2] These quotations are from Johnson, W., "Stuttering in the Pre-school Child," *Uni- versity of Iowa Studies in Child Welfare*, No. 37, 1934.

then she has repeated one or two words in almost every sentence, some-times repeating twice, and sometimes eight or nine times. It doesn't seem to bother her but I'm worried about it as it gets a lot worse when she asks questions or when she is tired, and I'm afraid other children will start laughing at her. One of her playmates has already imitated her several times. No one else in our family has any trouble talking. What do you think we should do? Up to now we have just been ignoring it and hoping it will go away.

Unfortunately, stuttering does not always remain primary. It changes its symptoms as the child reacts to the penalties and evalu-ations of his parents, associates, or strangers. He begins to avoid and

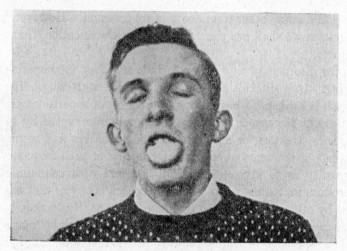

Fig. 2.   Stuttering.   It interferes with communication, calls attention
to itself, and makes its victim maladjusted.

disguise his speech interruptions. Struggle behavior develops. The repetitions change to prolonged fixations of the tongue, lips, jaws, or vocal cords. Breathing abnormalities of the most grotesque variety are adopted. Contortions of the face or body occur. All of these symptoms are lumped together under the term *secondary stuttering*.

Secondary stuttering occurs in many forms, since different indi-viduals react to their speech interruptions in different ways. One German authority carefully described ninety-two different varieties of stuttering (each christened with beautiful Greek and Latin verbiage), and we are sure that there must be many more. Stutterers have been known to grunt or spit or pound themselves or protrude their tongues or speak on inhalation or waltz or jump or merely stare glassily when in the throes of what they call a "spasm" or a "block." The late Irvin S. Cobb described a certain Captain Joe Fowler [3] who manifested his stuttering through the use of profanity. Captain Joe was able to speak very well under ordinary circumstances, but when he got angry or excited, his speech stopped entirely, and he was only able to get started again through the use of a stereotyped bit of cursing. Some of the imitations of stuttering heard in the movies and on the radio may seem grotesque, yet the reality may be even more unusual.

Some stutterers develop an almost complete inability to make a direct speech attempt upon a feared word. They approach it, back away, say "a-a-a-a" or "um-um-um," go back to the beginning of the sentence and try again and again, until finally they give up communication altogether. Many stutterers become so adept at substituting synonyms for their difficult words, and disguising the interruptions which do occur, that they are able to pose as normal speakers. We have known seven severe stutterers whose spouses first discovered their speech impediments after the wedding ceremony. Stutterers have preached and taught school and become successful traveling salesmen without ever betraying their infirmity, but they are not happy individuals. The nervous strain and vigilance necessary to avoid and disguise their symptoms often create stresses so severe as to produce profound emotional breakdowns.

Cluttering. Another disorder of rhythm is cluttering. It is characterized by slurred and omitted syllables, by improper phrasing and pauses due to excessive speed. Clutterers speak by spurts and their speech organs pile up like keys on a typewriter when a novice stenographer tries for more speed than her skill permits. An old text in speech correction has this description: ". . . a torrent of half articulated words, following each other like peas running out of a spout"; [4] but the torrent is also irregularly interrupted in its flow. People constantly ask the clutterer to repeat. They are empathically irritated by his uneven volleys of hasty syllables. They find themselves interrupting during his panting pauses and then in turn being interrupted by a new overwhelming rush of jumbled words.

Spastic speech frequently involves a disorder of rhythm. It is difficult for the victims of cerebral palsy to make smooth transitions

---

[3] Cobb, I. S., *Exit Laughing*, page 80. Indianapolis: Bobbs-Merrill Company, 1941.
[4] Wyllie, J., *The Disorders of Speech*, Edinburgh, Oliver and Boyd, 1894.

or to marshal an air flow constant enough to produce a polysyllabic word or a phrase without a break. Even when their articulation and voice quality is fairly normal, these interruptions in the fluency are noticeable enough to interfere with communication.

Articulation. Under disorders of articulation we include all those disorders characterized by the substitution, omission, addition, and distortion of the speech sounds. There are many somewhat synonymous and overlapping terms in common use for these disorders, among which we can name *baby talk* (infantile perseveration), a disorder with no organic basis but characterized by stereotyped substitutions similar to those used by the normal child in the early stages of speech development; *lalling*, characterized by defective *r, l, t, d,* or *s* sounds, and largely due to inactivity or sluggishness of the tongue tip; *lisping*, a disorder of the sibilant sounds, especially *s* and *z*, characterized by the substitution of the *th* (θ; δ) consonants (a lingual or frontal lisp), a mushy *sh* ($\int$) or *zh* ($\mathfrak{z}$) sound (a lateral lisp), *t* or *d* (occluded lisp), or the nasal snort resulting from the attempt to make an *s* or *z* through the nose (nasal lisp); *delayed speech*, characterized by a narrow repertoire of consonants and unintelligibility; and *oral inaccuracy*, which is a wastebasket term for any mild articulatory defect.

Actually these names do not denote different types of disorders. They are not mutually exclusive. Lallers often lisp, and lispers talk baby talk, and all of them show oral inaccuracy. The important features of all articulatory disorders are the presence of defective and incorrect sounds. The forty-year-old farmer who wept when he heard his voice on a recording of a children's rhyme did so because of the defective and incorrect sounds he had produced:

> Tinko Tinko itto tah,
> How I wondah wheh you ah,
> Up abuh duh woh soh high
> Yike a diamon' in duh kye.

As the above selection indicates, most articulatory cases have more than one error and are not always consistent in their substitutions, omissions, insertions, or distortions. This is not always the case, however. Thum lingual lithperth merely thubthitute a *th* for the *eth* thound. Otherzh shkwirt the air shtream over the shide of the tongue and are shed to have a lateral lishp. Others thnort the thnound (nasal lisp). Many children have been known to buy an "ite tream toda" or an all day "tucker."

It would be impossible to portray the acoustic characteristics of some of the distortions used by articulatory cases even if we used the phonetic alphabet. Seldom does an adult substitute a true *w* for the *r* as he attempts such a phrase as "around the rock." He usually produces a sound "something like a *w* and something like the velar *r* made with the back of the tongue elevated and the tip depressed" (16). In some lateral lisping, the sound produced is more of a salivary unvoiced *l* instead of the *s*, a sloppy slurping sound which not only disgusts its hearers but its speaker too.

Many of the omissions heard in articulation cases are merely weakly stressed consonants. When in a noisy room, an eighteen-year-old boy in describing a winter scene would seem to say, "The 'ky and 'no in wintuh." The missing sounds, however, were evident in quiet surroundings and were perfectly formed, but their duration was so brief that any noise seemed to mask their presence. Many cases, however, do entirely omit sounds they cannot produce.

Additions of linking sounds are frequently found in blends ("the buhlue-guhreen color of spuhruce trees"), and when a child adds *ee* to every final *r* sound, as one of our cases did, the peculiarity is very noticeable.

To many persons, articulatory defects seem relatively unimportant. But severe articulation cases find the demands of modern life very difficult. We knew a woman who could not produce the *s*, *l*, and *r* sounds and yet who had to buy a railroad ticket to Robeline, Louisiana. She did it with pencil and paper. Another man with the same difficulty became a farmer's hired hand after he graduated from college rather than suffer the penalties of a more verbal existence. Many children are said to outgrow their defective consonant sounds. Actually, they overcome them through blundering methods of self-help, and far too many of them never manage the feat. One man, aged 65, asked us bitterly when we thought he would outgrow his baby talk.

In severe cases, communication is almost impossible. Mothers cannot understand their own children. The delayed-speech case, deprived of normal verbal outlets for his emotion, becomes a behavior problem. Try, for instance, to translate the following nursery rhymes as transcribed from phonograph recordings:

> Ha ta buh, Hah ta buh,
> Wuhnuh peh, two uh peh,
> Ha ta buh.

Tippo Tymuh meh a pyemuh,
Doh too peh,
Ted tippo Tymuh to duh pyemuh
Yeh me tee oo weh.

ə drjə, ə dɑjə, ə tɛnə tɑ tɑjə,
Wɑ meɪ ju tʌm toʊ tun,
ju juːt tə tʌm æ tɛn əta,
bʌt naʊ ju tʌm æ nun.

Voice disorders. Under disorders of phonation (voice) we have three major divisions: disorders of pitch, of intensity, and of timbre (voice quality). Typical pitch disorders are the *monotone*, the *too high pitched* or *too low pitched* voice, and the voice that is characterized by *stereotyped inflections*. Typical disorders of intensity are *aphonia*, the lack of any voice, often characterized by strained whispering; and the *too loud* or *too weak* voice. Under disorders of voice quality we find two frequent types, *hypernasality* (including cleft palate) and *hyponasality*, and a multitude of other types which have been described in the literature by as many names as there are appropriate adjectives. Among these we shall mention the *pectoral*, the *guttural*, the *harsh* or *strident*, the *husky*, and the *hoarse* voice. Certain voice disorders such as the *falsetto* voice involve both pitch and timbre abnormalities.

The following description was uttered by a two-hundred-pound football player in his high, piping, shrill child's voice:

Yes, I was one of those boy sopranos and my music teacher loved me. I soloed in all the cantatas and programs and sang in the choir and glee clubs and they never let my voice change. I socked a guy the other day who wise-cracked about it, but I'm still a boy soprano at twenty-two. I'm getting so I'm afraid to open my mouth. Strangers start looking for a Charlie McCarthy somewhere. I got to get over it, and quick. Why, I can't even swear but some guy who's been saying the same words looks shocked.

A high-pitched voice in a male is definitely a handicap, communicative, economic, and social.

When a woman's voice is pitched very low and carries a certain type of male inflection, it certainly calls attention to itself and causes maladjustment. The following sentence, spoken by a casual acquaintance and overheard by the girl to whom it referred, practically wrecked her entire security: "Every time I hear her talk I look around to see if it's the bearded lady of the circus."

On every campus some professor possesses that enemy of education, a monotonous voice. A true monotone is comparatively rare, yet it dominates any conversation by its difference. To hear a person laugh on a single note is enough to stir the scalp. Questions asked in a true monotone seem curiously devoid of life. Fortunately most cases of monotonous voice are not so extreme. Many of them could be described as the "poker voice"—even as a face without expression is termed a "poker face." Inflections are present, but for fear of revealing insecurity or inadequacy they are reduced to a minimum.

By stereotyped inflections we refer to the voice which calls attention to itself through its pitch patterning. The sing-song voice, the voice that ends every phrase or sentence with a falling inflection, the "schoolmaam's voice" with its emphatic dogmatic inflections, are all types of variation which, *when extreme*, may be considered speech defects.

The intensity disorders need little illustration. Many of us have experienced *aphonia*, after prolonged abuse of voice through screaming or when laryngitis has caused us to "lose" our voice. People who earn their living by their mouths—among them, singers, train announcers, clergymen, and schoolteachers—are subject to aphonia, hysterical or otherwise. Most very soft or weak voices are due to insecurity or hearing loss. The extremely loud—to the point of irritation—voices are often due to personality problems or defective hearing. The *strident* voice combines excessive intensity with a harsh voice quality to pierce the ears and rasp the sensibilities of its victims. One of the most difficult voices to correct is that which is marked by sudden bursts of loudness or by the "trailing off into nothingness" at the end of each phrase. Both irritate their listeners.

That the disorders of voice quality are difficult to describe is indicated not only by the names which we listed earlier in our classification but also by the names we omitted. Voices have been called *thick, thin, heavy, sweet, round, brilliant, hard, metallic,* and *rich* as well as *poor*. The terms we have used are not much better, but at least they do not confuse auditory perceptions with those of taste or touch. The science of experimental phonetics has not yet been able to provide a better classification for variations in timbre.

The quality of *excessive nasality* (hypernasality, rhinolalia aperta) is easily recognized. Its possessor not only seems to speak his *m*, *n*, and ŋ sounds through his nose, but also many of the vowels and voiced continuants such as *r*, *v*, and *z*. When combined with certain inflection patterns it has been described as a "whining" voice. In certain sections of the country a variety of hypernasality is dialectal and of course in this setting it would not be a speech defect. In *assimilation nasality* only the sounds preceding or following the *m*, *n* and *z* sounds are excessively nasalized, but these can occur frequently enough to provoke audience irritation.

In *hyponasality* (denasality, adenoidal voice, rhinolalia clausa) the speaker does not or cannot utter the nasal sounds through the nose. The voice quality if deadened and muffled, as though its owner had a perpetual cold or post-nasal drip. The *m* resembles a blend of *m* and *b* spoken simultaneously, and the other nasals have similar cognates. Often habituated during the presence of adenoidal growths in early life, it persists long after the adenoids have been removed. People listening to denasal voices find themselves swallowing and clearing their throats and consumed by the urge to get out of range.

Other voice-quality disorders are occasionally noted by the teacher doing speech correction in the public school. Many boys' voices become husky and hoarse during the two or three years prior to voice change and become clear again after that event. Overstrain due to prolonged yelling, screeching, or shouting can cause this quality in any of us. Perhaps the *strident, hoarse, husky*, and *breathy* qualities of voice indicate a two-factor continuum involving (1) breath expenditure and (2) muscular strain. The strident voice shows a preponderance of tension in the muscles that squeeze the pharynx while the breathy voice represents a minimum of strain and a maximum of breath expenditure.

The words *throaty* and *pectoral* as adjectives to describe voice quality are probably identical save for the sex of the persons concerned. Throaty voices in the female are paralleled by the voice of hollow booming pectoral timbre in the male. Both involve lower pitch levels, rounded mouth openings, and retracted chins. Pectoral voice has been called the "rain-barrel voice." There are echoes in it. It reverberates like song in the bathtub. It was formerly much used by preachers and politicians and by undertakers and insecure high-school teachers.

The *falsetto* voice is a grievous burden to its owner unless he yodels for a living.   A complicated arrangement of the laryngeal cartilages and muscles causes only a portion of the vocal cords to vibrate, and the high-pitched tones thereby produced are amplified by constricted resonating cavities in the mouth and throat.   It is almost impossible to produce the falsetto with the head pulled backward as far as possible.

Cleft-palate speech involves both a voice and articulation defect. Not only are the consonants nasally emitted, but many of those which are not so emitted are slurred and distorted.   The voice quality is hypernasal.   Cleft-palate speakers honk their speech sounds in a manner which, once heard, is never thereafter mistaken.

Foreign accent is another disorder which involves both articulation and voice.   Speakers of a foreign tongue use sound substitutions and distortions, and they also use inflection patterns unfamiliar to our ears.   The rising inflection at the conclusion of the phrase as spoken by a Scandinavian speaking English may serve as an illustration.   In treating such a disorder we organize our therapy so as to attack both phases of the problem.

Symbolization disorders.   The problem of *dysphasia* (the general term for all disorders of symbolic formulation and expression) is rarely met in public-school speech correction.   Occasionally it occurs in mild form as a pronounced reading, writing, and speaking disability. In the speech clinic we often are required to help aphasics, and the end of World War II required the services of a good many speech correctionists to teach those who had received head and brain injuries. Children who have had meningitis or jaundice, and some adults who have suffered a paralytic stroke, often demonstrate the symptoms of aphasia.   Such persons find it difficult to use or comprehend linguistic symbols, whether they be written or spoken.   In the moto-expressive type of aphasia, the case may say "bum-bum-bum" for "cigarette," and "bum" for "shoe."   Another aphasic may grope for words in attempting to say "pencil" but say "eraser" or "pen" or "stick" instead.   Yet he knows his errors the instant they are spoken. In the receptive type of aphasia the difficulty lies in the perception. R. V. McKnight describes her own aphasic reaction to the word "your" as follows:

I mentally heard it but it had no meaning.   I felt that it was related to the word "you" but I could not figure out the relationship between the two.   I continued to puzzle over this until the speaker had finished his lecture and sat down. . . .   More generally when I do not recognize the meaning I do not recognize the sound.   The word is a jumble of letters.[5]

Children who have such difficulties are often mistakenly diagnosed as hard of hearing or feeble-minded.   Some cases of delayed onset or slow development of speech are probably due to aphasia.

Frequency of occurrence.   The disorders of rhythm, articulation, and voice represent all but a small fraction of the total number of speech defects.   The White House Conference[6] (1931), in reporting the number and types of speech defects, provides the following over-all figures:

Articulatory disorders	72%
(sound substitutions)	46%
(organically caused)	8%
(oral inactivity)	11%
(dialect)	5%
Rhythm disorders	22%
Voice disorders	4%

The frequency of occurrence is not entirely a true measure of the seriousness of the problem.   As West (16) points out, "Some of the most disabling defects and those requiring the greatest amount of time from the special speech teacher are those in the smaller groups.   In order of their seriousness, stuttering, hard-of-hearing speech, and paralyzed speech would probably be ranked first."

References

1. Backus, O. L., *Speech in Education*, New York, Longmans, Green, 1943.
The author classifies the various speech disorders according to their symptoms and compares them to the variations shown in normal speech.   Excellent illustrations are given.

2. Belgum, D., "Stuttering," *Hygeia*, May, 1944, Vol. 22, pages 346–347.
A college stutterer tells of his experiences in a speech clinic and afterward.

3. Brown, F., "Baby Talkers," *Proceedings of the American Speech Correction Association*, 1936, Vol. 6, pages 197–208.
A discussion of articulatory disorders in terms of their emotional causes and the types of symptoms shown.

[5] McKnight, R. V., "A Self-analysis of a Case of Reading, Writing, and Speaking Disability," *Archives of Speech*, 1936, Vol. 1.

[6] *White House Conference on Child Health and Protection, Special Education*, Chapter on "The Child Defective in Speech," New York, D. Appleton-Century, 1931.

4. Carrell, J. A., "A Comparative Study of Speech Defective Children," *Archives of Speech*, 1936, Vol. 1, pages 179–203.
A percentage study showing that 10 per cent of all school children had speech defects, and were inferior to the average in school achievement, intelligence, auditory acuity, and anthropometric measures. The most common sound substitutions are listed.

5. Despert, J. L., "Psychopathology of Stuttering," *American Journal of Psychiatry*, 1943, Vol. 99, pages 881–885.
A discussion of the theories and symptoms of stuttering. One typical case history with an account of the treatment is given.

6. Berry, M. F. and Eisenson, J., *The Defective in Speech*, New York, Crofts, 1942.
This book presents the picture of abnormal speech against a background of the normal. Interesting selections from the literature make it an excellent reference for the beginning student who needs a more adequate under standing of the different types of speech defects.

7. Greene, J. S., "Speech and Voice Disorders; Etiology and Therapeutic Procedures," *Medical Record*, 1943, Vol. 156, pages 599–601.
The various forms of speech disorders: dysphonia, dyslalia, dysarthria, dysphasia, and dysphemia are briefly described and the methods of treatment are indicated.

8. Huber, M. W., *The Practice of Speech Correction in the Medical Clinic*, together with Kopp, A. E., *Speech Correction from a Dental Viewpoint*, Boston, Expression Company, 1942.
This little book is especially valuable in providing the student with descriptions of the voice defects of organic causation. Cleft palate and aphonic, hoarse, and denasal voices are presented.

9. Louttit, G. M., *Clinical Psychology*, New York, Harper, 1936, Chapter 11, pages 423–453.
This chapter is still one of the best brief summaries of the nature, causes, and treatment of the various speech defects that have ever been written. Several interesting cases are presented in detail.

10. Louttit, G. M. and Halls, E. C., "A Survey of Speech Defects Among the Public School Children of Indiana," *Journal of Speech Disorders*, 1937, Vol. 2, pages 73–80.
A questionnaire study of 30 per cent of the total school population in Indiana, showing that 3.7 per cent of these children had reported speech defects, and that there was a greater incidence among boys and subnormals. Other statistics on incidence are also given.

11. Mills, A. W. and Streit, H., "Report of a Speech Survey, Holyoke, Massachusetts," *Journal of Speech Disorders*, *1942*, Vol. 7, pages 161–167.
This reference outlines the procedures and results of a survey of the speech defectives in a public school system.

12. Ogilvie, M., *Terminology and Definitions of Speech Defects*, New York, Teachers College, *Columbia University Contributions to Education*, Number 859, 1942.
This monograph represents an attempt to translate the many varying terms

for speech disorders into a unified and systematic classification.   It is especially useful as a dictionary, and also as a source for references. A large bibliography is appended.

13. Seth, G. and Guthrie, D., *Speech in Childhood; Its Development and Disorders*, pages 146–162, London, Oxford University Press, 1935.
A classification of disorders of speech which result neither from deafness nor mental deficiency.   A description is given of these disorders: audimutitas, logorrhoea, dyslalia, idioglossia, and sigmatism.

14. Travis, L. E., "Diagnosis in Speech," *Yearbook National Society Study of Education*, 1935, Vol. 34, pages 399–434.
An estimate that 5 per cent of school children have speech defects necessitating remedial attention, including 1 per cent stutterers.   Factors in diagnosing articulatory disorders and stuttering are mentioned.

15. Travis, L. E., *Speech Pathology*, Chapters 2 and 3, New York, D. Appleton-Century, 1931.
A brief outline classifying speech disorders and a discussion of general causes of speech disorders, including many summaries of studies of causal factors in speech defects.

16. West, R., Kennedy, L., and Carr, A., *The Rehabilitation of Speech*, Chapters 3-9, New York, Harper, 1937.
A consideration of symptoms and treatment, both for those speech disorders directly caused by a physiological or anatomical defect, and those whose causes are in the realm of abnormal psychology or psychiatry.

III

Understanding the Speech Defective

Why we must know our cases. The essential task of the speech correctionist is to help his articulatory, voice, or stuttering cases to overcome their speech handicaps. He is often asked for exercises or drills which will accomplish this, but the mere fact that no ethical worker in the field will ever guarantee a cure should indicate that the problem is not simple. First, the techniques used in speech correction all involve learning and unlearning. New habits must be taught and old ones broken. People differ in their modifiability. Motivation can vary all the way from:

I've burned my bridges behind me. I've told everybody I know that I'm not coming back until I can talk right. I told my girl our marriage was off unless I licked this speech impediment. I'll do anything, even if it takes three years of my life. This is it. Tell me what to do first.

to:

My vacation starts in June but I want to go up to the cottage for a few weeks first, to rest up and play a bit. I would prefer to come the last two weeks of July if you find you cannot help me by correspondence. My stuttering is not very severe and many times I do not stutter at all. I am sure it would not take long if you could just help me get confidence in myself.

Besides motivation, we must always take into account the presence of emotional factors which might prevent the person from facing his speech defect as a problem in re-education. A lisper who has been severely penalized for his sibilant errors finds it very difficult to accept the temporary partial failures which always accompany the type of learning process involved in speech correction. The stutterer who has always tried to hide or disguise his disorder will be tempted to escape any therapy which necessitates the exposure, manipulation, and con-

29

trol of his stuttering spasms. Neurotic or psychotic tendencies always affect the progress and outcome of the treatment. Therapy must always be tailored to fit the person we are trying to help. Some methods just will not work with a given individual. For example:

Ordinarily, we use phonograph recordings of the speech of our foreign accent cases for purposes of phonetic analysis and ear training. While there is often a first shock on hearing one's own errors, it usually passes quickly and the case soon looks forward to the convenience the recording provides in recognizing and eliminating errors. In one of our cases, an American-born woman who had learned three languages simultaneously before the age of five—(her parents had planned a ballet career for her), each recording provoked an emotional outburst and retarded her progress. We attributed her reactions to her hatred of the speech defect but she told us later that she went into a frenzy whenever she heard any phonograph record since it reminded her of all the wasted hours of her youth, spent in the rigid discipline of the classic dance.

Most of our failures in speech correction are due to ignorance, and most of that ignorance concerns the person whom we are treating. Every worker in our field makes mistakes in helping any child or adult to overcome his speech handicap. Most of these mistakes are minute. They may concern timing, for instance. If a lisper has finally learned a good *s* in isolation, how soon should we require him to start using it in familiar words? When dare we ask him to alternate syllables such as *see* and *thee* at fast speeds? Other mistakes are more vital and we lose completely our opportunity to help the person who has come to us. These mistakes are the ones that haunt us and keep us humble in the profession of speech correction. Most of them could be avoided, if only we could get to know our speech defective more thoroughly.

If we neglect our study of the person we are treating, we may work in vain. Emotional conflicts of which we may be entirely ignorant may cause relapse. This is well known in such psychosomatic disorders as asthma, ulcerative colitis, and peptic ulcer. In speech correction, relapses in stutterers have been so common that attitudes of pessimism are held by every esteemed authority in the field. Even simple articulatory defects, such as the substitution of *w* for *l*, may return years after the errors have been eliminated from all ordinary speech, and we remember very well that case of ours who lost her voice on the first of every month. Her husband disliked paying her bills and was very verbal about it. A few of these unfortunate episodes soon teach the speech correctionist to study his cases.

A good share of the total handicap which most adult speech defectives possess is emotional in nature. They suffer from fears, shames, and embarrassment, and their reactions to these penalties interfere with communication. Many a stutterer could talk undetected were it not for the marked fear and embarrassment which themselves attract attention. But more handicapping still are those inner emotional reactions which no listener ever sees but which govern the speech defective's life and shape his personality. So closely linked is the inner emotional burden with the outer speech handicap that the one can seldom be treated without doing something about the other. Travis (21) has said:

The primary concern of speech correction is the person. . . . It is not enough to know what sort of a speech defect a person has. In addition, one should know what kind of a person has a speech defect. The speech defect has no particular meaning apart from the person who presents the defect. We are not interested in speech defects, but in speech defectives.

In these words, Travis expresses the reason for this chapter. Speech correction is but one small area in the field of clinical psychology, and the speech correctionist who thinks that he deals with lisping rather than lispers, and with stuttering rather than stutterers, will find discouragement at every turn.

Emotional conflicts may also serve as predisposing, precipitating, and maintaining causes of speech disorders. The literature is thronged with case studies showing the influence of personality and behavior problems in producing speech disorders, but we cite two that are more clear cut than those usually found.

Just before school opened after the holidays, C. K., a Junior High School teacher, age 38, was jilted by her fiancé. She had never been able to maintain discipline among her students and had not enjoyed teaching, according to the report of her principal. A slight cold caused her to lose her voice completely. Two months later, she was still unable to speak above a whisper, although the physician's report stated that no inflammation or other pathology existed. He diagnosed her disorder as hysterical aphonia.

A. T., a girl of 15, suddenly began to lisp and substitute w for r. She had previously spoken without any articulatory defect for at least six years, although her first-grade teacher declared she had some kind of speech disorder when she was seven years old. Three months later the disorder disappeared as suddenly as it had appeared. The only explanation which seemed to have any evidence to support it was that the girl knew of her parents' plan to get a divorce and adopted the symptoms of an earlier age level when no family conflict was threatening to disrupt her security. At any rate, the disorder disappeared as soon as a parental reconciliation was effected.

It is easily seen from these cases that a thorough knowledge of the speech defective's personality and history is vital to successful treatment.

Speech defects are so conspicuously different that they themselves can serve as the cause or the nucleus of personality problems. A stutterer who reacts to rejection, pity, or humor by attacking will be likely to have antagonistic responses toward the speech correctionist. The lisper who withdraws when penalties are threatened is prone to avoid and postpone those very measures that may solve his basic problem. Often these aggressive and retreat reactions are disguised so cleverly that only careful study will disclose them. In any event, these personality problems can interfere or entirely frustrate our corrective efforts unless we understand them well enough to fit them into our remedial program. We should solve them if we can. We dare not ignore them.

How to study your cases. Since it is vitally important for us to know the people with whom we work, we should also know the methods commonly used. In speech correction we always take a case history; we sometimes require a verbal or written autobiography; we employ psychological tests of intelligence, vocational aptitude, personality, and school achievement; we collect as much information as we can from the speech defective's associates; we interview the case himself, sometimes at great length; and we observe his behavior in both ordinary and controlled situations.

The extent of this exploration usually depends on the severity of the speech defective's emotional handicap. Many of the younger children, especially those with mild articulatory defects, require no great amount of detailed investigation. The following report by a public school speech correctionist will illustrate about how much information may be gathered on one of the milder cases.

I am writing this brief summary of what I know about J. S. at the request of his mother, who has informed me you are planning to work with him this summer. He has a simple frontal lisp substituting the *th* sounds for the *s* and *z*. All other sounds are good, and he can make these sounds when he is careful, but only at slow speeds. All of the *s* blends are bad. His mother tells me that formerly he had difficulty with other sounds but outgrew these errors. No one else in the family lisped. His hearing is adequate but he has been slow to recognize errors except in isolated sounds. No one seems to tease him about it, and he is not at all self-conscious. He has always enjoyed coming to speech class. He has been very co-operative, but I only see him once a week for a fifteen-minute period and then only as a member of a group of six. He is bright and doing excellent school work. His reading is superior for a third grader. No dental abnormality, though his mother thinks a former thumb-sucking habit caused the lisp. Never has been a behavior problem at home or school. All he needs is a more thorough retraining than we can give here and I am glad you are going to help this summer. I'm sorry I cannot tell you more about him but I have over 150 other children and I've only seen the mother once. His third-grade teacher says that he is no problem to her. He will probably come out of it anyway, but I think perhaps the mother is overanxious because she said an aunt of hers still lisps.

At the other extreme are the very difficult cases, some of whose folders in the clinic files are several inches thick.

The case history. Although the case history as an instrument for exploring another human being is incomplete, unsatisfactory, and unreliable in many ways, no convenient substitute for it has ever been found. Its function is to serve as an outline of questioning and prompting, as a system of signposts pointing out pathways that should be followed, as a land-marked map of unexplored territory. It tends to prevent superficiality and snap judgment during diagnosis. It conserves time and energy. When used by a trained examiner who appreciates its weaknesses and limitations and who is alert to follow up any significant leads that appear, it gives us a picture of the individual which is of inestimable value. When used by a poor examiner who merely asks the questions and records the answers, or who loses himself in a mass of irrelevant information, it is practically worthless. A sample outline of the general case history and the special case histories for articulation, voice, and stuttering disorders will be found in the Appendix at the end of this book.

A typical general case history summary is now given, not so much as a model of what a case history should be but as a practical illustration of the information usually procured by this means.

CASE HISTORY SUMMARY

Informant: Mother.

Family: Paternal grandfather stuttered; paternal uncle left-handed.

Economic status: Isolated farm; very poor; insufficient food at times. Insufficient clothing.

Home conditions: Father very brutal to members of family; beats mother and children, including case; "terrible temper," almost killed son-in-law by kicking in head; taunts mother with inability to get divorce or to live afterward; boasts of extramarital relations; eldest two daughters left home "to get away from him"; "chased daughters out in middle of winter"; shames and beats boy for lack of speech; "very smooth talker when authorities come" and declares wife is crazy; (*Note.* We found no evidence of paranoia in informant); angry when each new baby comes (nine children, seven living; two miscarriages), but no sexual control.   Mother works in fields and woods; in great fear of being hurt or possibly killed; once "loved the very ground he walked on but not now"; interested in helping child; child is very fond of mother and co-operates with her; will speak a few words when she coaxes him; mother wants a divorce but is afraid. Child is very much afraid of father but identifies himself somewhat with the man; child has always been forced to do things by father; father beats child for not repeating correctly; the other children adopt the father's attitude and tease, shame, and brutalize the boy; boy seems much more afraid of men strangers than of women.

Development: The child's physical development was normal; no birth injuries or accidents; no serious illnesses; had bad temper tantrums, beating head on floor; some of these still continue; speech development fairly normal; lalling, vocal play, and inflection practice coming at the proper time; said "mama" and "papa" at 18 months; made peculiar sucking and throat noises; breathes very heavily; has had tonsillectomy and adenectomy (July, 1936), but still shows some nasal stoppage and mouth breathing; thyroid disturbance suspected; hearing was tested and seemed adequate, although attention lapses occurred (we could not test for auditory aphasia, and it may be a possible explanation); at certain times does not seem able to understand, but does so under adequate motivation; the child uttered the words "Oh boy" under strong emotion, but has never said them before or since; he does not seem to be using silence as an attention-gaining device; mother said that child first refused to make any speech attempt and showed the negativism when he put "watermelon seeds up his nose at the age of three or a little earlier."   I.Q. could not be determined, but went above the 5-year level on the Grace Arthur tests; seems ambidextrous.

Speech: The boy has said the following words: "Junior, Wright, Oh boy, Spot (dog's name), here, Maud and Molly (horses' names), pig, chicken, automobile."   The child will repeat words after mother by watching her mouth, but only at certain times.   Learned "one-two-three; a-b-c" at school the first day (when substitute teacher taught) but refused and was rejected when regular teacher came back.   Said "No" to examiner.   We could not make examination for organic defects, because of child's fears. We were able to get him to say a few words when mother was present.

The autobiography.   Adults are often asked to write or give orally an autobiography.   Instructions for such an autobiography might run as follows:

The purpose in our asking you to write an autobiography is to become well enough acquainted with you to fit our treatment to your needs. We must know as much as possible about:

> your parents and brothers and sisters
> your friends and enemies
> your teachers
> your employers or fellow workers
> strangers who have played an important part in your life.
> achievements you have been proud of, or praised for
> talents you possess (your good points)
> your bad points
> things you have done for which others have punished or rejected you
> unpleasant experiences
> things which made you unhappy
> how you react when you are praised or appreciated
> how you react when you are punished

Note. Write down your character sketches and your memories as they come to you. Put them on cards or individual sheets of scratch paper. Then organize later into three chapters: Chapter I. My preschool period; Chapter II. School days; Chapter III. Since. The autobiography should run about ten pages or more. Give us a good picture of the people who were important in your life and why. What have been your assets and liabilities? How have others reacted to them? What kind of a person were you during each period?

Here are a few excerpts from actual autobiographies to illustrate the kind of information which they can contribute to our understanding of the speech defective:

My family life at home was very unsatisfactory. I felt that Mother and Dad hated my stuttering intensely, that they thought it unfair that a daughter of theirs should be so afflicted. I felt that I was a disappointment to them. I was impulsive, nervous and "bull-headed" in their eyes. I quarreled with my sisters. I was indeed a problem.

When I was in the second grade, "spit-balling" was all the rage. I never threw any but the boy behind me sure did. One day when he was caught he laid the blame on me so artfully that I was kept after school and quizzed by my teacher. She was an old witch anyway and couldn't understand what I was trying to say. But then when I got excited nobody could understand me. She then said that as a result of my throwing the spit balls she was considering putting me back in the first grade. All I could do was cry.

Observation of behavior. Probably the most valid of all the methods tor getting to know and understand another human being is that of careful observation. Every worker in the field of speech correction relies upon this method of checking his interpretations and his information. One of the statements in the code of ethics prescribed by the American Speech Correction Association states that no treatment shall ever be administered entirely through correspondence. The reason for this statement is obvious. We cannot truly know an individual except through observing his behavior. The student of speech correction should train himself in this method for studying his cases. He should avail himself of every opportunity to predict human behavior. He must learn to observe and appreciate the little human dramas which roll up their curtains in the most unexpected places. He should make an intensive and systematic study of a few of his acquaintances, writing down his findings in a notebook with examples of correct and incorrect predictions of their behavior. Here is one of the examples from a student's notebook:

My batting average in predicting the behavior was pretty poor today, though I had one good success. Into the lunchroom where I eat my breakfast came a man. I told my companion that I would wager a nickel that he would stir his coffee with the spoon in his left hand. I had based my prediction on the following observations. His hat was tipped slightly to the left on his head, and although he removed it with his right hand, he put it into the rack with his left. He took off the right sleeve of his coat first and I have previously observed that most people take off the sleeve of the nonpreferred arm before the other. Then, too, he rubbed his chin with his left hand as he contemplated the menu on the wall. I won the nickel.

It is always important to separate observation from interpretation. The following passage is entirely free from the latter:

When his mother carried him into the room, his chin quivered and then he began to cry. She shook her head and he stopped momentarily, then began to cry more loudly. She shook him and covered his mouth with her hand, saying, "Don't cry like that! The doctor will spank you. See the pretty chair. Do you want to sit in it?" The child yelled more loudly. She shook him again. "Tell the doctor your name. Bobby! Say, 'Bobby.'" She sat him down forcibly in the chair and turned to the examiner. "He won't ever do what I say. He's bull-headed just like his no-account father." She got up and looked out of the window, then returned to the child. "Now look here" she said, "I brought you thirty miles to talk to this man and you better do it, dummy. You won't get any ice-cream cone either."

The following excerpt will represent the same experience but with interpretations, some of which are not justified:

The child was forcibly carried into the room by the mother who scolded him for not talking. She threatened and reproached him for not co-operating. She was disgusted with the child's behavior and told him she would punish him for his obstinacy. She could not control him at all. The child knew that he could refuse to talk and get away with his refusal. He cried bitterly during most of the period. The boy's delayed speech is probably due to negativism.

Interpretations are inescapable in any study of another human being, but most of our clinical errors result from mistaking them for factual observations.

It is often possible to learn a lot about a person by introducing him into situations that have been designed especially to bring out hidden conflicts. For instance, we have used psychodrama to demonstrate the existence of family frictions of which we had no previous knowledge. We have sent stutterers into situations where we knew they would be laughed at for their disorder, so that we could observe their reactions to this penalty. We have watched their response to praise which had been prearranged. We have given small children clay images of their fathers, mothers, and brothers, and have seen their play reveal hostilities which were never revealed in any other way. The use of fist puppets with appropriate dialogue between the puppet and the child has often yielded material that was very important to treatment. For instance:

The parents of the six-year-old girl, a lisper, had been divorced a year before the child was brought to the clinic. Our problem was to determine who should carry on the remedial speech work which we had started. Neither the mother nor the father was available. The first-grade teacher had forty-two children in her room and was reluctant. The father's sister, who lived with him and the child, was very intelligent and pleasant. She had taught school successfully and was eager to help. The child seemed to be very fond of her. However, a puppet named "Aunty" and another named "Teacher" first held a pleasant dialogue with each other, then with the child. The child enjoyed the drama very much and took part in it freely. She refused to speak to the aunty puppet except briefly. She told her to go away and fall down and get run over by a car. She told the teacher puppet to spank Aunty and make her go home. When this was carried out in pantomime, she laughed and clapped her hands. She also accepted a correction of her speech when the teacher puppet asked her to say an *s* word correctly. When Aunty tried the same correction later, she told her to shut up and "go home and be dead."

Needless to say, the girl's aunt was not chosen to do the speech correction.

Interviewing. The art of interviewing, both as a diagnostic and a therapeutic device, is receiving the increasing emphasis in clinical psychology which it richly deserves. We feel that all teachers or clinicians who deal with problem children or adults should be trained in methods of interviewing. The moment a person begins to discuss his difficulties, he opens the shell that protects his hidden insecurities. Speech is always revelation, and never more so than when it is free and uninhibited. Much of the art of interviewing centers about the creation of attitudes which encourage free spontaneous expression.

There are two main varieties of the interview, the *directive* and the *nondirective.* In the first type, the speech correctionist does most of the talking. He asks the questions and their answers are usually of the yes or no variety. He gives advice or explanations of the speech defective's emotional conflicts. He interprets and amplifies the speech defective's remarks so as to define the problem or its solution. This method of interviewing has certain applications in the field of speech correction, but it has many disadvantages. Weiss and English, in their excellent text on psychosomatic medicine (23), give this advice to physicians who are confronted by cases with personality problems: "Inexperienced physicians often have a great urge to interpret things to the patient, to talk a lot to the patient about mental mechanisms. We advise that it is better to listen than to talk."

The nondirective method of interviewing might be termed dynamic listening. The speech correctionist gets his case to talking about his problems, places most of the responsibility for this discussion on the case, and when pauses or requests for comment occur, he merely tries to repeat in his own words the emotional attitudes which the case has been expressing. He must be the perfect listener, always in tune with the speaker's thoughts. When he responds, he should respond primarily to the feelings expressed by the speech defective rather than to the intellectual content of his disclosure. The speech correctionist neither approves nor disapproves of what is told him. He does not judge. He merely keeps trying to understand. If the case is kept talking freely and feels that he is understood, he can hardly fail to verbalize his basic conflicts.

It might seem to the uninitiated that the nondirective method of interviewing is easily mastered. We have not found it so. There are many pitfalls for the unwary dynamic listener. He finds himself listening intellectually rather than emotionally. He finds himself talking too much, interpreting, directing, and pointing out implications.

No, the nondirective method of interviewing is not easy, but it is extremely productive of insight, not only for the speech correctionist but also for the speech defective himself. We heartily recommend the book *Counselling and Psychotherapy* by Rogers (19), from which the following partial transcription of a phonographically recorded interview is taken:

Subject. When I wax enthusiastic philosophically, I oftentimes have quite a blocking in my speech—maybe you notice how I hesitate. Now, my hesitation is not a groping for words, although that's a sort of a—well, I want to make it seem so, for what you might call protective coloration.
Counsellor. Defend yourself a little bit that way?
S. Yeah. I like to make people think that I'm groping for just the exact word—that I'm a careful thinker, but actually I know right off what I want to say, and when I am fluent, I get very exact and nice diction without having to grope for a word.
C. So that in that particular situation your blocking keeps you from being your best and fluent self. And in that situation, it's speech blocking that is primarily . . .
S. Well, yes. I mean it seems like—well, there wouldn't be any other blocking. No other form of activity than speech is going on, and that's the thing, of course, which I notice—that is, of course the thought—my thought is also to a certain extent blocked—that is they sort of go hand in hand. When I'm able to speak more fluently, I'm able to think more fluently.
C. M-hm.

Integrating the information. The techniques described above will produce a great deal of information, much of which may have little meaning for speech correction. Even the significant facts by such methods will be worthless unless they can be interrelated so as to give an organized picture of the person we are studying. A mass of disorganized historical facts is not a history, nor is a scattering of environmental data a geography. Some form of organization is likewise necessary in the study of personality. Despite the risk of creating certain artifacts, we have found it clinically convenient to organize and orient our personality information with respect to the following three questions:

1. What marked differences of physical appearance, behavior, or environment distinguished this person from his associates?
2. Which of these differences were approved, which were penalized, and by whom?
3. How did this person react to this approval or penalty?

If our information is sufficient to give an adequate answer to all three questions (at each of the various age levels or stages of social interaction), we shall have gained an excellently integrated picture of the person possessing the speech defect. Although the preceding method for integrating personal data is the result of clinical technique, theoretical justification may be found in its defense. There are almost as many definitions of personality as there are authors who have written about it, yet the majority of them concern themselves with "traits," "reaction tendencies," and "adjustment." These terms indicate that clinical psychologists and psychiatrists, however they may phrase their common problem, are concerned with: (1) physical, environmental, and behavioral differences; (2) social approvals and penalties; and (3) reactions on the part of the individual to these penalties or approvals. In other words, personality is based on *evaluated individuality*.

The importance of physical, environmental, and behavioral differences. Individuality itself is based on the ways in which a person differs from his associates. Those characteristics which he possesses in common with all other members of his group contribute little to his personality. A white skin will not affect his personality development unless he numbers among his associates someone who is not Caucasian. Surpassing beauty, low intelligence, a long nose, pronounced athletic ability, a hearing defect, an ability to use picturesque language, extreme shyness, a speech defect, and many other differences can affect personality development if they set the person apart from his fellows.

Twenty severe stutterers undergoing treatment by the author were studied very intensively through interviews, autobiographies, conferences with parents and associates, and other devices. Among other results, it was found that many differences in addition to their speech defect had influenced the development of their personalities. Some of the differences that seemed most determinative of their insecurities were: protruding teeth, effeminacy due to the influence of seven older sisters, lack of sufficient spending money to maintain position in exclusive girls' school, a habitual facial grimace (tic), extremely short stature, illegitimacy, a father in an institution for the insane, red hair, and a reading disability. On the other hand, certain differences were viewed as securities, and among those that seemed most significant were: athletic ability, personal beauty, ownership of a pony and many playthings, pronounced musical talent, prestige of having traveled widely, younger playmates, a brother who was a prize fighter, and high intelligence. It may be pointed out that, in each case, the difference in itself was not so important as its interpretation by the speech defective's associates. In some instances, the same difference was interpreted by one speech defective as an asset and by another as a liability.

Since individuality depends upon the persons who are the speech defective's associates, we must know something about his companions at the various age levels. At the preschool level, these are largely confined to the father, mother, brothers and sisters, servants, relatives or friends of the family, and a few playmates. When the child enters school, the teacher and schoolmates may entirely alter the pattern of his differences. Later on, other new associates will enter the person's sphere of social, educational, sexual, or economic contacts, and these will either create new or accentuate old differences. Each of us recognizes that our personalities vary somewhat with the group we join. We are not the same persons to our parents that we are to our students. In studying the speech defective, then, we must know his associates if we would recognize the differences about which his personality was built.

A speech defect is naturally an outstanding difference. Most of us speak without breaks in rhythm, peculiar speech sounds, or inadequate tones. Although small children do not tend to perceive a speech defect as quickly as adults, their games and activities depend upon communication, and the speech defect is usually discovered sooner or later. Occasionally we meet a child from a family in which most of the other members have a similar speech defect. Again, we find cases in which the parents have grown accustomed so gradually to a child's defective speech that they fail to recognize it. Children from these families will be likely to develop personality and behavior problems when they first enter school. A speech defect must always be perceived by others before it can become a significant difference.

Penalties and approvals. The second of the three questions previously mentioned in this chapter asked what penalties or approvals by the person's associates contributed to his personality problem. This question is necessary because personality is not merely individuality but *evaluated* individuality. Differences in themselves are not of vital importance to their possessor. They assume their significance because they are judged or evaluated by his associates. They may be judged as assets, as liabilities, or as neither one. If they are evaluated as assets—as helping to fulfill the desires of his associates— the group will tend to welcome him. If they are judged to be lia- bilities, the group will tend to reject him. Thus approval and penalty are the results of the group's evaluation of the differences the indi- vidual possesses. Fortunately, most groups base their final rejection or acceptance of an individual bidding for inclusion upon more than one difference. They note all of his liabilities and all of his assets, and if the latter outweigh the former, he probably will be accepted. Thus it is possible for a severe speech defective to go through life with a minimum of rejection, even though he never overcomes his liability.

Moreover, different groups will evaluate a speech defect in dif- ferent ways. A debating society would evaluate it as a much greater liability than would a baseball team. The group will accept the speech defective's difference if its members feel that it is not conspicu- ous enough to penalize them socially, thwart their free communication, or cause them uncomfortable emotional reactions. If it is over- shadowed by other differences, such as a good sense of humor or an ability to listen effectively, it will be tolerated and its possessor ac- cepted. Rejection, acceptance, and toleration are the three possible resultants of evaluating a difference. If we are to understand the speech defective's problem, we must know what rejections, tolerances, and acceptances he has met, and in what groups or through what individuals they have occurred. Many types of penalties are used by society to ensure conformity and to prevent the liabilities of any one individual from handicapping the other members of the group. Some illustrative penalties from stutterers' autobiographies follow:

Most clerks always look away when I get stuck and begin to force. It always infuriates me that they don't even have the decency to look at me. Once I even went to the manager of a store about it and he looked away too.

My father wouldn't ever listen to me when I stuttered. He always walked off. I finally got so I'd say everything to him by having mother give him the message.

People do not usually laugh at my other kinds of stuttering, but when I begin to go up in pitch, they always smile or laugh right out loud. I was phoning a girl today and hung up when I heard her snickering.

My mother always hurried to say the word for me whenever company was in the house. I often asked her not to but she couldn't help herself. It used to shame me so, I'd go up in my room and cry and I never went visiting with them.   Sometimes I'd eat in the kitchen when we had strangers come for dinner.

The other boys in the school used to call me "stuttercat" and imitate me whenever I came to school.   At first I always managed to be tardy and stay after school to avoid them, but my folks got after me and then I began to fight with them.   I got to be a pretty good fighter, but the bigger boys always licked me and the teacher punished me when I hit the girls. I still hate girls.

After I came to high school from the country, everybody laughed at me whenever I tried to recite.   After that I pretended to be dumb and always said "I don't know" when the teacher called on me.   That's why I quit school.

Every time I'd ask for a job a funny look would come over their face and some of them would say no right away even before I finished what I was going to say.   Some of the others, and one of them was a stutterer too, just waited till I finally got it out and then they'd shake their heads. One storekeeper was so sympathetic I could hardly get out of there fast enough.

The worst time I ever had was when a hotel clerk saw me jumping around and called a doctor.   He thought I was having a fit.

These are but a few of the many penalties and rejections which any speech defective or any other individual with an unpleasant difference is likely to experience.   Imitative behavior, curiosity, nicknaming, humorous response, embarrassed withdrawal, brutal attack, impatience, quick rejection or exclusion, overprotection, pity, misinterpretation, and condescension are some of the other common penalties.

The amount and kind of penalty inflicted on a speech defective are dependent on four factors: (1) the amount or peculiarity of the speech difference; (2) the speech defective's attitude toward his own difference; (3) the sensitivities, maladjustments, or preconceived attitudes of the people who penalize him; and (4) the presence of other personality assets.

In general, the more frequent or bizarre the speech peculiarity, the more frequently and strongly it is penalized.   Thus a child with only one sound substitution or one that occurs only intermittently will be less penalized than one with almost unintelligible speech, and a mild stutterer will be penalized less than a severe one.   Second, as Bryngelson[1] has so clearly pointed out, the speech defective's own attitude

---

[1] Bryngelson, Bryng, "The Reëducation of Speech Failures," *Quarterly Journal of Speech*, April, 1933, pages 227–229.

toward his defect often determines what the attitude of the auditor will be. If the speech defective considers it a shameful abnormality, his listeners can hardly be expected to contradict him. Empathic response is a powerful agent in the creation of attitudes. Third, the worst penalties will come from those individuals who are sensitive about some difference of their own. Since many speech defectives have parents or siblings with similar speech differences, they are often penalized very early in life by those persons. Moreover, many individuals have such preconceived notions or attitudes concerning the causes or the unpleasantness of speech handicaps that they react in a more or less stereotyped fashion to such differences, no matter how well adjusted the speech defective himself may be. Finally, as we have pointed out, the speech defective may possess other abilities or personal assets which so overshadow his speech difference that the latter is penalized very little.

In considering the effects of these penalties on the personality, we must remember that penalty need not be overt to produce a reaction. Insecurity, a common term in this clinical field, refers to the fear of penalty rather than to its actual presence, and insecurity alone can warp a personality. Speech defectives often become very suspicious and paranoid. They vividly remember the penalties which were inflicted by a few individuals and imagine that all other people have the same attitudes but are too polite to express them. These imaginary or expected penalties can affect an individual as well as the real ones can.

Reaction to penalty or approval. We have now considered two of the three major factors contributing to the development of the personality: the differences themselves, and the accompanying approvals or penalties. The third factor is the person's reaction to these approvals or penalties. The penalties themselves would have little effect on the speech defective's personality were he, for example, to ignore them. But his reaction to the penalty is probably the most important of all these factors.

A speech defective or any other individual can react to the penalties inflicted by his associates upon his difference in three main ways: (1) by regressive or withdrawal behavior, (2) by aggressive or protest behavior, or (3) by understanding, unemotional acceptance. These reactions themselves may be considered as differences.

Regressive or withdrawal behavior as a reaction to penalty. When a difference such as that of a speech defect is so conspicuous that a group will not accept its possessor, that person may retreat from further attempts in group activity. He may isolate himself as much as possible from others and lead a sedentary life. He may refuse to attempt to cope with reality, and indulge in daydreaming and fantasy. He may retreat completely from the problem of his difference and develop an interest in other things. These other interests may be developed so highly that he will overcompensate for his weakness. Compensation in a small degree does not harm a person. It may develop talents and skills which will add to his personality assets. But if all attention is focused upon the compensation, and the difference is completely disregarded, other serious personality problems will arise. The overcompensation itself may be evaluated as a weakness by the group. Finally, an individual may regress to a former stage of life and revel in his past achievements. He may deny that he has any such difference. He may overemphasize his former acceptances by groups and dwell in the remembrance of the days when he made satisfactory adjustments and had his parents and teachers to reinforce his strength if those adjustments failed. All of these mechanisms denote a retreat from reality, a refusal to struggle further with the problem caused by his rejection.

Some speech defectives react in the ways just described. They are especially prone to indulge in such substitute satisfactions as creative writing, music, or reading. They hunt for havens wherein they can avoid the penalties that communication usually provokes. Sometimes the speech clinic itself becomes such a haven. Withdrawal behavior is often fostered by misinformed parents and teachers, but it never solves the speech defective's problem. Indeed, it frequently causes him to avoid the speech correctionist who could help him. Moreover, when the associates of a withdrawing speech defective are constantly confronted by his attitude of avoidance, they respond in the same way, and so reinforce the total maladjustment.

Aggressive or protest behavior as a reaction to penalty. Penalty and rejection by his associates may lead an individual to react aggressively by attack, protest, or some form of rebellion. He may employ the mechanism of projection and blame his parents, teachers, or playmates for his objectionable difference. He may display toward the weaknesses of those in the group the same intolerant attitude which they have manifested toward his own. In this way he not only temporarily minimizes the importance of his own handicap, but also enjoys the revenge of recognizing weaknesses in others. He may attempt to shift the blame for rejection. He will say, "They didn't keep me out because I stuttered—they just didn't think I had as nice clothes as the rest of them wore." In this way he will exaggerate the unfairness of the group evaluation and ignore the actual cause. Another attack reaction may be that of focusing all attention upon himself. He can refuse to co-operate with the group in any way, can belittle its importance openly, and can refuse to consider it in his scheme of existence. Finally, he may react by a direct outward attack. A child, or an adult with an easily provoked temper, may indulge in actual physical conflict with members of the group which has not accepted him. He may spread pointed criticism of the group in a resentful manner. In any of these methods, the object of the rejection does not retreat from reality—he reacts antagonistically and attacks those who made his reality unpleasant.

Among the speech defectives the author has examined, the behavior problems that seemed due to a protest reaction against the group's penalty include: lying, enuresis, constipation, temper tantrums, stealing, arson, suicide, use of obscene language, cruelty to pets, truancy, fighting, destruction of property, disobedience, attempted suicide, sexual promiscuity, and feeding difficulties.

Some speech defectives show few outward signs of these reactions except attitudes of sullenness or non-co-operation; in others, the protest is unmistakable. Unfortunately, these protest reactions do not solve the problem. They merely increase its unpleasantness.

The more the speech defective attacks the group, the more it penalizes him. Often such reactions interfere with treatment, for many of these speech defectives resent any proffered aid. They attack the speech correctionist and sabotage his assignments. The inevitable result of these attack reactions is to push the speech defective even further from normal speech and adequate adjustment.

Intelligent unemotional acceptance as a reaction to penalty. The two reactions previously discussed ignored reality. This third type of reaction involves an admission of reality. A person may honestly state the reason for the group's rejection of him. He may even tell why his difference would be a weakness to that group. There are two kinds of admission: (1) the individual accepts the rejection in an emotional and pessimistic manner; (2) he admits the basis for the group action, but regrets it, and accepts the inevitability of future similar defeats. The second method of admission is an unemotional one in which the person realizes the validity of the group's action. He accepts the rejection wholesomely and takes an objective attitude toward both the group's action and his handicap. The basis of his reactions is the short sentence uttered by the greatest of all mental hygienists, the cartoon character Popeye, who says, "I yam what I yam." The individual with such an attitude says, "Of course I have a difference. I stutter (or have red hair, or weigh two hundred and fifty pounds, or have a big nose), but what of it? That's just the way I am." This type of reaction destroys much of the emotionality and abnormal behavior usually built around a difference. It provides no necessity for using the tricks and subterfuges which always accompany attempts to hide or to minimize a defect. It furnishes the essential basis for subsequent remedial speech work as it brings the defect into the open and allows its possessor to study it thoroughly and to work on overcoming it. No speech defect can be eradicated when it is hidden. It must be seen as a problem to be solved before its possessor can solve it. Johnson[2] gives some excellent examples of this reaction in his monograph on the personality of stutterers, and Bryngelson[3] has discussed the theory of the "objective attitude" in several publications. The student is urged to master these concepts, since they serve as a basis for much speech-correction therapy.

If a speech defective honestly admits his difference, the group will accept it unemotionally. If he states his determination to work on his speech problem, the group's support will reinforce his determination. The group will criticize and encourage him, and, realizing that the disappearance of the handicap will ultimately strengthen its own power, will refuse to penalize him during the remedial process. It not only will enable the defective to enjoy group association devoid of deceit and its accompanying nervous strain, but also will give him a more normal personality and increase his motivation during the period of speech retraining.

Intelligence tests. Since learning and unlearning depend greatly upon intelligence, some estimate of this factor must always be made.

The part played by low intelligence in producing articulatory and voice disorders is well known. Not only are children of low intelli-

---

[2] Johnson, Wendell, "The Influence of Stuttering on the Personality," *University of Iowa Studies in Child Welfare*, 1932, Volume 5.

[3] Bryngelson, Bryng, "Psychological Problems in Stuttering," *Mental Hygiene*, 1937, Volume 21, pages 631–639.

gence slow to learn to talk, but their speech patterns are frequently slurred, confused with sound substitutions, and complicated by peculiar intonations. Motor skills are retarded, and speech, the most complicated of all motor skills, certainly demonstrates the effect of this retardation. The feeble-minded child's lack of discrimination, his distractibility, and his lack of response to social stimulation—all contribute to inaccurate and defective speech. Moreover, the same factors make rapid remedial work impossible and necessitate techniques other than those ordinarily employed.

On the other hand, the child of average and superior intelligence can be expected to respond to adequate therapy if his emotional reactions do not interfere. The brilliant child especially can be relied on to take charge of his own case to a large extent, and such self-reliance should be encouraged. These and other equally obvious observations point out the great necessity for a valid estimate of the child's intelligence. An excellent discussion of personality and intelligence tests from the point of view of the speech correctionist will be found in the text *Speech Pathology* by Travis.

An excellent paper-and-pencil test which does not stress language skills is the California Test of Mental Maturity. We must always remember, however, that defective speech may interfere with expression. Stutterers may prefer to remain silent rather than suffer exposure of their difficulty. Delayed-speech cases are so deficient in vocabulary that they are penalized by any verbal test. Articulation cases are often retarded in reading skills.

Personality tests. Although personality tests can never serve as an adequate substitute for the intensive personality study which much of speech re-education demands, they can often give us a quick picture of general tendencies toward maladjustment. Analysis of the items of such paper-and-pencil tests as the Mooney Problem Check List, the Haggerty-Olson-Wickman Behavior Rating Scale, or the Bell Adjustment Inventory can often open up avenues of exploration that might otherwise be overlooked. In our own clinical practice we have found the Minnesota Multiphasic Personality Inventory (18), the Murray Thematic Apperception Test, and the Rorschach Ink-Blot Test to be especially valuable in detecting infantile emotional reactions or hidden anxieties and frustrations.

Achievement tests. These tests are used in speech correction primarily for discovering whether or not a child's educational retardation is due to the influence of his speech defect on reading skills. Articulatory disorders commonly reflect themselves in reading, producing similar errors there, and stuttering and voice cases frequently dislike oral reading so much that it affects their silent skills.   Remedial reading can easily be combined with remedial speech work, and improvement in both will frequently solve the child's other scholastic problems.   Two excellent batteries are the Stanford Achievement Tests and the Unit Scales of Attainment, but these should be supplemented by the diagnostic reading tests of Gates and Monroe.

Aptitude tests.   Since severe speech defectives are often unemployed or are situated in occupations ill-suited to their abilities, they generally need some vocational counseling.   We have found the Kuder Preference Record and the Cleeton Vocational Interest Inventory to be valuable aids in this counseling.

References

1. Bender, L. and Woltmann, A. G., "The Use of Plastic Materials as a Psychiatric Approach to Emotional Problems in Children," *American Journal of Orthopsychiatry*, July, 1937, Vol. 7, pages 283–300.
Children's activities in playing with modeling clay are observed and interpreted in the light of their emotional conflicts.

2. Bingham, W. V. D. and Moore, B. V., *How to Interview* (third revised edition), New York, Harper, 1941.
This is probably the best book on interviewing techniques in all fields.   It provides an outline for the training of interviewers which any student could follow.

3. Bryngelson, B., "Psychological Problems in Stuttering," *Mental Hygiene*, 1937, Vol. 21, pages 631–639.
A discussion of the stuttering personality and of the "objective attitude" as a basis for all therapy.

4. Cattell, R. B., *Crooked Personalities in Childhood and After: An Introduction to Psycho-Therapy*, New York, D. Appleton-Century, 1938.
This book considers the psychological treatment of nervous children and discusses fundamentals related to the origins of maladjustment, heredity, the family and its relation to the child, and the obligations of society in mental hygiene.

5. Despert, L. J., *Emotional Problems in Children*, Utica, N. Y., State Hospital Press, 1938.
The various emotional problems of children including speech defects are discussed in terms of environmental influences, parental attitudes, and developmental factors.

6. Gesell, A., Castner, B. M., and Amatruda, C. S., *Biographies of Child Development*, New York, Hoeber, 1939, pages 139–146.
The development of a delayed speech case is described according to the physical and social background.   The influence of a new social environ-

ment and new attitudes on the part of the parents and nurse are discussed.

7. Glauber, I. P., "Speech Characteristics of Psychoneurotic Patients," *Journal of Speech Disorders*, March, 1944, Vol. 9, pages 18–30.
Ten brief case histories of neurotic patients are given to illustrate the point that emotional conflicts reflect themselves in the speech of these individuals.

8. Greene, J. S., "Functional Speech and Voice Disorders," *Journal of Nervous and Mental Disease*, March, 1942, Vol. 95, pages 299–309.
Speech disorders due to emotional causes are presented and discussed.

9. Harms, E. (Editor), "Approaches to the Problem of Anxiety and Fear Disturbances in Young Children," *Nervous Child*, January, 1946, Volume 5, pages 8–95.
A description of children's fears, their development, prevention, and treatment.

10. Hunt, W. A., and Stevenson, C.. "I. Psychological Testing in Military Clinical Psychology: II. Personality Testing," *Psychological Review*, 1946, Volume 53, pages 107–115.
A good description of various personality tests and their application to psychotherapy.

11. Johnson, Wendell, *Because I Stutter*, New York, D. Appleton-Century, 1930.
An account of the influence of stuttering upon the personality, written by a stutterer. He also gives a description of the cause of his speech difficulty, as it was ultimately diagnosed.

12. Johnson, Wendell, "The Influence of Stuttering on the Personality," *University of Iowa Studies in Child Welfare*, Vol. 5, 1932.
A monograph of a study to evaluate the influence of stuttering on the personality, and the principles underlying the development of stutterers' attitudes. It considers stutterers' adjustments in school, the relation of age to adjustment difficulties, the chief wishes of stutterers, and their greatest personality problems. Many case studies are included, and the autobiography as a valuable technique is discussed.

13. Kanner, L., *Child Psychiatry*, Springfield, C. C. Thomas, 1937.
Deals directly with speech disorders and also treats many other childhood problems, including: the methods of studying and handling children's psychiatric problems, the age factor, the emotional factor, the sex factor, the environment factor, work with the family, emotional disorders, thinking difficulties, antisocial trends, the major and minor psychoses, and specific therapeutic aids.

14. Louttit, G. M., *Clinical Psychology*, New York, Harper, 1936.
Contains a complete chapter on speech defects (Chapter 11), and also considers school retardation, specific disabilities in school subjects, superiority, behavior and conduct problems, personality problems, juvenile delinquency, sensory defects, psychoneuroses and psychoses, and neurological and physical disabilities.

15. MacKenzie, C. M., "Facial Deformity and Changes in Personality Following Corrective Surgery," *Northwest Medicine*, August, 1944, Vol. 43, pages 230–231.

Patients with facial deformities usually withdraw from society. Remarkable changes in personality may result from corrective surgery.

16. Marquit, S. and Berman, A. B., "Psychological Techniques and Mechanisms in Guidance," *Journal of General Psychology*, 1942, Vol. 27, pages 231–240.
Seven case summaries are presented to show the types of psychological tests and methods used in guidance.

17. Marzolf, S. S., *Studying the Individual; a Manual on the Case Study for Guidance Workers and Psycho-clinicians*, Minneapolis, Burgess, 1940.
In this manual the student will find a good discussion of the usefulness of the case history, techniques for eliciting information, and a set of problems and questions which provide an opportunity for training in administration and interpretation.

18. Richardson, L. H., "A Personality Study of Stutterers and Non-stutterers," *Journal of Speech Disorders*, June, 1944, Vol. 9, pages 152–160.
This reference illustrates the use of various personality tests in speech correction.   The author discusses the value of the Rorschach, the Thematic-Apperception test, the Personality Inventory, and other diagnostic aids.

19. Rogers, C. W., *Counselling and Psychotherapy*, Boston, Houghton Mifflin, 1942.
This text has already become a classic in its field: the indirect interview as a device for conflict diagnosis and psychotherapy.   Every speech clinician should not only read this book but also train himself in the techniques so clearly illustrated therein.

20. Rotter, J. A., "A Working Hypothesis as to the Nature and Treatment of Stuttering," *Journal of Speech Disorders*, 1942, Vol. 7, pages 263–288.
The author stresses the importance of working on the whole personality of the stutterer rather than on his symptoms.

21. Travis, L. E., "A Point of View in Speech Correction," *Quarterly Journal of Speech*, 1936, Vol. 22, pages 57–61.
A statement of the basic principles which should underlie speech correction, with especial emphasis on treating the speech defective rather than the speech defect.

22. Thorn, K. F. and Bryngelson, B., "An Analytical Study of the Social and Speech Adjustment of Good and Poor Speakers by Means of the Autobiographic Method," *Speech Monographs*, 1945, Vol. 12, pages 61–73.

23. Weiss, E. and English, O. S., *Psychosomatic Medicine*, Philadelphia, Saunders, 1944.
One of the best textbooks on psychosomatic medicine.

IV

Psychotherapy in Speech Correction .

A certain amount of psychotherapy is employed by every speech correctionist with every case. When a teacher says to a little child who has finally been able to produce a correct *r* sound, "That's fine, Dorothy; now let's practice it so you can show your mother that you can say the word 'radio' just like big people say it," she is using psychotherapy. When the speech correctionist attempts to persuade the schoolteacher to give the young cleft-palate child a position of some responsibility in the classroom (even if it is only to take care of the chalk supply), we are witnessing a form of psychotherapy. Speech correction is much more than the making and breaking of speech habits. Many of the cases seen by the speech correctionist can only be helped by preliminary or concurrent psychotherapy. Some need psychotherapy and nothing else.

The amount of psychotherapy used with any given case can only be determined by studying his history and behavior. Generally speaking, it is wise to plan a careful program of psychotherapy when the speech defective (1) shows very obvious peculiarities of physique, speech, or behavior; (2) has a history of frequent rejection or other social penalty; (3) reacts by marked aggressiveness or withdrawal tendencies to the normal challenges of life; (4) shows great tension or stress in ordinary situations; (5) rejects or sabotages the efforts of the speech correctionist to improve his speech. The last three of these items can also be used to measure the progress of psychotherapy. When the antagonistic stutterer becomes more friendly, when the tense falsetto-speaking girl becomes more calm and relaxed, when the speech defective approaches his conferences with eagerness and co-operation, the treatment is progressing satisfactorily. When the opposite reactions are in evidence, the speech correctionist should revaluate his methods and diagnoses.

The methods of psychotherapy vary from simple suggestion to

52

profound psychoanalysis. Yet they all seem to be focused on the attainment of the following goals: (1) *to help the speech defective understand his problem;* (2) *to let him get the emotional poison out of his system by freely expressing his true feelings;* (3) *to help him organize and carry out a campaign which will* (a) *increase his social assets and eliminate or minimize his abnormalities;* (b) *eliminate or minimize the penalties inflicted upon him;* (c) *develop attitudes toward his speech defect and other social liabilities which will not handicap him.* We italicize these goals because far too many speech correctionists perform their psychotherapy in a hit-or-miss fashion. Through lack of planning and integration, the result is often so sketchy and incomplete that basic conflicts are untouched. When this happens, progress in speech rehabilitation is slow or entirely blocked.

Fluency for the stutterer or satisfactory *s* sounds for the lisper may be temporarily attained but later lost in a mysterious relapse. If we are to do our work thoroughly and well, we must plan and carry out a systematic program of psychotherapy.

Helping the speech defective to understand his problems. We once asked a small child who had received some speech-correction help in the public schools to tell us what his speech difficulty was. Although he had a very bad lateral lisp, he finally said, "I don't know. I guess I don't talk slow enough." There is no excuse for such blind treatment. The speech defective should always know what his problems are, and this holds true whether they deal with pronunciation errors or profound emotional conflicts.

A far too common practice in speech correction is the imposition of the problem by the speech correctionist. The latter makes his diagnosis and then forces it upon his victim. He tells the adolescent girl, "You still talk baby talk because you don't want to grow up or accept the responsibilities of maturity. You are afraid of rejection by others of your own age. You still wish to be the child that you once were, protected and loved by your parents and playmates." Even when such a diagnosis is correct, it is unwise to try to foist it upon the case. She will probably reject it anyway, and even when she accepts it as the intellectual truth, she will be unable to change her basic emotional attitudes. It is always wise to let the person with a problem find it himself. The task in psychotherapy is to provide the means whereby this insight can be achieved.

The best method for getting a person to locate and define his problems is free, uninhibited talking. If anyone talks long enough and freely enough he will reveal his basic maladjustment not only to others but also to himself.   The art of the speech correctionist comes in creating a situation where the person can feel this freedom of expression.   It is not wise to give this assurance directly ("You may feel free to talk to me frankly about anything").   Instead, the speech correctionist should endeavor, by his responses to what the case tells him, to make clear that he is fundamentally interested only in trying to understand.   He does not judge.   When he does speak, he merely restates the attitudes which have been expressed by the speech defective.   He may clarify them, but he never tries to modify them in the direction of better adjustment.   The case will do that himself, if permitted to.   The speech correctionist never tries to reassure the case that expresses pessimism or hopelessness.   He is merely interested. He does not try to convince his case that the latter's fears, hostility, or guilt feelings are exaggerated or unreasonable.   If they exist, they are important enough to merit the dynamic listening described in the previous chapter.

Letting the speech defective express his repressed feelings.   The usefulness of catharsis in psychotherapy has long been recognized.   The adolescent girl without a girl friend to whom she can confide the difficulties and emotions of those troubled years is in sad straits indeed. There are more confessionals outside the church than within, for the good reason that the need to express our emotional conflicts is even more universal than religion.   Psychoanalysis is founded upon this need.   Rogers (9), in his excellent book on counseling, has this to say:

We have learned that catharsis not only frees the individual from those conscious fears and guilt feelings of which he is aware, but that, continued, it can bring to light more deeply buried attitudes which also exert their influence on behavior.   In recent years we have learned new ways of using this old approach.   The whole technique of play therapy is based on the fundamental principles of catharsis; the use of finger paints and psychodramatics and puppet shows all have a relationship to this old and well-established category of psychotherapy.

The speech defective especially has great need for some emotional expression.   The child with delayed speech so garbled that even his parents cannot understand him frequently shows pronounced behavior problems which disappear as soon as he can talk well enough to express his frustrations verbally.   The stutterer who attempts to talk away his troubles usually only succeeds in increasing his speech difficulty. These individuals need the relief that can come from talking out their problems to an interested and understanding person who will not penalize their speech defects. The speech correctionist is the ideal person to satisfy this need.

It is very difficult for younger children to express their repressed emotions verbally to the speech correctionist, even when they have surrendered their affection and confidence. But when free play is permitted and the child can use materials creatively, many of the hidden attitudes are aired and dissipated.

One of our cases, an eleven-year-old stutterer, brought a picture of a guillotine and asked if he could build one in our shop. He said that he had started one at home but his father had broken it up. We gave him the razor blade he requested and gave him access to a workbench and tools. His finished product was crude but the weighted razor blade was sufficiently adequate to cut a match in two. He then brought from his pocket a clothespin with eyes and nose and mouth inked on the top. "Watch this!" he said with great enthusiasm. The blade descended but it did not do much more than nick the clothespin. He became enraged, picked up the little machine and pounded it viciously, saying, "I'll get you. I'll beat your head off. I'll cut it off. You will break it up, will you! I'll break you up. All in pieces and throw them away."

This experience led to a series of interviews with the father which altered a good many of the environmental pressures on the boy.

Finger painting has likewise served as a means of expressing hostility and other repressed emotional material. Puppet play, in which the child tells the puppet what to do and say, is another excellent vehicle. Even with adults we frequently use some psychodrama before sending the speech defective back to face his old environment. Certain individuals are chosen to take the part of the parents or employers or whoever seems to figure in the situation. Then the case describes the situation and, taking his own part, also directs and corrects the spontaneous interplay between the characters. Phonographic recordings of dramatized speech-conflict situations have also been used successfully to tap the repressed emotions and to channel them into nonharmful activities.

Not only does this catharsis facilitate speech therapy by removing the tensions and emotional blockings which prevent its successful administration, but also, in some cases, it frees the speech defective from his symptoms.

In many cases it is necessary to do much more than provide the case with an understanding of his problem and relieve him of his repressed emotional attitudes. *We must also do all we can to increase his assets, minimize his liabilities, decrease his social penalties, and develop normal attitudes toward his disabilities.*

Earlier in this chapter we pointed out that the speech correctionist should attempt to help the speech defective solve his personality or behavior problems whether they were the cause or the result of his speech defect. Treatment is thereby made much more efficient and effective. In certain instances, the psychiatrist or clinical psychologist must be asked to help. It is even more usual to enlist the aid of parents, teachers, and associates in carrying out the program. Of course, the amount of personality treatment depends upon the nature of the problem.

Clinical psychologists often make the paradoxical statement that the best cure for personality disorders is prevention. It is certainly true that wise parents and teachers often can prevent the child from developing sensitivities and inadequate reactions to speech or other differences which society penalizes, and that they can foster other differences which will be considered sufficiently attractive social assets to forestall rejection. The speech correctionist should always consider it part of his duty to provide the necessary information and to educate the general public concerning proper parental and pedagogic management of the handicapped individual.

Unfortunately, the majority of the cases seen by the speech correctionist have already developed their personality and behavior problems, and while the occurrence of new inadequate reactions or the growth of old ones may be prevented, the urgent problem is concerned with the solution of those problems that are causing or contributing to the speech defect or interfering with its treatment. The treatment of these individuals varies with the nature of the problem, with age and intelligence, with the amount of parental co-operation, and with so many other factors that it is difficult to discuss the subject save in general terms.

Certain principles, however, seem to govern the methods used: (1) The differences about which the personality problem developed must be discovered, eliminated as far as possible, or recognized (consciously and objectively) as features which good adjustment will minimize and poor adjustment will amplify. (2) The penalties that are being inflicted upon the individual because of his differences should be eliminated as much as possible, and those that occurred earlier in the individual's development should be discovered, brought up to consciousness, and subjected to unemotional analysis or abreaction. Similar procedures should be carried out for those approvals that are not merited or that contribute to the personality problem. (3) The inadequate reactions to penalty or approval must be discovered. Those that are most characteristic should be identified, and a strong attempt should be made to inhibit them. Their contribution to the emotional handicap, to unpleasant social reactions, and to the speech disorder must be clarified. Finally, (4) the objective attitude of intelligent unemotional acceptance of the speech defect and other differences should be substituted for the withdrawal or aggressive reactions.

Discovering and eliminating the nuclei of personality problems. The methods used in discovering what physical, environmental, or behavioral differences served as nuclei for the development of the personality have already been mentioned. There are various ways of eliminating these differences after they have been discovered. If the difference is of a physical nature (cross-eyedness, protruding teeth, obesity, club feet, and so on), we may be able to find surgical, dental, or medical methods for eradicating it. If the difference is environmental or economic, we may be able to eradicate it by enlisting the various social agencies or by removing the child from his present environment. If the difference is behavioral, we may be able to re-educate his parents and associates or to alter his environment so as to remove the irritating stimuli that set off the inadequate behavior. We must always remember that a *difference* implies a relationship, a comparison between two or more individuals, and we may eradicate a difference by having its possessor join a group of individuals who possess similar traits. Thus we often find a swift release from emotional conflict when the speech defective enters a speech clinic and discovers many other individuals with similar peculiarities. His own difference is minimized by such association. When he is able to include himself as a part of normal society by perceiving that its members, too, possess penalizable differences to which they might react inadequately, much progress has been made. For this reason, one technique useful in speech correction is the conduction of a class dealing with personality and behavior problems or a class in public speaking, taught from the mental-hygiene point of view. The speech defectives in these classes soon learn that the so-called normal speakers have their own differences and insecurities. When carried out under the direction of an able clinician, exhibition and discussion of these differences seem to have much value.   Confession and verbalization provide excellent means of reducing their influence, and good-humored admissions or exaggerations tend to diminish the emotion with which they are invested.   At any rate, the first task in the management of a personality problem is an attempt to eradicate or minimize those differences about which the individual has built his inadequate behavior. One case study may be cited:

E. G. was a cross-eyed girl of nineteen with a very severe stutter. Although of superior intelligence, she left school in the ninth grade and, from that time on, she very seldom left the confines of her home.   She dominated her wealthy parents in every way and shirked every type of responsibility.   When guests came for dinner, she had the servants serve her in her room.   She spoke very little to anyone but read a great deal. Simulated heart attacks were used to control her parents.   She refused to see any physician.   Financial reverses and the death of her father forced her to do something about her speech defect after an attempt at suicide failed because of lack of courage.   Enrolled in the speech clinic, she immersed herself in the literature on stuttering but failed to carry out any assignment which entailed any persistence, courage, or exhibition of her speech defect.   Faced with dismissal, she pleaded that she wanted to cooperate but did not have the will power.   She declared that she thought she would acquire some if she were permitted to remain.   She was told that she could return if she would have an operation for her strabismus and carry out a certain set of assignments at home.   The operation was very successful, and, when she returned a year later, her personality seemed to have changed entirely.   She had performed not only all of the assignments given her but many more difficult ones as well.   She had prepared herself for college entrance examinations, had taken dancing lessons, and had obtained and held a job in a restaurant for some time.   For the first time she seemed to have some self-respect and courage to undergo temporary unpleasantness in order to achieve a future goal.   Her stuttering was still present though its severity had decreased.   She co-operated in every way and progressed rapidly in her speech work.   Her explanation for the change was succinct: "Having my eyes fixed gave me my chance."

Eliminating and minimizing the penalties and unmerited approvals that produce maladjustment.   Psychiatrists have often pointed out that the most inadequate behavior shown by maladjusted individuals occurs in situations in which there are features similar to those of traumatic or extremely unpleasant situations in the early history of the individual.   This is especially true of penalties.   Even the so-called normal person tends to react childishly at times, and those times are characterized by the presence of people or penalties bearing some important resemblance to childhood conflict situations. These present situations which are reminiscent of old maladjustment are the danger spots for which our speech defective must be prepared, and through our intensive study of the person, we teach our cases to recognize those persons and penalties which bear dangerous resemblance to old conflicts. This very recognition helps to prevent the almost involuntary response which is aroused by such reminiscent conditions. Many adults are not lying when they claim that they "just couldn't help" their inadequate behavior when confronted by old penalties. After the clinician helps them to be on their guard, they can develop the ability to inhibit the sudden overwhelming impulse to withdraw or attack.

Another useful technique in preventing the person or penalty from acting as a cue to set off the old response is to associate with it some other incompatible response, such as one that is humorous or absurd. The clinician may also deliberately create experimental situations, warning the speech defective beforehand, in which the old penalties or unmerited approvals are used. The speech defective is asked to react as adequately as possible and to substitute an adequate response for that which he commonly uses in such situations. He may also be asked to use similar penalties himself and to see how others react to them. Occasionally, the clinician should set up an experimental situation with the old penalties and give the student permission to react in the old way. With permission, the reaction becomes absurd. Paranoidal tendencies may be checked by assignments to exaggerate and burlesque them on a verbal level. A written diary of all suspected penalties as compared with those which are overt will also help.

Above all, it is necessary that all penalties and rejections be verbalized and confessed to someone—the speech correctionist or psychiatrist, as the case may be. Much of the emotion can be dissipated in this way, and the confession will serve as an excellent opportunity for dispassionate analysis and proposals of alternative reactions. Speech is one of the best forms of emotional catharsis we have in our clinical repertoire.

Of course, many of these suggested techniques cannot be used with young children. With them, it is necessary to educate the parents and associates to refrain from using those penalties and rejections that are producing the inadequate behavior. Occasionally this is not possible because of the personality problems or resistances to clinical recommendation which the parents or associates themselves possess.

In this event, it is wise to try to take the child out of the old environment, at least for a time. Visits to more co-operative relatives are
useful. Occasionally summer camps, private schools, or boarding
homes provide such a change. It is also possible to change the environment to some extent by getting the speech defective to join new
groups or to make new acquaintances who will react less savagely to
the objectionable difference. Even when the parents seem willing to
co-operate, it is wise to provide some clinical supervision, since parents
find it difficult to change their ideas and penalties. Family conferences at the end of the day and weekly reports to the clinician in which
the parents confess to each other, or to the clinician, their failures in
following the new regime will help to ensure its success.

*Eliminating the withdrawal and attack reactions which characterize
the maladjustment.* We must remember that eliminating the objectionable differences themselves will not always remove the inadequate
behavior shown by the maladjusted speech defective. Withdrawal
and attack reactions may become habitual responses to almost any
type of insecurity. They may have originally been born and nursed
by some former difference which no longer exists. Arising as specific
responses to a specific situation, they tend to become generalized and
stereotyped. Since they themselves become behavioral differences
that are penalized by the group, they attain a permanence that is independent of their original causes. It is necessary, therefore, to focus
some therapy directly upon the reactions themselves.

In general, the procedure to be followed is similar to that described
in the last section. The withdrawal and attack reactions must be
brought up to consciousness, confessed, guarded against, voluntarily
practiced in unemotional or clinical situations, exaggerated, associated
with humorous and other incongruous attitudes, freed from their satisfactions, penalized, and inhibited. Above all, their motives must be
analyzed. They must be understood in terms of the past history of
the individual and in terms of their contribution to the personal unpleasantness and social handicap.

It is not sufficient or possible merely to teach the speech defective
to give up or inhibit his old withdrawal or attack reactions. He must
be taught some substitute response to rejection, penalty, and all the
other forms of insecurity. The substitute response usually taught is
that which we have described in an earlier part of the chapter as the
"objective attitude," or the intelligent unemotional acceptance of the
objectionable difference as a problem capable of some solution. With

some cases, it is impossible to teach this objective acceptance immediately, and a clinician will occasionally teach withdrawal reactions to an individual who habitually attacks, or aggressive reactions to the person who characteristically retreats. Even with these cases, the final aim is always the acquisition of an attitude that will face the facts realistically.

The nature of the objective attitude has already been discussed. Intelligent and well-informed parents teach it to their handicapped children when they are very young, and these children find it just as natural as other children find withdrawing or attacking. Among children as well as adults, the objective attitude is most easily taught through example. Attitudes are notoriously contagious, and if some of a child's associates, parents, or teachers adopt such an objective attitude, he will usually acquire it almost unconsciously. Occasionally, it will be necessary for him to be taught some verbalization of it, so that its expression will not be too hesitant or floundering when challenged by his associates. When possible, the child should be taught to accompany his unemotional admission of the difference with a statement of belief in its eventual disappearance. Thus one untutored cross-eyed child was overheard saying to his teasing associates, "Sure I'm cross-eyed and I'm going to Chicago some time and get it fixed." All teasing stopped. A difference about which the possessor was not sensitive was not worth wasting teasing upon—so reasoned the group. A well-conducted speech-correction class in which groups of children are taught together is a very efficient agent in the teaching of this attitude. They learn it from one another as well as from the teacher.

When working with older children or adults whose maladjustment is very marked, one must utilize the same indirect methods for teaching the objective attitude; but, in addition, more direct methods can be employed. The philosophy behind the objective attitude should be taught with emphasis on its reasonableness. The speech defective, for example, should be shown, through analysis of actual situations, how his withdrawal or attack reactions contribute to the present unpleasantness and perpetuation of his handicap. He should be shown that the speech defect is but a small part of his total handicap, that an emotional handicap is usually added to every physical or behavioral one, and that often the former far overshadows the latter.

The student should be required to outline a program of self-reeducation under the guidance of his clinician. Daily assignments should be formulated, first by the clinician and later by the student himself. These should be constructed in such a fashion that the student will have to enter new situations in which his difference is subject to penalty. They should provide devices for checking the occurrence of old reactions. Daily reports should be made to the clinician in written or verbal form. The student should make a confession of each day's inadequate reactions, adding an honest analysis of reasons for his failure and a statement of the more adequate reactions that he might have used. Whenever possible, the teacher and student should formulate assignments to cancel the failure. Occasionally, some associate of the student who consistently uses the same penalty can be found. Such associates provide excellent opportunities for demonstrating improvement in adjustment.

A system of good-natured but vivid penalties should be devised to take care of the failures that cannot be canceled. The student is assigned to use the inadequate reactions in situations in which he is not insecure. For example, a girl with a falsetto voice due to hypertension resulting from social and economic insecurities constantly reacted to all persons whose social poise she envied by sarcastically attacking them. With those to whom she felt socially superior, she never showed this reaction, and her voice was not falsetto. She was therefore assigned to be devastatingly sarcastic to three of the latter individuals. The assignment was very difficult, but, when finally performed, it so convinced her of the inadequacy of the sarcasm that she seldom used it again, and, when she did, the memory of its distastefulness soon curtailed its use.

The value of such negative practice is that of increased insight. The student is assigned deliberately to create situations in which the former insecurities and inadequate behavior would tend to be present. The old inadequate reactions, however, are not to be used, but, instead, the appropriate behavior is to be carried out. Such deliberate entrance into insecure situations not only teaches new reactions, but also gets rid of a great deal of the fear associated with them. The student is required to state his problem and his attempts at solution whenever opportunity presents itself. Admission of the problem and evidence of intention to improve will often change the attitudes of groups which formerly rejected the individual. Often the speech correctionist can contact the persons who have previously exerted these penalties, informing them of the situation and requesting their cooperation. A systematic program of self-improvement should be worked out to provide the maximum future economic, social, and sexual security. Subgoals for each of these securities should be formulated, and assignments leading to their fulfillment should be systematically carried out. Most of this personality work is individual and very time-consuming, but it is truly effective.

Treatment of individuals with certain special personality and behavior problems. Whenever faced by penalty or the threat of penalty, certain speech defectives with a history of thoroughgoing withdrawal fail to co-operate with the speech correctionist despite their urgent need for help. They often claim that they would like to co-operate but that either (1) they do not have the energy or will power to carry out the assignments, or (2) they do not have the time because of the great demands made upon them by their music or writing or other form of overcompensation. These two defenses are rather difficult to break down, but the task can be accomplished. Occasionally it is advisable to let the overcompensating individuals start their speech-correction work and then to terminate it suddenly because of their refusal to co-operate. They can then be readmitted whenever they agree to give up the overcompensation. Strong realistic attitudes on the part of the clinician, together with examples and powerful propaganda in behalf of the objective attitude, will usually solve the problem.

Teachers of speech correction often fail to make much headway with speech defectives of the weak-willed variety, and they attribute their failure to this characteristic itself. Although such students are exasperating in their seeming refusal to put forth any real effort of their own toward alleviating their handicaps, it will be found that proper training in self-discipline will produce excellent results. However, before the teacher can hope to train another person in such discipline, it is necessary that she train herself, a process that will usually be of more than academic value.

Before one begins such training in self-discipline, it is necessary to make a behavior analysis to determine wherein the weakness lies. Such an analysis would require examples of behavior which indicate: (1) inability to make a prompt decision; (2) avoidance of responsibility or opportunity; (3) procrastination of inevitable tasks; (4) leaving tasks or projects unfinished; (5) refusal to undergo temporary unpleasantness for a future good; (6) disorganized and wasteful effort; (7) half-hearted effort, obviously inadequate to the task; (8) inability to perceive or respond to a subgoal leading to fulfillment of a strong desire; (9) self-deprecation; (10) daydreaming and other substitute satisfactions. The relative frequency of behavior falling under these categories will indicate the proper direction of training in self-discipline.

The majority of individuals will have little difficulty in carrying out a program of remedial work based upon these weaknesses once they are clearly seen, for there is a formula which almost forces them to carry out their projects. That formula may be stated as follows: (1) State your task and your determination to someone whose respect you greatly desire or wish to keep; (2) plan a definite time and place for its accomplishment and tell that other person what they are; (3) insist that he check up on your performance as soon as possible.

It should be stressed that the motivation for these assignments or tasks should be the fulfillment of a desire to improve oneself rather than the consequences of the task itself. When working with a very weak willed speech defective, it is at first necessary to subordinate his will entirely to your own, to compel him to carry out the tasks which you assign and to make the reports you demand. But it is wise to wean him psychologically as soon as the effect of the new regime has built up his own self-respect. At first the assignments should be so constructed that their unpleasantness will never be greater than the unpleasantness of reporting a failure. As he continues to fulfill them, his pride in himself will increase, and consequently his desire for approval. As his pride grows, so, too, can the difficulty of the assignments. The assignments and tasks should always be appropriate to the patient's weakness, but they may range far and wide within the category. Thus, a speech defective who habitually refuses to undergo temporary unpleasantness for a future good is assigned to have a dental cavity filled. Self-discipline assignments need not be confined to speech work. Occasionally, when the patient absolutely refuses to carry out a speech assignment, it is well to perform it yourself, insisting that he accompany you. As you carry it out, verbalize the thoughts he would have verbalized, were he doing it, and exaggerate his symptoms. However, no refusal must go unchallenged, and it is better to give up a case than to continue without his co-operation.

As soon as possible, the speech defective should be acquainted with the entire plan of his treatment so that he can see the relation of his daily assignments to his subgoals, and their relation to the end goal— normal speech. Too many teachers ignore the importance of this type of motivation, not realizing how much they are retarding the patient's progress. Blind work is usually worthless. In so far as possible, it is well to make speech improvement merely a phase of general improvement. Improvement in the patient's personality will improve his speech, and vice versa. The speech-correction teacher should train herself in outlining such general campaigns for self-improvement by outlining one for herself.

When the speech defective is characterized by aggressive and attack behavior, the speech correctionist must expect to find these attitudes focused on him by that defective. Hidden or open antagonism to speech-correction work will occur, sometimes expressing itself in subtle sabotage and sometimes in direct conflict. The author has found it wise to provide some form of outlet for the impulse to attack or rebel in these cases. Some associate is delegated to provoke the antagonistic reactions at every turn, keeping a detailed report of the case's behavior. Other associates are designated as individuals to whom the case must present a picture of modesty, submissiveness, and withdrawal. All expressions of antagonism or justification should be recorded, and the student should be required to recite them over and over until they lose their satisfaction. Exaggerated behavior of this type should be assigned to be displayed in nonappropriate situations.

The clinician should never allow himself to react to the antagonism shown him, but must always show an attitude of tolerant interest in that behavior. He may duplicate the student's behavior in some other situation, requiring the student to observe the mechanisms demonstrated. In a few cases, the negativism and antagonism can be used as actual motivation for speech work if the clinician expresses his belief in the student's inability to achieve certain goals or perform certain tasks. If the environment of such an individual is altered so that it provides a minimum of penalties or empathic reactions to his attack, and if other methods of reaction are taught to him, he can usually be brought to make an adequate adjustment.

References

1. Allen, F. H., *Psychotherapy with Children*, New York, Norton, 1942. Chapter 3 of this stimulating book, "The Therapeutic Process," has a great many concepts and methods for the speech correctionist who has to deal with problem children or children with problems.

2. Beckey, R. E., "The Children's Speech Clinic," *Hygeia*, 1944, Vol. 19, pages 663–664.
A popular description of speech therapy through play.

3. Bryngelson, B., "Psychologic Factors in the Management of the

Exceptional Child," *Journal of Exceptional Children*, 1938, Vol. 5, pages 65–67.
The role of the teacher in managing the handicapped child is presented from a mental-hygiene point of view.

4. Conn, J. H., "The Child Reveals Himself Through Play," *Mental Hygiene*, January, 1939, Vol. 23, pages 49–69.
In this article the student will come to understand that the child not only reveals himself through play, but also relieves himself of a good many emotional conflicts.

5. Despert, J. L., "A Therapeutic Approach to the Problem of Stuttering in Children," *The Nervous Child*, 1943, Vol. 2, pages 134–147.
The importance of maternal attitudes in affecting the treatment of stuttering in young children is clearly presented. The attempt to solve the child's anxieties is described.

6. Hollis, F., *Social Case Work in Practice*, New York, Family Welfare Association, 1939.
The importance of this book for speech correction lies in its exposition of attempts to alter the family situation in which the emotional conflicts are centered.

7. Gustavson, C. G., "A Talisman and a Convalescence," *Quarterly Journal of Speech*, 1944, Vol. 30, pages 465–471.
An excellent account of the introspections of an adult "cured" stutterer which is especially useful in illustrating the withdrawal reactions as the person himself feels them and in portraying the individual's attempts to free himself from their frustration.

8. Lemert, E. M. and Van Riper, C., "The Use of Psychodrama in the Treatment of Speech Defects," *Sociometry*, 1944, Vol. 7, pages 190–195.
Many different types of psychodramatic activity are cited to show their application to speech correction. Puppets, phonographically recorded dramatizations of interview material, and other similar agencies are used in the diagnosis and treatment of personality problems.

9. Rogers, C. W., *Counselling and Psychotherapy*, Boston, Houghton Mifflin, 1942.
The final part of this book is a transcription of a phonographically recorded series of interviews with a neurotic stutterer which led to excellent insight into the nature of his problems and provided their solution. The student can here see psychotherapy in action.

10. Whiles, W. H., "Treatment of Emotional Problems of Children," *Journal of Mental Science*, 1941, Vol. 87, pages 359–369.
A common-sense approach to children's emotional problems with emphasis on environmental alteration.

11. Whitten, I. E., "Therapies Used for Stuttering: A Report of the Author's Own Case," *Quarterly Journal of Speech*, 1938, Vol. 24, pages 227–233.
In this case report of a successful treatment of stuttering a preliminary psychiatric therapy was followed by speech therapy. Both are described in sufficient detail to give proper perspective to both.

12. Will, N., "A Six-Month Report on the Personality Development of a Thirteen-Year-Old Stuttering Boy," *Quarterly Journal of Speech*, 1944, Vol. 30, pages 88–95.

The picture of the child's personality at the beginning and end of therapy is given, together with a description of the methods used in altering his behavior patterns.

V

How Children Learn to Talk

The problem. Many new parents seem surprised when asked if they know how to teach their baby to talk. They usually answer that babies learn to talk just as they learn to breathe or swallow. Let us examine this common assumption. James IV of Scotland deliberately isolated two children at birth under the care of a mute nurse, and it is said that when they first spoke they "spak very guid Hebrew," a conclusion which conveniently confirmed the royal prediction that any child exposed to such an environment would learn to speak in that tongue. However, Kaspar Hauser, who had been forcibly imprisoned when a child and kept in an isolated cell for sixteen years, had no speech at all. Nor did Lucas, the Baboon Boy of Africa, Victor, the Wild Boy of Aveyron, or Kamala, the Wolf Girl of India. An eight-year-old boy, Tamasha, when found in the jungle of Salvador in Central America, had only one actual word among his animal grunts and growls. Only after a long and difficult course of training did he develop a meager vocabulary.

It is true that many children learn to speak without any conscious or deliberate teaching on the part of their parents. Indeed, some children develop speech despite incredibly poor teaching methods, emotional conflicts, and parental neglect. In a similar manner, even though some children have learned to read by spelling out Burma-Shave signs along the highway, we still employ elementary school-teachers who spend years preparing for their task of teaching children how to read. The skills involved in speech are far more complex than those in reading, yet, how many parents have ever read a word on the subject of teaching a child to talk? It is even difficult to find material related to the teaching of talking. Anyone who has observed the average parent bombarding his baby with the wrong type of speech material at the wrong time and in the wrong way will not marvel that there are so many speech defectives. Nor will he be surprised to learn that most of the speech disorders begin during the first years of life. Libraries are crammed with books on how to teach everything from advertising to zoology, but you will search long and far for a book on the teaching of talking, the most useful of all our communicative skills. Because of this basic neglect, the speech defective is with us still, usually as still as possible.

A question almost impossible to answer is "When did your child learn to talk?" The skills involved in speech begin to be acquired as soon as the child is born and are seldom perfectly mastered, even during a lifetime. Much of the speech learning during the first six months is relatively independent of the stimulation given by the child's parents. Even in the crying and wailing of infants the short, sharp inhalation and prolonged exhalation so fundamental to true speech are being practiced. Lip, jaw, and tongue movements involved in the production of all the speech sounds in all human languages are repeatedly performed. The early awareness of these movements and their accompanying sounds provides the foundation for speech readiness. Throughout the first years of life there are many ways in which parents can help or hinder the development of speech. Their knowledge or ignorance determines whether the child shall learn to talk because of his parents' efforts or in spite of them. Their application of principles, so obvious that we wonder why they should ever be violated, will determine whether the child's speech will be an asset or a handicap. Time after time the speech correctionist tries to trace the cause of a stutter or an articulatory defect, only to lose it in the vague parental memories of childhood. It is vitally important for the student of speech correction to know how speech develops.

First Through Sixth Month

Crying, whimpering, reflexive sounds. The child is learning to talk when he draws his first breath and lets out the yell that announces his arrival. He is learning to talk as he sucks and swallows, belches and smiles, for co-ordinations used in these activities are used in speech.

However, many of these activities are reflexive in nature. The birth cry itself seems to be nothing more than the automatic intake of air across taut vocal cords. During the first two weeks, most of the infant's vocalization is of this sort. It seems to have no intent or meaning. Variations in intensity account for practically all the variety that can be heard in the squall. Most of the vocalization occurs during pain, hunger, cold, or some other discomfort, but the nature of the irritation cannot be distinguished from the type of squall.

Even during the first month, the vocalizations vary from child to child. One infant may coo and laugh when taken from the breast; another may whimper; and still another may kick and scream. Research indicates that even at this period there are more vowels and consonants used in noncrying vocalizations than in whimpering, and more sounds used in whimpering than in ordinary crying.

The noncrying sounds are composed of grunts, gurgles, and sighs, and include most of the front vowels, the consonants k, l, g, and the glottal catch. These particular consonants involve contacts and tongue movements similar to those used in swallowing. All of these sounds are accompanied by movements of the arms, legs, or trunk. They sometimes occur during the act of sucking or immediately after feeding. Compared to later vocalizations, the noncrying sounds produced by a healthy baby during the first month are relatively infrequent. More crying is done than whimpering, and more whimpering noises are produced than noncrying ones. Perhaps it was this fact which led one scientific father (4), faithfully and no doubt solemnly, to record his baby's wails, first phonographically and then in the phonetic alphabet. After a profound mathematical analysis of the records, he concluded that the wails increased in pitch. Most night-walking fathers would agree that the wails also increase in loudness and meanness.

Many parents seek to prevent all crying, although a certain amount of it does exercise the child's vocal and respiratory co-ordinations as well as its parents' patience. They jounce their baby up and down, juggle it back and forth, or rock it, pat it, and whirl it until it is dizzy enough to end its crying through unconsciousness. Other parents resolutely ignore their newborn's howls because of a mistaken fear that they might spoil the child. These babies may cry away so many of their waking hours that their speech-sound repertoire will be necessarily limited. As we have seen, fewer sounds are used in crying than in noncrying speech. Again, many parents interrupt their children's automatic vocalization by embracing them or conversing with them. They should let the vocal play period complete itself. During this first period the muscular development of the tongue may be delayed and abnormally high palatal arches may be produced by bottle feeding with improper nipples. These organic conditions may delay speech development.

TABLE 1

SUMMARY OF MOTOR AND SPEECH DEVELOPMENT
(First Through Third Month)

	Motor Development	*Response to Adult Stimulation*
FIRST MONTH	Occasionally can lift head. When one part of the body is stimulated, the whole body becomes active.	Reflex smiling movements to tactual organic or kinesthetic stimulation. Will push away adult's finger if pressed against baby's chin. When laid prone on flat surface, makes crawling movements.
SECOND MONTH	Able to follow a horizontally moving light with eye movements. Can lift head and chest off the floor when prone. Can turn from side to side.	Soothing voice will occasionally stop crying. Social smiling and laughter if eye contact and smiling accompanies adult's voice.
THIRD MONTH	Sits with support. Holds head steady.	If adult interrupts child's vocalization by voice, child will either increase own vocalization or stop altogether. Occasionally will imitate exact intonation and phonetic form, but usually automatically responds to adult speech by own formerly practiced sounds. Responds to angry vocal tone by crying; to pleasant one by cooing, sighing, and other noncrying vocalization.

Speech Development
(type of vocalization and conditions under which it occurs.)

	Type	*Conditions*
END OF FIRST MONTH	Crying: Vowels (usually nasalized): æ, ɛ, ɪ, ɛ, ʌ. Consonants: l, h. Whimpering: Vowels (often nasalized): i, ɪ, ɛ, ɛ, æ, ʌ. Noncrying (sighs, grunts, explosives, etc. Not likely to be nasalized): Vowels: i, ɪ, ɛ, ɛ, æ, ʌ, ʊ, u. Consonants: h, k, g, l.	Hunger, pain, discomfort, fatigue, lack of exercise, strong sensory stimuli. Has intense conditions of the types listed above. Relief from conditions of discomfort.
END OF THIRD MONTH	Same sounds as above, plus a very few more. Pitch of crying slightly higher. Relatively more noncrying vocalization. If the child's attention is attracted (eye movements fixated on adult, who smiles and speaks to child) he will often respond by vocalization. Crying begins to be differentiated according to type of discomfort: pain, hunger, etc. In some children, repetitive chains of sounds ("gagagagaga") appear in states of comfort. Back consonant (k, g, ŋ) sounds relatively frequent.	

71

Table 2

SUMMARY OF MOTOR AND SPEECH DEVELOPMENT

(Fourth Through Sixth Month)

Motor Development	Response to Adult Stimulation	Speech Development (type of vocalization and conditions under which it occurs)
Will reach for, but miss, dangling objects. Will accept and hold an object. Sits up easily with support.	The typical (imitative) response of infant vocalization to the mere hearing of speech and voice seems to decrease in frequency at this time, not to reappear until the ninth month. Interruption of babbling by adult speech usually causes silence unless adult is not sensed as a meaningful stimulus.	More babbling and vocal play (repetitive chains of syllables) than ever before. They occur more frequently when the child is alone. They are accompanied by smiles, laughter, gurgles, and other sounds indicatory of comfort and well-being.
Sits alone momentarily. Turns from back to side. Pulls hair and nose.	Responds to human voices in absence of visual contact by head and eye turning. Responds automatically to friendly tone by smiling and angry tone by crying. Vocalizes displeasure if loved toy is removed.	Occasional reinforcement of babbling if parents interrupt with the syllable being spoken by the child and speak it softly in the proper rhythm so it creates no interruption.
Squeaks a rubber doll. Can reach for object and put it in mouth. Rolls from back to stomach. Can grasp dangling object. Sits alone thirty seconds or more. Can hold two cubes.	Child no longer reacts automatically to friendly or angry tones but rather to the accompanying features of the situation. Follows a vertically moving object with eyes.	The babbling not only consists of more or less regular patterns of phonetically similar syllables but there is also a marked rhythm. These chains of sound often begin in a whisper, rise to a crescendo of intensity (though not of pitch), and then subside. More noncrying sounds than at three months. Nasal sounds begin to appear in babbling as well as in crying.

72

In the baby's second and third month he begins to respond to human speech by smiling and vocalization. This vocalization has little resemblance to adult language. The coos, gurgles, clicks, grunts, and sighs do include a few consonants and vowels that we may recognize, but the father should not become discouraged if he says "Daddy! Daddy!" and the child responds with "wah." At least the baby is producing vocalization, and as anyone who has ever worked with a deaf-mute knows, that achievement is no small one. Parents should encourage this almost instinctive tendency to vocal play by combining a few gentle vowels with smiles, and then waiting the four or five seconds the baby needs before he responds. Most parents never give their children this necessary time interval. They should!

A good share of this vocal play is carried on when the child is alone and it disappears when someone attracts his attention.

One child played with her babbling each morning after awakening, usually beginning with a whispered "eenuh" (Lina) and repeating it with increasing effort until she spoke the syllable aloud, whereupon she would laugh and chortle as she said it over and over. The moment she heard a noise in the parents' bedroom this babbling would cease and crying would begin.

The parents who joyfully rush in and ruin this speech rehearsal are failing to appreciate its significance in the learning of speech. The child must simultaneously feel and hear the sound repeatedly if it is ever to emerge as an identity. Imitation is essentially a device to perpetuate a stimulus, and babbling is self-imitation of the purest variety. When the babbling period is interrupted or delayed through illness, the appearance of true speech is often similarly retarded. Deaf babies begin to babble at a normal time, but since they cannot hear the sounds they produce, they probably lose interest and hence have much less true vocal play than the hearing child. Mirrors suspended above the cribs of deaf babies have increased the babbling through visual self-stimulation.

Babies babble most freely after food and drink—even as you and I—and yet most parents use this postfeeding period to bombard the infant with such a hodge-podge of verbal, visual, and tactual sensations that they are bound to inhibit the self-stimulation that might occur. They tickle his feet, tell him he looks like his Uncle Oscar, lift him up to test his poundage, and flood his ears with endearing verbiage. It must be difficult to be a baby trying to learn to talk.

Table 3

SUMMARY OF MOTOR AND SPEECH DEVELOPMENT
(Seventh Through Ninth Month)

Motor Development	Response to Adult Stimulation	Speech Development (type of vocalization and conditions under which it occurs)
Sits alone easily. Stretches out arms to mother. Cutting first teeth.	Usually rejects adult demands for imitation but occasionally will form sounds with silent mouth movements. Responds by pursuit or flight movements to coaxing or threatening gestures if accompanied by vocalization.	Much more variety, occasional disyllables heard in babbling—occasional periods when same sounds are repeated for several days.
Stands with help. Begins to crawl. Will offer toy. Cutting first teeth.	Begins to combine babbling with gestures of reaching, rejecting. Calls for attention. If adult interrupts by imitating child's rhythmic pounding, clapping, or the motor play, the child will show marked perseveration in the activity. Toward the end of the eighth month, the child will imitate adult's physical rhythmic movements (clapping, nodding, etc.).	Toward the end of the eighth month the child begins to inflect his babbling, changing the pitch suddenly, repeating the commanding, complaining, declaring, questioning intonations of adults. Begins to duplicate in his own private vocal play the "mama" "dada" and "bye-bye" words spoken so often by his parents but does this as a form of babbling rather than as a response to adult stimulation.
Stands, holding furniture. Sits up alone. Stepping movements. Sways to music.	Responds to strangers by retreating or crying and to other children by exploration or crying. Beginning about the ninth month the child will hold out arms if adult prepares to pick child up by showing same activity.	More phonetic variety in crying as well as in babbling. More back vowels used in both. Higher pitch level and more pitch variation. Crying (yelling) often used to get attention. Babbling proportionately more frequent form of phonation than at five months.

74

The next major advance in the use of speech material may be called the stage of socialized vocalization, and it begins, in the majority of children, about the fifth month.   The child begins to use his vocalization (with more vowels than consonants) for getting attention, supporting rejection, and expressing demands.   Frequently he will look at an object and cry at the same time.   He voices his eagerness and protest.   He is using his primitive speech both to express himself and to modify the behavior of others.   This stage is also marked by the appearance of syllable repetition, or the doubling of sounds, in his vocal play.   He singles out a certain double syllable, such as *da-da* and frequently practices it to the exclusion of all other combinations. Sometimes a single combination will be practiced for several weeks at a time, though it is more usual to find the child changing to something new every few days and reviewing some of his former vocal achievements at odd intervals.   True disyllables (*ba-da*) come relatively late in the first year, and the infant rejects them when the parent attempts to use them as stimulation.

Seventh Through Ninth Month

Practice of inflections.   The next stage appears during the seventh to ninth months and is marked by the appearance of tone variation and inflection in the vocal play.   The child practices inflections of every sort, those of questioning, command, surprise, and many others never used by the parents.   It is interesting to note that during these months the child frequently repeats over and over sounds and inflections which are too complicated for an adult to imitate.

We have previously spoken of various stages of development, but it should be made very clear that, although most children go through these stages in the order given, the activity in any one stage does not cease as soon as the characteristics of the next stage appear.   Grunts and wails, babbling, socialized vocalization, and inflection practice all begin at about the times stated, but they continue throughout the entire period of speech development.

It is during this period that the baby begins to use more of the back vowels (u, ʊ, o, ɔ) in his babbling.   According to Irwin and Curry (10), 92 per cent of all vowels uttered by babies are the front vowels as compared to the 49 per cent figure for adult speech.   They say, "It is evident that a fundamental process of development in early speech consists of the mastery of the back vowels."   It is interesting that when we work with adult articulation cases we prefer syllables such as *see* and *ray* and *lee* to those involving the back vowels like *soo* and *low*. Front vowels seem to be more easily mastered.

The baby, through his vocal gymnastics, gradually masters the co-ordinations necessary to meaningful speech. But it must be emphasized that when he is repeating *da-da* and *ma-ma* at this stage, he is not designating his parents. His arm movements have much more meaning than those of his mouth. It is during these months that the ratio of babbling to crying greatly increases. Comprehension of parental gestures shows marked growth. As the summary (Table 3) indicates, the second period of imitation begins. The child now responds to the parent's stimulation, not automatically, but with more discrimination. His imitation is more hesitant but it also seems more purposive. It begins to resemble the parent's utterance. If the father interrupts the child's chain of *papapapapapapapapa* by saying *papa*, the child is less likely than before to say *wah* or *gu* and more likely to whisper *puh* or to repeat the two syllables *puh-puh*. During this period, simple musical tones, songs, or lullabies are especially good stimulation. The parent should observe the child's inflections and rhythms and attempt to duplicate them. This is the material that should be used for stimulation at this period, not a long harangue on why mother loves her little token of heaven.

After the Ninth Month

Some time during the period between the tenth and eighteenth month the normal child learns to say his first true words. Comprehension shows a great spurt of development at this time. As Table 4 indicates, gesture and imitation grow in complexity. The baby suddenly becomes a very human being. He learns to walk and to talk and to feed himself, three of the most fundamental of all human functions. He's quite a fellow indeed. Let us see how he masters his first words.

Teaching the child to say his first words. It is usually thought that the child learns to talk by imitation, but if by imitation is meant the exact reproduction of that which is seen or heard, certainly no such imitation occurs. It is true that, during the last months of the first year, most children seem to make some attempts to reproduce movements which they witness, but rarely are these movements exact. Imitation, as used in the larger sense to denote attempted reproduc-

TABLE 4

SUMMARY OF SPEECH DEVELOPMENT

(Tenth Through Twelfth Month)

Response to Adult Stimulation

Begins to comprehend a few words when accompanied by gestures or presentation by adults ("no-no," names of family).

Will fix object with eyes when its name is pronounced.

Responds discriminatively to words spoken in friendly and angry tones.

Will patty-cake when parent pronounces the words or even the rhythm of the rhyme when other vowels are used.

Great interest and attention paid to isolated adult words if they are always associated with things or activities important to his needs.

Fights with playmates for desired objects.

Will imitate two tones sung by adult.

Should imitate "dada" by twelve months.

Child will occasionally imitate sounds produced by clocks, dogs, cows, and adult exclamations without demand.

Child often responds to parental demand for imitation by a partial duplication. He will say "p" for "pap." If parent gives a disyllabic word, child often responds by reduplication.

Speech Development

Pronounced efforts to imitate are marked at this stage, especially if adult interrupts vocal play by speaking the sound being produced.

Will imitate number of syllables as well as sounds involved.

Readily imitates sounds already practiced and occasionally sounds new to the child or ones not present in the contemporary vocal play.

Echolalia occurs if the adult's words are introduced unobtrusively into the child's vocal play. (Echolalia—in a dream—is much more accurate than voluntary imitations.)

Occasionally, the child will respond to adult verbal stimulation by a delayed speech attempt.

Will accompany gestures by vocalization.

Some children acquire first true words.

tion, seems to be motivated by the desire to perpetuate the stimuli which intrigue one's interest. It is the child's way of maintaining his interest. The child's memory span is very weak and short, and to compensate for this deficiency he seeks to perpetuate the stimulus by repeating it. This accounts for the doubling and repetition of syllables in the vocal play and for the persistence with which he pounds the rattle on the table.

When the process of speech imitation is studied, we discover that it begins when the parent starts to imitate the child. This may sound paradoxical, but its truth will be apparent when the situation is defined. During vocal play the child happens to be repeating the syllable *ma*. The hearing of the sound interests him, and so he repeats it again. Suddenly the sight of his mother interrupts his response to his own stimulation, and he lapses into silence. But the mother, unaware of the perfection of her technique, says to him, "Mama? Did you want mama?" and immediately the interesting stimulus is there again. Wishing it to continue, he makes the same vocal co-ordinations he made when alone, and again the same interesting sounds are heard, *mamaamaama*. Whereupon the mother rushes to the phone to tell her husband that the child has spoken his first word.

This, of course, is not strictly true, for only when the child uses the word as a definite tool of communication with such a meaning as "Mother, come here," or "Mother, lift me up!" can we say with certainty that he has acquired his first word. Nevertheless, the process of word acquisition has been described. The first step in teaching a child to talk should be the imitation of the sounds being made by the child during his vocal play. This should be preceded, if possible, by the parental imitation of other movements, such as pounding the table. If the child can be stimulated to return to his own former pounding by watching the parent pound, half the battle is won, for the first requisite is gained: the perpetuation of a stimulus given by another person. In imitating the speech of the child, the parent should seek to interrupt the child's activity before it is completed. For example, if the child is saying *da-da-da* over and over, it is wise to interject the parental *da-da* as soon as the child's first *da* has been produced. This will produce the most favorable conditions for getting the child to return to his own former activity, and usually he will maintain it much longer and much more loudly than he usually does. At first only a few sounds should be used in this way, preferably those that later can be used to represent the people doing the training. Thus the child will acquire *mama* in a situation which always represents her presence, and it is wise for her to say the word whenever she picks the child up. Thus the child will come to associate the interesting sound with the person, and it will thereby come to have meaning.

The child should be given such training until he responds consistently with eager repetition whenever the parent has interrupted vocal play by imitating his vocalizations. After that it is wise for the parent to utilize the silence periods which occur during the babbling as intervals of strong stimulation with the sounds previously used by the child. For example, the child has been babbling and suddenly becomes silent. The parent then attracts his attention and repeats *mamama* (or any other syllable which the child has been practicing). If the child will respond to this stimulation by attempted repetition, a second step in word acquisition has been taken. After considerable training involving the practices of both steps, the parent having been careful to pick the appropriate times, the child will suddenly surprise everyone by using the word very meaningfully, perhaps accompanying it with the gesture of reaching. In similar fashion, other early words may be taught.

In one sense, it may be said that the first words are acquired through stabilization. Out of all the vocal tangle of sounds produced by the baby, certain monosyllables or repeated syllables appear as familiar entities. They already have meaning for the child since they have expressed his needs or bodily conditions. He has played with them on so many pleasant occasions that they are old friends. He knows them well. Now, these same syllables become associated with certain conventional gestures (*bye-bye*) or consistent objects (*mama*) which appear repeatedly in his daily life. The first words have been his for a long time. They merely get a stabilized adult meaning.

One parent, whom we studied with some interest, tried by every device of conditioning known to educated idiots to have his boy say the word "Ralph" (the father's name) as his first meaningful word. He worked with the boy for hours. When the first word did arrive (fourteen months late) it was "teetee" and referred to a cat.

Even as certain gestures such as reaching become stabilized from the wild undifferentiated arm-swinging of the infant, so, too, do the first words from their early matrix of vocal play.

Gesture is very important in stabilizing the first words. Sometimes it is almost too powerful.

We observed one child who had the following history. At nine months the mother stretched out her arms to the child whenever the latter asked through gestures to be taken up. At nine months, eight days, the child would imitate the mother by reaching out bimanually whenever the mother did so. The mother then began to say "mama" whenever she used the gesture. At 9; 14, the child would say it with the mother as they stretched out their arms.   At 9; 16, the child said "mamama" as she responded to the mother's silent gesture of reaching.   On the same day she also said "mama" as she reached for her cup.   At 9; 19 she said "mama" to the father when he reached out to take her.   Long after she could say "Daddy" imitatively and spontaneously, the gesture of reaching was always accompanied by "mama."

Fortunately, the effect of the accompanying gesture is seldom so persevering.   Phonetic and intonation patterns of adult vocalization usually accompany the gesture and are perceived by the child as a whole.   He responds not merely to the warning shake of the parent's head but to his own imitative head wagging and to the peremptory tone of the phrase "No.   No!" and, if these fail, to the swat on his bottom as well.   Even the mother's turning of her head or body as she recognizes and says "Daddy" is a meaningful gesture.   Comprehension of speech for the baby consists of his interpretation of gesture, intonation patterns, and the presence of syllables which he has previously practiced.   Those gestures spontaneously used by the child are much better than any that parents could think up.   If you interrupt his hand-waving by your own similar gesture, and say "bye-bye" and then take him out doors, the word will be learned fairly easily. But if you try to teach him to kiss his father's picture and say "Daddy" at the same time, the work will be long and hard and perhaps useless.

These first words of the child may sound very much like those of adult speech, but they differ greatly in meaning.   Some of them are no doubt "abracadabra" words.   The child says "mama" and magically she appears.   Other early words are mere signs of recognition or acquaintanceship.   "Ba" may mean, "I know you.   You're a ball. You're that round smooth thing I throw and bounce."   He utters it with the same smug self-satisfaction that our friends manifest when, hearing a familiar musical phrase, they pat their egos and murmur, "Brahms, of course!"

Speech at eighteen months.   At eighteen months, the child is toddling about the room pushing chairs and toys from one position to another.   He climbs without discrimination.   He spills with a spoon but manages to feed himself after a fashion.   His handedness is pretty well established.   Extremely active, he seldom plays with any one object or activity very long.   As fond of music as before, he now prefers marches to lullabies except before bedtime.   When angry, he screams, kicks, or holds his breath, but this mass activity is not focused or directed against any particular person.   He initiates games such as

"Peekaboo" and seems to take great pleasure in "making" adults co-operate. A large empty box is his dearest toy. He usually plays beside other children rather than with them, and he plays better alone. He relies on adults for assistance and attention but shies away from strangers. He should never be asked to speak to them at this age.

At eighteen months the child's speech activity consists of *a few meaningful words*, a little solitary *vocal play*, some *echolalia*, and a great deal of what we shall call *jargon*. Again, let us repeat that we are discussing the mythical average child. The average child has acquired from ten to twenty meaningful words with which to manipulate his elders and express his needs. He not only has names for members of his family but for many other things. Some typical examples are: (mo) for *snow;* (ɔgɔn) for *all gone;* (baɪbaɪ) for *bye-bye;* (aɪt) for *light;* (kækə) for *cracker;* (pap) for *pot.* Many of these are used as one-word sentences and they are very general in their reference. (kækə) can refer to *cracker* or *bread* or even to the fact that the dog is chewing a bone. Many parents lose a great deal of pleasure by not trying to solve these little crossword puzzles of infancy.

Parents of our acquaintance put the problem to us in these words: "Why does our eighteen-month-old daughter refer to both the cat and a champagne bottle by the same word *dih* (dɪ)?" At the time we could not answer, but during the child's third year the word *dih* changed to *ding* (dɪŋ), then to *dink* (dɪŋk), and finally to *drink*. The child had been fascinated by the sight of the cat drinking its milk.

Occasionally the use of one word will spread to include a great many unrelated objects. The child feels little of his parents' confusion when he uses the word *behbuh* (bɛbə) to mean first "baby" then "bib," then "bread and butter." In this instance, the referential spread was no doubt due to the phonetic similarity of all these words. Had the parents taught them at different times or with different intonation or stress, the spread would not have been so great. Soldiers and others who suffer damage to the brain show these same symptoms.

Many early words are generalizations because they are so few and must serve a child so often. When a child who learns the word *puppy* as the designation for his varying perceptions of dogdom is suddenly confronted by a pony, he must needs make *puppy* do for both until he gets a new term. One child used the sound *fffff* as a generalized word for flowers. We also use a similar generic term. But he used *fffff* for perfume, for cigarette smoke, and for the figures on the wall paper.

As the child comes to discriminate between objects, he needs terms to fix the contrasts involved. As long as ponies and dogs are merely big creatures with four legs on the corners and a hairy coat, they require but one word, and *puppy* is adequate. But when he realizes that ponies neigh, and he can ride on them, and they are bigger and eat carrots and never sleep by the fireplace—then a new word is needed, and it is acquired.

How, then, do children acquire these new words? The answer seems to be that at the moment when the child is undergoing some new experience in perception, or has an urgent desire to manipulate some new object in order to know it better, the adult intervenes, supplying a new word. If the child perceives this vocalization as part of the total experience, and at the same time produces the word through imitation, he finds he has a more efficient tool than the old generalized word. As the process repeats itself, the child comes to realize the greater expressiveness of conventional language forms. The whole process is, of course, also influenced by other factors: by the child's growing discrimination, by the strength and constancy of adult intervention at the crucial moments, and even by the natural responsiveness of the child.

These first words are used by the child even in his play. He yells "bell-bell-bell" (or a reasonable facsimile thereof) to himself as he rings it. He repeatedly labels the eyes, nose, and ears, not only of the mother who taught him but of his dog or doll, and he pokes them in the labeling. The early words are still accompanied by gesture or pertinent activity. He needs the parents' gestures in order to comprehend their utterances, and so he gestures and speaks in his turn. Only about one fourth of his speech attempts on these words can be understood by strangers. Each family seems to elect one of its members as interpreter. Nevertheless these first ten or twenty words of the eighteen-months-old child are a wonderful achievement. His manner shows that he knows it even if you do not. One child beat his chest and war-whooped whenever he used a new word successfully.

Jargon. The largest share of the average eighteen-months-old child's speech is *jargon*. This unintelligible jabber is probably more important for speech development than people realize. It is the lineal descendant of vocal play, but it differs from the earlier babbling in its rich variety and its seeming purposiveness. The child seems to be talking to other people or to his toys, rather than playing with the sounds themselves. He seldom repeats the same syllable.

One boy, aged 19 months, was observed banging a teddy bear with a hammer and between wallops addressing his victim as follows: "Gubba! Dadda bo-bo!" (Another hammering.) "Show gubba mahda." (Hammers again.) "Ashlee? Baá!" (Throws teddy bear over his shoulder.) In phonetics, the discourse was transcribed: gʌbə dædə bobo .... ʃo gʌbə mɑdɑ .... æʃli .... bɑ ...

Often this conversational jargon includes words he has mastered. Reaching out his dish for more ice cream he said, "ɛ:ɛ adə mamə i:ɪ næna aɪ kim ʃlæ?" The words which we have underlined are certainly understandable, and perhaps (nænə) refers to "banana," a favorite food, but the other syllables are difficult to interpret. And most of the child's jargon is even less intelligible.

As Gesell (6) phrases it, "At eighteen months her jargon was beguiling. She would talk confidentially for minutes at a single stretch, uttering not a single enunciated word but conveying much emotional content." As this quotation hints, jargon is probably the child's practice of fluency. Most young children swim in a river of fast-flowing meaningless adult jargon. Why should they not imitate their elders in fluency even as they copy their speech sounds and inflections? Certainly the gap between the few halting words of the child and the ceaseless ebb and flow of adult speech is very wide. Jargon is the bridge. It reaches its peak at eighteen months, dropping out rapidly, and it is usually gone by two years. A few children never use any jargon. When words fail they gesture or cry or remain silent. Most babies are like adults. They must talk whether what they say makes sense or not.

Vocal play and echolalia. The babbling play of infancy still appears, usually when the child is in bed or alone. He plays with repeated syllables or prolonged sibilant sounds. His new teeth enable him to produce new whistling sounds and so he must practice them. Often you can hear him whispering to himself and working up to the crescendo of vocalization. Prolonging sounds with his finger in mouth, or fumbling rhythmically with lips, he discovers again (and not for the last time) how fascinating he is. Jargon is his vocal response to a vocal world. Vocal play is his private rehearsal.

Echolalia appears very markedly in some children during this period, and it probably occurs in all children occasionally. By this term we mean the parrotlike echoing of words he hears. Occasionally whole phrases and sentences will be repeated so faithfully that the parent fairly jumps. In one instance a year-and-a-half-old girl almost wrecked a church service by saying, "and ever and ever amen!"

fourteen times in the middle of the preacher's sermon. She had only spoken a few words prior to this event and she never uttered the phrase again for years. Parents frequently use echolalia to teach their children nursery rhymes, most of which are first learned backwards. The parent says, "The cow jumped over the moon." "Moo," says the child automatically. Soon the parent begins to hesitate before the last word, and the child fills in.

Echolalia occurs almost instantly and unconsciously as if in a dream. The child's attention is elsewhere. Feeble-minded adults show a great deal of echolalia, as do aphasics and some psychotics. Any fairly normal person who has ever held a conversation with one of these echolalics will never forget the experience:

Are you ten years old?
Ten years old?
Yes.
Yes.
I mean . . .
I mean . . .
When is your birthday?
Birthday?
Yes.—Oh let it go!
Let it go.

There madness lies. But in little children echolalia is a normal stage of development and, sensibly, they pass through it in a hurry. It is seldom observed in the normal child after two and a half years.

Speech at two years. By the time the child reaches his second birthday he should be talking. Speech has become a tool as well as a safety valve or warning siren. He is saying things like: "Where Kitty?" "Ball all gone." "Want cookie." "Kiss baby." "Go bye-bye car." "Shut door." "Big horsie cry." "Put 'bacco in pipe."

Simple and compound sentences are often heard. The jargon is almost gone. His articulation is faulty; his speech rhythms are broken; his voice control ranges from loud to louder, but he has learned to talk. He may still turn out to have any of the speech defects, but he isn't mute. Not by a good many decibels, he isn't.

In summary, we may say again that children *learn* to talk. Their parents do the teaching, and it is usually very poor. Because of the widespread ignorance concerning speech development and the teaching of talking, many children: (1) fail to practice their speech sounds in vocal play; (2) do not learn how to imitate sounds; (3) do not learn that sounds can be meaningful and useful tools; (4) do not practice or profit from their jargon; (5) resort to gesture and other substitute behavior rather than develop a growing vocabulary, and therefore they (6) lay the foundation for defective speech.

The prevention of speech defects. Much has been written about the correction of speech defects but little about their prevention. The reason for this state of affairs is the general ignorance concerning the development of speech, especially during the preschool years. And yet it is precisely during these years when the majority of speech defects first appear. Stuttering begins during this period; the lispers fail to master the pronunciation of the sounds which other children are achieving; the whining voice of the little girl is reflecting that of her complaining mother. If parents knew how to teach their children to talk, and how to aid them in mastering the speech skills required in adult speech, there would be fewer cases for the speech clinic or the speech correctionist.

The young child has much to learn in the months that surround his third birthday. Prohibitions become important in his life and he becomes negative in turn. Bursting with energy, he meets frustrations at every turn. He must learn to become a social being, whether he wants to or not. The world of words becomes vastly important to the three-year-old. Through speech he finds expression for his emotion. By means of talking, he manipulates his associates and satisfies his needs. He has great need for fluency and precision of utterance.

The few infantile words that he learned during his first two years cannot possibly serve his growing needs. He now needs to express relationships and qualifications. He needs plurals and gender. He becomes conscious of the past and the future, and these demand new verb forms. The whole problem of English syntax presents itself as a challenge to the three-year-old. At the same time, his needs for a larger vocabulary are increasing. "What's that? What's that?" is a game which every parent learns to play, on the answering end. The three-year-old is into everything strange. He tests and tries everything, including the patience of his associates. These explorations yield him many moments of confusion when something never before seen has no name to identify its impact. Thus one three-year-old, who had shown precocious speech development with few if any breaks in fluency, suddenly observed a parachute descent and cried out "ε-ε-ʌ-ʌ-ε -bʌ (gesture of pointing and excited breathing), -bʌd-

bʌd- goʊ-bum." At the time, her normal speech was being recorded, and therefore the transcript was accurate. Her usual speech was rhythmic and fluent. It is interesting also that she showed a return to earlier phraseology: "go boom" for the "fall down" which she had been using for over a year. Under the pressure of haste, the unfamiliarity of the experience, the confusion of *airplane* (ɛɚ) and *bird* (bʌd), both of which were probably felt to be inadequate, the child's fluency broke down and she showed hesitant speech similar to that of primary stuttering.

Besides learning the conventional forms of syntax and acquiring a new vocabulary, the young child must also perfect his pronunciation and articulation. He has many errors to eliminate: the reduplications "goggy" for "doggy"; the use of the labial *w* for the tonguetip *l* and *r* sounds; the use of the *t* and *d* for the *k* and *g* plosives; the omissions of many of his final sounds. He also has many new co-ordinations and sound combinations to master: the precise grooving of the tongue for the sibilants; the transitional timing of the vocalization and movement on the affricatives (tʃ) and (dʒ) and the glide (j); the preparatory positioning of the tongue for the second sound in such blends as *sl, fr*, and *pl*. If these seem like a lot for a three-year-old to master, it must be said that we have only mentioned a few of them. All these and many other articulation skills must be mastered and perfected until they can be used at fast speeds and under conditions of excitement.

Finally, the child is attempting to conform to the patterns of the parent's speech with respect to fluency and phonation. Just as he imitates his father's pipe-smoking or his mother's sweeping with extreme fidelity, so, too, will he imitate their inflections and voice quality *and* attempt to imitate their fluency. It is in this last item that much of our trouble with stuttering begins. Children of this age do not have the vocabulary or the other skills well enough in hand (or mouth) to be able to keep their fluency up to adult standards. The adults about them speak to one another and to the children themselves in compound-complex sentences, in paragraphs that flow one after the other in endless series. If they pause, it is for so short an instant that the child cannot get his speech under way. Grown-ups often penalize interrupting children, but they will interrupt the child's speech with impunity. They finish the child's sentences before he has been able to get them half said. They interrupt to correct a plural or a pronoun or a past participle, and often seize the opportunity to rush on with their own flow of verbalization. When a child tries to adopt an adult fluency pattern of which he is not capable, or if he is bombarded by many of these parental interruptions, he will have hesitant speech. Anyone who has tried to speak a half-learned foreign language with a fluent native will understand what little children undergo. The average parent does not realize what has happened until the child's speech fails to develop normally.

If this childish urge to speak as fluently as his parents when he has neither the vocabulary nor the other necessary skills can precipitate stuttering, we should try to decrease its intensity. Whenever frustration is produced by having an aspiration level far above the person's performance level, we should try to reduce the former. In the case of the child learning to talk, the problem can be solved fairly simply. If the parents will speak to the child, using short phrases and sentences, using simple words whose meaning he can comprehend, using the simplest of syntax, the child will never need to feel speech frustration. He can achieve these fluency patterns without too much difficulty. We have been able, clinically, to free many children from primary stuttering by merely getting their parents to speak more simply. As an example let us quote from a parent's report:

Each evening, as you suggested, we have been holding a family conference and confessing to each other our errors in handling Ruth. Among other things, we found ourselves constantly talking over her head. Today, for instance, I said to her, "Ruth, do you suppose you could go to the bath room and bring down some of the dirty towels and wash cloths? Mama's going to wash." She looked at me intently, then went upstairs and came down with some soap, and said, "Woothy wa-wa-wa-wash bath bath. . . ." and she stuttered pretty badly. So I thanked her for the soap and said, "Ruthy go upstairs. Bring Mama wash cloth, please." Her face lit up, and she ran upstairs and down again in a hurry, bringing me the washcloth and a towel too. Then she said, "Woothy bwing wash coth. Nice girl." I begin to see what you mean by speaking more simply.

One need not talk baby talk in order to speak more simply. We must merely give our children fluency models within their performance ability.

If we are to prevent speech defects, we must prevail upon parents to change their present policy of sporadic correction and *laissez faire*. They must learn how to help the child master the difficult skills with

which he is confronted in adult speech.   They must learn how to keep
from making speech learning difficult.   They must not do all the
wrong things so blithely.

Helping a child gain vocabulary.   Most parents are eager enough to
help the child get his first twenty or thirty new words.   Some parents
are even too ambitious at first; they try to teach such words as
"Dorothy" or "Samantha."   But their teaching urge soon subsides.
The child seems to be picking up a few words as he needs them.   Why
not let him continue to grow at his own pace?   Our answer does not
deny the function of maturation in vocabulary growth.   We merely
say that parents should give a little common-sense help at moments
when a child needs a new word, a label for a new experience.   When
parents notice a child hesitating or correcting himself when faced with
a new experience, they should become verbal dictionaries, providing
*not only the needed new word, but a definition in terms of the child's own
vocabulary.*   For example:

John was pointing to something on the shelf he wanted.   "Johnny
want . . um . . Johnny want pretty pretty ball . . Johnny wanta pretty
. . um . ." The object was a round glass vase with a square opening
on top.   I immediately took it down and said, "No ball, Johnny.   Vase!
Vase!"   I put my finger into the opening and let him imitate me.   Then
we got a flower and he put it in the opening after I had filled it partially
with water.   I said, "Vase is a flower-cup.   Flower-cup, vase!   See pretty
vase!   (I prolonged the *v* sound slightly.)   Flower drink water in vase, in
pretty vase.   Johnny, say 'Vase!'"   (He obeyed without hesitation or
error.)   Each day that week, I asked him to put a new flower in the vase,
and by the end of that time he was using the word with assurance.   I've
found one thing though; you must speak rather slowly when teaching a
new word.   Use plenty of pauses and patience.

Besides this type of spontaneous vocabulary teaching, it is possible
to play little games at home in which the child imitates an older child
or parent as they "touch and say" different objects.   Children invent
these games for themselves.

"March and Say" was a favorite game of twins whom we observed.
One would pick up a toy telephone, run to the door of the playroom and
ask his mother, "What dat?"   "Telephone," she would answer, and then
both twins would hold the object and march around the room chanting
"Tɛpoʊn, tɛpoʊn" until it ended in a fight for possession.   Then the dominant twin would pick up another object, ask its name, and march and
chant its name over and over.

In all of these naming games, the child should always point to, feel, or sense the object referred to as vividly as possible. The mere sight or sound of the object is not enough for early vocabulary acquisition. It is also wise to avoid cognate terms. One of our children for years called the cap on a bottle a "hat" because of early confusion.

Scrapbooks are better than the ordinary run of children's books for vocabulary teaching because pictures of objects closer to the child's experience may be pasted in. The ordinary "Alphabet Book" is a monstrosity so far as the teaching of talking is concerned. Nursery rhymes are almost as bad. Let the child listen to "Goosey Goosey Gander, whither dost thou wander" if he enjoys the rhymes, but do not encourage him to say the rhymes. The teaching of talking should be confined to meaningful speech, not gibberish. The three-year-old child has load enough without trying to make sense of nonsense. When using the pictures in the scrapbooks, it is wise to do more than ask the child to name them. When pointing to a ball, the parents should say, "What's that?" "Ball." "Johnny throw ball. Bounce, bounce, bounce" (gestures). Build up associations in terms of the functions of the objects. Teach phrases as well as single words. "Cookie" can always be taught as "eat cookie." This policy may also help the child to remember to keep it out of his hair.

How to prevent hesitant speech. Hesitant speech (pauses, accessory vocalization, filibusters, abortive speech attempts) occurs as the resultant of two opposing forces. First, there must be a strong need to communicate, and second, this urge must be blocked by some counterpressure. Some of the common counterpressures which oppose the desire for utterance are:

1. *Inability to find or remember the appropriate words.* "I'm thinking of- of- of- of- uh- that fellow who- uh— oh yes, Aaronson. That's his name." This is the adult form. In a child it might occur as: "Mummy, there's a birdy out there in the . . . in the . . . uh . . . he's . . . uh . . . he . . . he . . . he wash his bottom in the dirt." Similar sources of hesitant speech are found in bilingual conflicts, where vocabulary is deficient; in aphasia; and under emotional speech exhibition, as when children forget their "pieces."

2. *Inability to pronounce or doubt of ability to articulate.* Adult form: "I can never say 'sus-stus-susiss-stuh—stuhstiss—oh, you know what I mean, figures, stastistics." The child's form could be illustrated by "Mummy, we saw two poss-poss- uh- possumusses at the zoo. Huh? Yeah, two puh-possums." Tongue twisters, unfamiliar sounds or words, too fast a rate of utterance, and articulation disorders can produce these sources of speech hesitancy.

3. *Fear of the unpleasant consequences of the communication.* "Y-yes, I-I-I- uh I t-took the money." "W-wi-will y- you marry m-me?" "Duh-don't s-s-spank me, Mum-mummy." Some of the conflict may be due to uncertainty as to whether the content of the communication is acceptable or not. Contradicting, confessing, asking favors, refusing requests, shocking, tentative vulgarity, fear of exposing social inadequacy, fear of social penalty in school recitations or recitals.

4. *The communication itself is unpleasant, in that it recreates an unpleasant experience.* "I cu-cu-cut my f-f-f-finger . . . awful bi-big hole in it." "And then he said to me, 'You're fi-f-fired.' " The narration of injuries, injustices, penalties often produces speech hesitancy. Compulsory speech can also interrupt fluency.

5. *Presence, threat, or fear of interruption.* This is one of the most common of all the sources of speech hesitancy. Incomplete utterances are always frustrating and the average speaker always tries to forestall or reject an approaching interruption. This he does by speeding up the rate, filling in the necessary pauses with repeated syllables or grunts or braying. This could be called "filibustering," since it is essentially a device to hold the floor. When speech becomes a battleground for competing egos, this desire for dominance may become tremendous. More hesitations are always shown in attempting to interrupt another's speech as well as in refusing interruption.

6. *Loss of the listener's attention.* Communication involves both speaker and listener, and when the latter's attention wanders or is shifted to other concerns, a fundamental conflict occurs. ("Should I continue talking . . . even though she isn't listening? If I do, she'll miss what I just said. . . . If I don't, I won't get it said. Probably never. . . . Shall I? . . . Shan't I?") The speaker often resolves this conflict by repeating or hesitating until the speech is very productive of speech hesitancy. "Mummy, I-I-I want a . . . Mummy, I . . . M . . . Mumm . . . Mummy, I . . . I want a cookie." Disturbing noises, the loss of the listener's eye contact, and many other similar disturbances can produce this type of fluency interrupter.

If we are to help prevent the disorder of stuttering from getting started, especially when there seems to be some familial or natural tendency toward fluency breaks, it would be wise to arrange the child's environment so as to eliminate these disturbing influences as much as possible. The situations which produce them can easily be avoided. When they have occurred and have produced hesitant speech, the parents can introduce other speech-play experiences which will facilitate fluency. Most parents have no knowledge of the influence of these conditions on speech, and forewarned is forearmed. We have been able effectively to change many a young stutterer's speech environment so that his symptoms entirely disappear by giving his parents this summary of influences productive of hesitant speech, and asking them to record and report each instance of their occurrence. Let us help our children learn how to talk and decrease the mal-influences that upset or retard speech development.

How to help the child master his articulation skills. There are three main ways in which parents can help their children eliminate baby talk and attain normal pronunciation skills: (1) Children should be taught the characteristics of the various speech sounds. (2) They should be given help in vocal phonics. (3) They should be taught to correct themselves. In a short five- or ten-minute period daily, simple speech games should be played to help the child identify the characteristics of each of the consonants. At first these games should consist of simple prolongations of some continuant consonant, the sound being used to identify the movement.

We used a little porcelain kitty of which he was very fond to help him get acquainted with the *s* sound. We played a sort of peekaboo game. Whenever we thought Bob was occupied we would poke the porcelain kitty around the corner and say *ssss*. Soon he was calling the toy *ssss*. He would say, "Gi' Bobby sssss kitty." Three weeks after we started this game he used his first good *s* in a real word, the word *ice*. Previous to this time he had either left off the *s* or used a *t* instead.

Many modern nursery schools are incorporating speech play as part of their daily activity. Here are the games used in one nursery school of four-year-olds. Modifications of them for individual home work are easily made.

1. *The "m" sound.* Have the children press a forefinger against one nostril then against the other as they hum *m m m m mee mee*. Have them pretend to be a band and play simple tunes using their noses as horns.

2. *The "p" sound.* Give each child a very thin strip of paper and, holding it vertically over the mouth by a finger pressed under the nose, make it move out as they say *puh, puh, puh*. Tell them they are motor boats and have them move across the room as they say *puh, puh, puh*, blowing the paper with little puffs of air.

3. *The "k" sound.* Tell them they are crows whose tongues got stuck under bottom teeth and can only whisper *kuh, kuh, kuh*. Show them how their tongues got stuck by anchoring your tonguetip below your front teeth and saying the sound. See if they can fly all the way around the room saying the crow whisper without having their tongues get unstuck. Look in their mouths as they come back and listen to their sounds.

4. *The "g" sound.* Tell them that in a kind of Indian talk "ugh ugh" means "yes" and "oog oog" means "no." Ask them simple questions and

have them answer you in Indian talk. Tell them that these Indians always hold their hand under the base of the chin when they answer questions. (This will help them feel the g sound.) Give them a feather for their heads and play an Indian game.

5. *The "f" sound.* Tell them to wet the side of their forefinger and hold it crosswise on the chin. Tell them to blow *f-f-f* until it feels cold. Call this the "freeze-your-finger" game. Feel the fingers to see which is coolest.

6. *The "v" sound.* Have them hold their fingers along the upper edge of the lower lip and make it buzz by prolonging the *v-v-v* sound (Do not say *vee*, just *v*). Tell them or show them that it gives a sound just like singing through the tissue paper over a comb. Have them sing some tunes with the finger-buzzing sound. See who can hold it the longest.

7. *The "sh" sound.* Choose one child to be the teacher and give each of the others a certain sound to say over and over until a hodge-podge or mumbo-jumbo of sound is produced. The moment the child-teacher puts her finger vertically to her lips and says *sh* . . . all the others must do the same thing. The one who stops last is the teacher.

8. *The "ch" sound.* Have the children form a line holding onto each other's hips and play train, starting up from the station when the conductor says "all aboard" and "choo-chooing" in unison as they move around the room. Have one person blow a whistle to stop the train. Repeat.

9. *The "j" sound.* Have the children sit on their haunches pretending to be frogs saying *jeo-joom* repeatedly. Choose a child to be a heron bird, and as he comes nearer the frog pond the children make their *jeo-jooms* softer and softer until finally they whisper and become silent. The bird says, "I guess there aren't any frogs here," and goes away.

10. *The "s" sound.* Have the child blow up his cheeks like automobile tires. As the teacher goes around the room she punctures them and they go *s-s-s-s* until all the air is gone. The one whose tire leaks the slowest gets to puncture the cheek tires the next time.

11. *The "z" sound.* Tell half of the children they are flowers and the other half they are bees gathering pollen to make honey. The bees hold a thin strip of paper in their teeth and must touch the flowers with it, saying *zzzzzzzzzzz* as they do so. After they have touched all the flowers they must return to the hive and drop the papers on the teacher's desk without using their hands. The bees then become flowers.

12. *The "r" sound.* Have the children go to the blackboard (or use arm movements in the air) and roll a chalk hoop ʊʊʊʊʊʊ all the way across the entire blackboard space saying *r-r-r-r*. Show them how to make the sound louder and softer as they draw continuous circles.

13. *The "l" sound.* Have the children open their mouths and do exercises with both their tongues and arms together. As their arms are swinging in a side arc over their heads, they lift their tongues up to the upper gums and say *lll* (not *ell*). As they drop their arms they also drop their tongues saying *ah*, thus producing *la*. Repeat, using other syllables *la-lo-lie-loo*.

14. *The unvoiced "th" sound.* Have the children cool off their tongues.

Tell them to pretend to eat some hot soup and then put their tongues just outside the door of their teeth and blow on it until it is cooled off. The sound which should be demonstrated is, of course, the unvoiced *th* as in *think*. Prolong it.

15. *The voiced "th" sound.* Make their tongues buzz against their fingers by holding their fingers vertically against the lips as they make the voiced *th* sound, as in *then*.

The above exercises can and should be varied in many ways as they are repeated. Different durations of the sound may be required, the sounds may be repeated any given number of times, or the intensity of the sound may be increased or decreased. Different vowels can be used to make up different nonsense syllables. They may be whispered or sung.

The important thing to remember in inventing new games or variations is to keep the identification of the sound as constant as possible. Thus the *f* sound should always be the "finger-cooling sound," the *s* sound the "punctured-tire sound," and so on. Thus the child can be asked to cool all of his fingers in turn with this *f-f-f* sound, or to cool another child's fingers, or to repeat the finger-cooling sound as he marches or until he finds a hidden object. Variation is excellent, provided the identity of the sound remains constant. The children are confused so far as the consonants are concerned. These games and exercises will help to eliminate this confusion.

Vocal phonics. Children during their third and fourth years are fascinated by rhymes and word play of every kind. They chant such sequences as these even when alone:

High chair, high tair, high bear, kigh kare, care care, bear tear, tear bear all up.
Sally, mally, silly sally, sabby, babby, sally babby.
I got a letter in the mail, in the pail, in the tail.
I like soup, sook, soos; do you like soot?

When their playmates seem puzzled by this punning, they laugh uproariously. If word play is the lowest form of wit, it may also be the earliest. But its major significance in the development of speech lies in its phonic training. Many children persist in their articulation errors because they never learn that words are composed of a series of consecutive sounds. They hear words as wholes—as chunks of sound. The word *fish* to these children is not a series of three sounds, *f*, ɪ, and *ʃ*, but a single sound. Thus the pronunciation of *fish* and *pish* if spoken quickly enough are much more alike than they are different, and the child fails to perceive any error. Very often, he may echo the word after his parent without error, and yet in the very next sentence he may use the *pish* again. Many parents consider their children obstinate because they do not use these words consistently with correct sounds. Yet, parrotlike repetition has little to do with mastery of true speech. The Mongolian idiot can often echo very long words and yet be speechless in the true sense of the word. The child must be able to perceive his own errors and to create his own standards of pronunciation before he can be expected to speak correctly.

The child must learn that words have beginnings and endings— heads, middles, and tails. He must learn that the word "fish" must start with the "lip-biting, breathy, finger-cooling sound" (or some similar identification) and with no other. He must learn that "cup" must end with a lip-popping puff of air. (kʌ) is not enough. There must be one more sound.

Most children learn these elementary facts of vocal phonics unconsciously through vocal play and listening. Many articulation cases never learn that words are made up of parts, and that if one part is wrong, the whole word is incorrect. These observations may seem absurdly simple to the student of this text, but he will appreciate their truth once he starts to teach some lisper an *s* sound.

> Say *sssssssssssss*.
> *Sssssssssssssss*.
> Fine! Now say *soup*.
> *Thoup*.
> Oh, oh. You said *thoup*.
> No, I didn't. I thaid it right: *ssssthoup*.

The best way of teaching vocal phonics to young children is through guessing games, rhyming, indexing, and rhythmic vocal play. Here are three typical vocal phonics games which we have used successfully with children of three to five years.

1. Make circles on the floor with chalk and give each circle a "sound name" (*ssss* or *mmmm*). The child must make that sound whenever he is in the circle. Thus, as he jumps from circle to circle, he could produce the word (s) (æ) (m) or *Sam*.

2. *Guessing game*. "Show me your *n-o-se* (noʊz)" Separate the sounds at first, but gradually shorten the intervals until the child realizes that (n-oʊz) is a slow way of saying *nose*. Then use other words such as (ʃ u), (f-eɪ s), (maʊθ), and so on.

3. *Collection game.* Give the child some gaily covered boxes and have him collect toys or objects whose names begin with an *s* sound and put them into the *m* box, and other objects whose names begin with an *s* sound and put them into the other box. Demonstrate first, and be sure to sound out the words so that he hears the *m* or *s* sound of the objects collected. Also demonstrate rejection thus: "Let's see. Here's a phone. Does this belong in the boxes? Let's see: *f-f-f-o ne.* No, that begins with a *fff* sound, not a *mmmm* or *ssss.* We don't say *mone* or *sone* do we? Let's just get things that begin with the *mmmm* or *sssss.* You bring them to me and I'll sound them out."

It is astounding to observe how a very few sessions of this vocal play will improve the young child's speech. Until the child knows one sound from another, and until he can analyze or synthesize words, he can hardly be expected to correct himself. If parents would spend half of the time they now waste in trying to correct the child's errors in a systematic effort to get him to recognize sound sequence and the characteristic features of the individual consonants, few articulation problems would result.

Teaching the child to correct himself. Once the child has become able to recognize the individual speech sounds, and has some concept of vocal phonics, the parents can begin to teach him to correct himself. It is odd that so few parents ever get this concept. They feel that they must do the correcting, that the little child is incapable of the task. No greater fallacy has ever produced so much speech difficulty. The methods used by the average parent to correct her child's errors are truly bad. The child is interrupted within the sentence; he is subjected to penalty; he is corrected sporadically rather than consistently; he is corrected on the whole word rather than on the sound that is mispronounced; no attempt is made to analyze the errors or to identify the correct sound. The parent merely yells: "Don't say wabbit; say *rabbit!* Why in the world can't you learn to talk like other children?"

Yet the child of three and four can easily learn to correct himself if the parents adopt a consistent policy of helping him to do so. First, they should confine their correction to those sounds that he should be expected to master at his age. We have known parents to try to get a child to say strawberry before he could even say the *s* or *r* sounds. The blends should never be subjected to correction in the early pre-school years. In general, we may say that the first sounds to be mastered are those that involve a few large and coarse movements rather than many small and delicate adjustments; those that are easily seen rather than those whose movements are made in the back of the mouth; those whose frequencies are closer to the frequency of the vowels rather than those of the very high frequency ranges; and those involving a few of the speech organs rather than those that demand the use of all.

Thus, the first sounds mastered are the vowels, then the labials, then the dentals and gutturals (front- and back-tongue sounds, "t, d, n, k, g, ŋ"), then the complicated lip and tongue sounds (f, v, l, r, s, z, ʃ, ʒ, dʒ, tʃ), and finally the blends ("st, gr, bl," and so on). The ages at which these sounds are mastered completely are given for the average child: labials at three years, dentals and gutturals at about three and a half to four years, the *f* and *v* at about five years, the complicated tongue sounds during the sixth year, and the sibilants and blends during the early part of the seventh year. These sounds, however, are mastered much earlier by children who have been given definite training.

Second, it is important that only one sound be subjected to parental attention at one time. Thus, for several weeks only the *k* sound should be the vehicle for teaching the child to correct his speech. Then the *f* sound, if that is incorrectly produced, may be worked upon. This concentration of effort on one sound at a time will do wonders to unravel the confusion which the average parental correction creates in the mind of the child.

Third, it is important that the parents help the child to locate his errors in terms of the sound sequences (the words) in which they occur, and that they help him identify both the correct and incorrect sounds. And finally it is important that all the correction be done without emotion and at appropriate times.

Suppose, then, that the parents have carried out the identification and vocal-phonics games and exercises and that the child continues to make some errors. How then can the parents help? We believe that the general procedure could be illustrated thus: As soon as the child has finished his sentence, say to him something like this: "You know, Johnny, you didn't say one of the words the way big people do. You said *dipper* instead of *zipper*. You forgot that *zipper* starts with the bumblebee sound: zzzzzzz. Hear it? *Zzzzzipper, zzz-ip-er*. Now let's pretend we've got some zippers on our shirts. Watch me *zzzip* mine up! Now you pretend you are that bumblebee, and make your sound zzzzz as you zip up your shirt. Now say zzzzz-*ipper*. Fine, I knew you could." Yes, this type of teaching takes a bit longer than

"Oh, don't say *dipper* say *zipper!*" but it will save time in the long run.

In summary, then, let us say that parents should help their children to recognize the individual speech sounds, should train them in vocal phonics, and should teach them to correct themselves. This sort of a policy in the home will solve much of the speech-correction problem in the school. Speech defects can be prevented if parents will try intelligently to teach their children to talk.

References

1. Allport, F. H., *Social Psychology*, Boston, Houghton Mifflin, 1924, pages 181–183.
The classic description of how children learn to say their first words: 1. The child stimulates himself to repeat a syllable by hearing it. 2. Adults who pronounce the same syllable evoke the same response. 3. Perception of object at same time that others pronounce the syllable and evoke the child's response associates the syllable with the sound. 4. Perception of object evokes the child's production of the syllable.

2. Anderson, J. E., "The Development of Spoken Language," *Yearbook, National Society Studies in Education*, 1939, Vol. 38, Part 1, pages 211–224.
A general summary of language growth from birth, with especial emphasis on its development during the preschool years.

3. Blatz, W. E., Fletcher, M. L., and Mason, M., "Early Development in Spoken Language of the Dionne Quintuplets," *University of Toronto Studies; Child Development Series*, 1937, No. 16.
The children were more retarded than twins in language development, due, perhaps, to their mutual imitation. Annette was imitated more than the other children. Graphs and charts of language development are provided.

4. Fairbanks, G., "An Acoustical Study of the Pitch of Infant Hunger Wails," *Child Development*, 1942, Vol. 13, pages 227–232.
The author applies scientific analysis to the auditory characteristics of his infant's crying. The pitch varies, and so does the intensity!

5. Fröschels, E., *Psychological Elements in Speech*, Section II on "Infant Speech," Boston, Expression Co., 1932.
A discussion of the development of infant speech, pointing out analogies in the development of infant speech and in disorders of speech. The disorders of speech mentioned in this connection are aphasia, articulatory disorders, initial stuttering, and development stuttering.

6. Gesell, A., *The Psychology of Early Growth Including Norms of Infant Behavior and a Method of Genetic Analysis*, New York, Macmillan, 1938.
A scientific discussion of the transformation of motor capacities into motor abilities in the child, and his achievements in health and uninterrupted progress. It considers five fields of behavior for human psychomotor development—postural, prehensile, perceptual, adaptive, and language.

7. Hawk, S. S., "Can a Child Be Taught to Talk," *Journal of Speech Disorders*, 1939, Vol. 4, pages 173–179.
The concept of speech readiness is explained, and with it the motokinesthetic method for teaching the sounds and words suitable to a young child's speech.

8. Hurlock, E. B., *Child Development*, New York, McGraw-Hill, 1942, pages 124–156; 157–186.
The first section of this book listed in the above reference gives an excellent account of the child's motor development. The second summarizes language development from birth onward. The material is presented interestingly and thoroughly.

9. Irwin, O. C., "Research on Speech Sounds for the First Six Months of Life," *Psychological Bulletin*, 1941, Vol. 38, pages 277–288.
A summary of the studies on infant vocalization.

10. Irwin, O. C. and Curry, T., "Vowel Elements in the Crying of Infants Under Ten Days of Age," *Child Development*, 1941, Vol. 12, pages 99–109.
Data interpreted comparatively to show a trend during speech development to increased use of back vowels.

11. Leopold, W. F., "Speech Development of a Bilingual Child: A Linguist's Record. Volume I. Vocabulary Growth in the First Two Years," *Northwestern University Studies in the Humanities*, 1939, Vol. 6.
All the words, both English and German, were transcribed phonetically, with the date and circumstances under which they were produced.

12. Lewis, M. M., *Infant Speech*, London, Paul, Trench, Trubner, 1936.
A book outlining the development of a child's speech from the birth cries to the beginning of conceptual use of speech. This is based upon some statistical observations, and to a large extent upon the observation of a particular child. It discusses early utterance, babbling, imitation, comprehension of conventional speech, meaningful utterance, the mastery of conventional forms, the expansion of meaning, and further progress in conventional use. The appendices contain charts of the various data collected.

13. Low, A. A., *Studies in Infant Speech and Thought. Part I: The Development of Sentence Structure in Infancy from the Viewpoint of Grammar; A Quantitative Analysis of the Continuous Speech Record of Two Infants*, Urbana, University of Illinois Press, 1936.
The report of a study to evolve a method that would show the language development of a child. It gives the observations of two mothers, and records and analyzes the utterances of their two children. The study includes many charts and tables summarizing the analyses of the language responses.

14. Merry, F. K. and Merry, R. V., *From Infancy to Adolescence*, New York, Harper, 1940, Chapters 3 and 4.
This book not only summarizes the motor, physical, and social development of very young children but also language growth. There are many excellent transcriptions of the speech of children at the different age levels.

15. Miller, N. E. and Dollard, J., *Social Learning and Imitation*, New Haven, Yale University Press, 1941.
This book is especially noted for its exposition of imitation as a form of learning. It clearly illustrates the proposition that one cannot imitate any activity one has not previously practiced. Examples of imitation in children are given.
16. Murchison, C., *A Handbook of Child Psychology*, Chapter 9, Worcester, Clark University Press, 1931.
A survey of the whole field of infant speech by Dorothea McCarthy. It includes developmental stages of speech, the growth of vocabulary, the development of the sentence, the functions of language, the relation of language development to other factors, and speech tendencies at higher ages, with many summaries of individual studies under each heading.
17. Poole, I., "Genetic Development of Articulation of Consonant Sounds in Speech," *Elementary English Review*, 1934, Vol. 11, pages 159–161.
A study of the ability of 140 preschool children to articulate consonant sounds in words. The results showed that a child who is developing normally both physically and mentally may be expected to have reached maturity of articulation at least by the age of eight, with the median girl reaching that stage shortly after the age of six, and the median boy at age seven. The author concludes, then, that, unless definite pathological conditions were present to alter prognosis, no special help in articulation need be given to children younger than these ages.

VI

The Child Who Has Not Learned to Talk—
Delayed Speech

Many terms have been used to describe the case of the child who has not learned to talk. He has been said to have "baby talk," "idiolalia," "speech retardation," and "delayed speech." He has been called "the slow of tongue." The parents complain that these children have not learned to talk or cannot learn this skill. Indeed, some of these children have no true speech but rely on grunts and gestures to make known their wants. Others vocalize a lot, but the speech flow resembles the jargon of the young baby, and it is unintelligible.

One of the children we examined vocalized every minute of her stay with us. She was a restless, wandering child whose attention constantly shifted. As she picked up one toy, threw it down, ran to the window, tapped at the pane, shook her skirt, sucked her thumb, laughed at her reflection in the mirror, and performed a hundred other consecutive activities, she accompanied each with a constant flow of unintelligible jabber. By using a hidden microphone, we were able to record some samples of her speech. The speech sample together with the object of her attention ran like this:

Yugga boo booda . . . iganna mim . . ." (jʌgə bu budə ɪgænə mɪm.) Picked up the toy automobile and threw it down. "Annakuh innuhpohee . . . tseeguh . . . teekuh . . ." (ænakə ɪnəpohi tsigʌ tsikə.) Looked out window and tapped at pane.

In this case we were unable to recognize any mutilations of familiar words, though in most cases of delayed speech careful analysis will isolate a few words, consistently used, which bear some resemblance to their conventional cognates. Both of these general types of delayed speech can result from fixation at an infantile level of speech development. They can also occur regressively as the result of a

sudden accident, illness, or emotional shock, even when the previous
speech development has been excellent.   Both mutism and unintelligibility are relative terms, since noises are made by all mutes, and even
in the worst jargon faint resemblances to meaningful words are occasionally found.   The problem of delayed speech, however, is more
than that of a severe articulation defect.   These children are also
handicapped linguistically and semantically.   They often do not
comprehend the language of others, nor are they particularly interested in vocal symbols even when they can understand them.   The
longer they go without receiving help in attaining a normal method of
communication, the more they tend to ignore the speech of others.
There certainly does seem to be a time when each child is ripe for
speech learning.   According to Stinchfield, the *speech readiness period*
lies primarily between the ninth and twenty-fourth months of a child's
life.   He may be taught to talk much later, but it is during this period
that he will learn his speech skills most quickly and thoroughly.   However, our own clinical practice has independently convinced us that
any child who does not begin to speak intelligible two-word phrases by
thirty months should be referred to the physician and the speech correctionist.   The longer speech is delayed, the more difficult it is to
teach.

Causes of delayed speech.   In the treatment of delayed speech it is
important that a careful and thorough study of the child's development and environment be made.   Every child will learn to talk unless
some important factor prevents speech acquisition.   In no other
speech disorder is it so necessary to find and eliminate the cause, and
the teacher should leave untapped no source of information which
might lead to a knowledge of the origin of the child's lack of intelligible
speech.

The common causes of delayed speech, all of which should be considered in exploring the child's history, are: low mentality, deafness,
poor co-ordinations due to disease or paralysis, prolonged illness (especially in the first two years of life), lack of necessity or motivation
for speech, improper teaching methods used by parents, shift of
handedness or confused hand preference, necessity for learning two or
more languages simultaneously, shock during the act of speaking,
emotional conflicts, and aphasia.   Each of these will be discussed in
turn.

Low intelligence.   The teacher must be careful in deciding that the
cause of the child's delayed speech is low intelligence.   Indeed, the

reverse relationship often seems to be the case, since several authorities claim that children gain from ten to thirty points in I.Q. as the result of having been taught to talk.   The Binet examinations are especially dependent upon the acquisition of speech, and even many of the performance tests presume a familiar acquaintance with activities that these speechless children would find difficult.   Recent studies in the field of intelligence testing have indicated that I.Q.'s can be raised by providing young children with a stimulating environment, and it is easily seen that a child who has no speech responses would not be likely to meet as much stimulation as would the speaking child. Nevertheless, children of low intelligence are generally retarded in speech and must be taught patiently and carefully by means of the special techniques known to the teacher of subnormal children.   These children need speech training even more, perhaps, than the usual course of study given them would seem to indicate.   Training in the manual and domestic arts should be supplemented by much speech training.

Hearing defects.   It is well known that children who are born deaf do not speak unless they are painstakingly taught to do so.   It is not so well known that children who have lost their hearing as a result of illness or accident frequently lose intelligible speech to such a degree that many of the speech sounds are never regained.   Nor is it well enough known that there are types of deafness which permit the child to hear certain pitches but not others.   So-called regional deafness, of which high-frequency deafness may serve as an example, can produce distortions of speech so peculiar that the child's parents are convinced of a lack of intelligence.   Some of these children have often been placed in schools for the totally deaf, although properly designed hearing aids could permit them to attain adequate speech.   These children should be referred to an otologist for a thorough examination. An audiometric examination is vitally necessary, and the physician should use some of the newer techniques suited to the responses of young children.

Poor co-ordination.   Although certain children present the picture of precocious speech together with defective or immature co-ordinations, the majority of children who are definitely retarded in the motor sphere are similarly retarded in speech.   The child with St. Vitus Dance (chorea), or the one who has suffered from infantile or spastic paralysis, seldom acquires intelligible speech before four or five years of age.   It is usually unwise to do much speech work with these children before they have acquired some degree of control over the larger movements. Physiotherapy, especially for the paralytics, will improve speech much more than concentrated speech correction in the early years of the child's life.

Illness. Prolonged illness during the first year usually interferes with the babbling and vocal play so necessary to the beginning of speech. The first speech attempts seem to emerge, not from the squalling of hunger, irritation, or pain, but from the noises of relief or contentment. An ill child seldom gets enough of this early speech practice, and since all the speech sounds used later in life are practiced during the babbling period, he usually presents delayed speech. Uninformed parents often fail to realize the importance of this babbling and, feeling that the child should then be talking, insist upon his learning meaningful words immediately. They should stimulate him to babbling as much as possible. His environment should be one of much vocalization, especially of the repetitive vocal play that many parents coo to their infants. Repetition of syllables immediately after feeding or when the child is content or free from pain will soon provoke a similar response from him. Meaningful purposive speech can be taught later, and the child should be encouraged to talk to his pets and toys, to accompany rhythmic movements with vocalization which is either sung or spoken, and to indulge in all the vocal play he wishes. Even six-year-old children with a history of early illness and delayed speech should be taught to babble.

Lack of motivation. One of the first causes of delayed speech which speech correctionists look for in the child of less than six years of age is that of a lack of motivation. Children will not learn to talk unless they realize the utility of speech. The law of least effort is a rather fundamental determinant of human effort, and when children can get their wishes fulfilled without employing speech, they never acquire this all-important tool. We adults, who speak so easily, often fail to realize that our vocal skills were not mastered without some difficulty. Children will avoid this difficulty if they can, and some parents seem to help them in this avoidance. Some mothers become so skillful at anticipating their child's every wish that the performance astounds the bystander. This appalling situation arises especially when the child is an only child or has been ill a great deal or is handicapped in some way. Excessive overprotection and solicitude can not only delay speech acquisition but often prevent it altogether. The child develops an excellent understanding of the speech of others and frequently develops a gesture language which would do credit to a Charlie Chaplin, but he steadfastly refuses to make any speech attempt of his own.

Often the parent declares that she has tried to get the child to speak but he refuses, and that she does not know what to do. This is usually true, but when the manner of teaching has been examined, it will be found to be sporadic and perfunctory. Only a consistent, patient, and extended program of speech teaching will be effective. This program must follow some such sequence as this:

1. Insist that the child accompany all gestures by some vocalization. This vocalization may be some meaningless vowel. The parent should sound the vowel whenever the child gestures so as to provide the stimulation necessary to produce the child's response. The parent should explain to the child that no wish will be satisfied until he does vocalize, and the parent must maintain this standard for at least a week before giving up. We have never had a failure when this has been done. Usually two or three days are necessary before all gestures are accompanied by vocalization.

2. Once vocalization has been accomplished, select some favorite plaything or favorite food, and demand a modification of the vocalization whenever the child desires the object. For example, if the child wants a ball, he should be told that he must press his lips together firmly before vocalizing, thus producing a sound similar to the *b* sound, in the syllable *ba*. Even if this sound is not exactly the true word for the object, it should be given him with much praise. Only one such "word" should be worked for at a time. If the child refuses the object and turns to others, he should be placed in an empty room where this object is the only toy. No normal child can resist such a program. The word should be reviewed frequently, and much social approval should be given. Pictures of the object can be hidden about the room and games may be invented to show the child the usefulness of naming. Once a word has been mastered, other words can be acquired in a similar manner. Monosyllabic words should be used and, as we have said, they need only approximate the real word. Babbling, echoing, and other speech games will help. Usually, when the child has acquired one or two words, the problem solves itself.

Poor speech standards. Another cause of delayed speech is poor speech standards in the home. This condition is closely related to a lack of motivation, although the latter usually refers more to the substitution of a gesture language than to the presence of a primitive vocal language which results from the parental acceptance of distorted speech. Many a child of four and five is brought to the speech correctionist with speech so unintelligible that no one save the mother can understand what the child is trying to say. Twins and children of similar ages often develop a serviceable speech of this sort. One pair of twins used much vocalization when communicating with each other but used only gestures when speaking to adults. In their primitive vocabulary, the following words seemed to be used consistently: "we-we" (meaning either "I" or "you"); "eee" (any adult); "bam" (ball); "bam-aa" (apple). There were other similar distortions and substitutions. In general, this type of speech consists of the more primitive lip, nasal, and tonguetip sounds used with the neutral or front vowels. Most of the words are approximations of those used by adults, with the distortions produced by substituting easier sounds for more difficult ones. Since the parents or associates of these children accept this counterfeit speech, the child has no incentive to improve it.

These poor speech standards are occasionally due to parental baby talk, but more often they are the result of illness or handicap which has made the parent reluctant to put any extra pressure on the child. After the illness, the parents resolve to insist upon good speech, and so they nag and correct and scold the child for a period of days. This procedure seldom produces any great change, because a strong penalty or pressure placed upon any activity as unconscious as speech tends to stamp in the error and to make it more permanent. Moreover, the mere command, "Don't say 'eee,' say 'mama'!" does not show the child how he can make the new co-ordinations. And again, constant nagging about the child's poor speech will surely arouse an emotional conflict, for not even an adult can watch his speech continually. Therefore, the parents usually give up the attempt and hope that the child will outgrow his poor speech habits.

Better methods than those suggested in the last paragraph will be discussed in some detail later in this chapter. But it can be emphasized that good speech standards must be built gradually and that the child must be shown how to make the desired words. The parents should concentrate their efforts on not more than five words, and these words should be composed of the easier speech sounds. The child must be taught to make the sounds which comprise these words and should be able to make them at will. This teaching of sounds should be confined to a few situations or speech periods which are part of the child's daily routine. Only good-natured and humorously vivid penalties should be used, and rewards should be stressed. When the child is first able to make the desired word, corrections should still be confined to these nucleus speech periods. But as these words and nucleus situations become completely mastered, the requirements may be extended until all words and all situations must conform to the adequate speech standards.

Improper methods used in teaching the child to talk. An authority on child care once said that children learn to speak, not because of parental teaching, but in spite of it. The average child certainly does seem to exhibit a remarkable ability to acquire speech when the teaching is so poor that it hardly merits the name. All that most young parents know of the teaching of talking is that they should hold out an object and repeat its name over and over. Meanwhile, they hope that the miracle will happen, and it usually does. But some children need more skillful teaching and do not acquire speech until such teaching is forthcoming. Some of the common errors made by parents in the teaching of talking are: stimulation at the wrong time, too much or too little stimulation, the wrong kind of stimulation, disregard of the need for motivation, and improper use of association to provide meanings.

Some parents begin to try to get the child to imitate them as early as the third and fourth months, whereas no attempts should be made until about the seventh month, and imitation of motor behavior should always precede imitation of speech. Stimulation at a time when the child has not reached the proper level of maturation is not only useless but also actually harmful, since it merely reduces the child's interest in the stimulation. Other parents will wake the child out of a deep slumber or will interrupt such prepotent activities as feeding to ask him to say "bye-bye." The first teaching of talking should be confined to the child's vocal play periods.

Even intelligent parents frequently overstimulate or understimulate the child and use improper types of stimulation. Children who are neglected, even in the interests of modern child education, will be delayed in their speech. Then, too, children who are bombarded from every side by crowing parents, by masses of endearing or admiring verbiage, can hardly be expected to respond selectively. Parents who have heard of the evils of using baby talk (which certainly is an evil at a later stage of speech development) confine their stimulation to such words as *bicycle*, *mother*, and *nurse*, and they occasionally rebuke their unlucky offspring for such achievements as *ba* for *ball*. As we have seen, the first stimulation should be the imitation of the child's own vocal play; and the next should be monosyllables or double syllables which the child has practiced previously. Later, after the child has learned to enjoy and to use speech and shows eagerness for new names, the true disyllables (such as *water*) can be used.

Many parents, made unintelligent by the presence of a new object for their self-love, seek to anticipate their child's every wish. They rush to give the ball to the child if he so much as looks at it. Were they wise, they would move it a little closer and provoke some speech attempt, thus using the situation for the teaching of talking. Probably the most frequent functional cause of delayed speech is this parental overeagerness. Children won't talk unless they profit from the attempt. Speech is a tool, and if it is not needed, it will not be used. Parents should be very careful to prevent the formation of such a condition, for only by careful and systematic retraining can it be broken down.

Finally, parents make the mistake of tearing down associations as fast as they are built. Instead of concentrating their teaching on a few simple words and their associated objects, they overwhelm the child with synonyms and adjectives and terms of endearment, a hodgepodge of stimulation which would make a nonspeaking adult with an I.Q. of 150 give up in despair. The use of a little applied intelligence, and some consideration of the child's outlook, will solve this problem.

Shift of handedness. A relatively infrequent cause of delayed speech is the shift of handedness insisted upon by many parents of left-handed children. Occasionally a child is found with no definite hand preference and speech which is very much delayed. Most of these children show a spontaneous acquisition of speech as soon as they show a preference for one hand. Studies in aphasia demonstrate that the part of the brain which controls speech is also that which is responsible for the control of the preferred hand. Therefore, it is wise to determine which hand the child naturally prefers and to prevent any prejudice on the part of the parents from affecting his natural choice. The child should be observed in those activities which have been least affected by environmental training, and these activities are those which demand little speed, strength, or accuracy. Writing, sewing, or cutting with scissors are not good criteria of natural handedness. The teacher or parent should make careful observations of the child's one-handed activity and then take the child to some psychological or speech clinic where the proper apparatus is available for diagnosing the true hand preference.

Once this has been done, a program of manual activity should be initiated. New skills should be acquired with the correct hand, and the old skills should be transferred to the proper side. It is often wise to ask the child to vocalize as he uses his hand in such activities as ball tossing, writing, and hammering. The child should be trained in larger activities first, and then in those which involve the use of specialized movement. Almost miraculous results follow a program of this sort. With no speech training, but with intensive concentration on motor skills, the child suddenly begins to speak.

Bilingual conflicts. Some parents deliberately attempt to teach their children two languages at the same time, a procedure which is usually disastrous. Studies indicate that inefficiency and confusion result from such training even in adulthood. Most children in foreign-language homes learn the foreign speech first, and then make the shift when they enter school. This can usually be done without much danger, but when older children in the family insist upon speaking English, the situation becomes dangerous. The teacher must educate the parents to insist upon one language until the child has acquired a mastery of it. If this procedure is followed, no delayed speech will result.

Emotional shocks and accidents. As we have mentioned, speechless children are often found whose histories show that they talked at one time. These individuals often lose their speech because of some accident, severe illness, or shock to the central nervous system. Occasionally a severe fright or other powerful emotion will produce a speechlessness which persists. One child injured his tongue and mouth cavity with a pair of scissors and refused to talk long after the wounds had healed. Another child of five was talking to his mother when knocked down by a large dog. At eight years he was still using pantomime for all communication.

The majority of these cases will respond to the intensive treatment to be described later. However, when the loss of speech followed a strong psychological or emotional shock, it is often wise and necessary to take measures to minimize the effects of the shock. The procedure usually consists of the following steps: (1) Someone, such as a teacher, psychologist, or psychiatrist, who has had no former connection with the child's unfortunate experience, wins his confidence and respect. (2) The original shock situation is re-experienced in such a way as to provide a successful solution. The child must somehow recreate the original situation and master it. (3) Attitudes of humor should be associated with the experience. (4) When speech does return or is relearned, the child should verbalize both the situation which caused the shock and the one which canceled it.

As an illustration, the treatment of the child who lost the power of speech after being knocked down by a dog may be described.

The speech correctionist to whom the child was referred spent a week of fifteen-minute daily periods in gaining the child's confidence. In these periods games were played in which the child's dominance over toys, teddy bears, and so on, was stressed. The clinician never spoke to the child but used sign language entirely. Gradually, games were introduced in which activity was accompanied by vocalization. There was a spiral maze in which a little train traveled the grooves when pushed by the humming clinician. If the child pushed the train without humming, the clinician shook his head and took the toy away from him. Pictures of dogs were hidden about the room and the child learned to say "dah-dah-dah" until he found them. A stuffed toy dog was provided and the child was encouraged to roll a large ball in the attempt to knock it over. The clinician then held the toy dog and made it prance and dodge the ball. All activity by this time was accompanied by some kind of vocalization, and the clinician occasionally used one or two words such as *dog*, *train*, and *here*. A puppy who had previously been trained to play the ball game was brought in, and when the child appeared for his conference the clinician was playing ball with it. The child was given the ball, and, rolling it at the puppy, knocked it over. "Look, look, I did it," he said spontaneously, and from that time on, speech returned swiftly. The child seemed very cruel to the puppy for a while, but gradually this attitude changed. Later, the clinician taught the game of "Knock-down," in which alternately the child and the clinician and the puppy pretended to attack and to be knocked over. The child was very amused by this game and kept a running conversation going all the time in imitation of the clinician.

Emotional conflicts. Another frequent cause of speech loss is emotional conflict. One child stopped talking when the courts, after his parents were divorced, assigned him to the custody of the father. Another, the youngest child and only boy in a family of six children, all of whom were extremely rapid speakers, finally gave up the battle for speech until he entered school, where the competition was not so great. Another child, urged to confess his guilt in a rather serious misdemeanor, refused and was punished severely. He did not speak again until after a course of psychological treatment. Other emotional speech conflicts which have produced speech loss are: forcing the child to recite or perform when he feels himself incapable of doing so successfully; too high speech standards in the home; constant repression at home or in school; deprivation of attention or so much overattention that an abnormal hunger for attention is created, both resulting in speech loss as a symptom which will satisfy this thwarted desire; and subjection to unreasonable (from the child's point of view) compulsion to such an extent that the only way in which he can resist is to refuse to talk. In each of these instances, the treatment requires elimination of the cause by treating the environment rather than the child.

Speech teachers who do not realize the importance of emotional etiology frequently find themselves working vainly. The child will appear to make progress and then will unaccountably relapse into as much or more error than he had at the beginning. The speech correctionist is frequently required to map out an entire program of home adjustment before her work can begin. She must teach the parents how to react to the child's negativism and demand for attention. The former may be taken care of by commanding and requesting the child to do things he really wants to do, and then, when he refuses, accepting his refusal. An example of this may be given:

The teacher said to the child in a rather peremptory tone, "Johnny, you go down to the drugstore this very minute and get yourself an ice-cream cone!" The child answered "No!" and the teacher asked another child, who accepted and returned to eat the ice-cream cone under Johnny's regretful nose. Such a program soon brought a discriminatory answer to requests and commands, and when reward for positive response was added, together with humorous attitudes toward the negativism, the child's whole attitude changed, and his speech soon became normal.

At times, the child's refusals may be chalked up on the board and matched by the teacher's or parent's refusals. The demand for attention, if reasonable, should be satisfied in other ways. If unreasonable, it can be eliminated by teaching the child that he will get a lot of attention at certain times during the day but not at other times. Penalize all unreasonable demands by humorous disregard.

In addition to the emotional etiology, emotional conflicts will frequently produce a rapid, careless speech, or a repressed speech with minimal articulatory movements, which lead to sound substitutions, omissions, and distortions.

Poor auditory memory span. Another cause of delayed speech seems to be an inability on the part of the child to retain sequences of sounds. He frequently can repeat a sound or a word immediately after it has been pronounced but seems to be unable to retain it for more than a few seconds. Simple sounds appear to be retained more easily than words of one syllable, and polysyllabic words present insuperable difficulty. Many parents who fail to recognize this condition attribute the child's speech failure either to stubbornness or to a lack of intellect, and penalize the child severely. This causes a negativism which complicates the situation.

Most of the children who possess short auditory memory spans can be trained to retain auditory impressions long enough to acquire good speech. The training must include teaching the concept of sequence and the delayed response. Many exercises for teaching these factors will be found in the chapter on the treatment of articulatory disorders. Young children must be taught the concept of sequence by identifying sounds with objects. Thus, in one case, the concept of sound sequences was attained in the following manner:

Three different dolls were named "wa," "ba," and "ma." After the child learned their names, the teacher pretended that the dolls were going to school, and as they entered the door the child was to say their names. Sometimes, two entered the door in a hurry, and so the child had to say "ma" and "ba" in swift sequence. By varying this situation in many ways, the child soon learned to point out the dolls in their proper sequence and to give their names in proper order. By insisting that the child cross the room to whisper the names to her mother, the delayed response which necessitated the retention of sound sequences was taught, and from this simple beginning a sound plan of treatment was constructed which resulted in good speech.

Aphasia. One of the more uncommon causes of delayed speech is aphasia, which is usually the result of a severe birth injury or an injury to the head. It is always necessary to rule out the other causes, especially those of high-frequency deafness and feeble-mindedness, before aphasia is considered.

The child may appear to be congenitally deaf, but if there is a history of occasional response to air-borne sound (rather than to sounds which might be carried through the floor or other vibrating bodies), the child should be carefully examined by a specialist in this field. Highly emotional situations often produce such responses when they are not apparent in ordinary activity. Other signs of aphasia manifest themselves in what seems to be a "forgetting" of the purposes of well-known objects such as a pencil or spoon. The treatment of these cases is difficult and must be carried out through the development of a service-able gesture language, to which vocalization may later be added. The kinesthetic method of teaching speech sounds is effective with many of these children. In any event, the parent and teacher should seek to find other avenues of speech teaching than those normally used, and they should study carefully the more recent works on this subject. The references at the end of this chapter will serve as a primary bibli-ography. The disorder is so rare that few teachers ever see an aphasic child.

General principles of treatment. In the preceding discussion we have suggested several methods for retraining the child with delayed speech. The general principles upon which that treatment is usually founded will be outlined briefly.

Although a few exceptional parents possess the temperament and understanding necessary to carry out the remedial program, it is usu-ally well to have someone who has had no previous history of failure in teaching speech to the child do the work. A specialist in speech correction is probably best fitted to handle the situation, but we have seen excellent results obtained by interested primary teachers. In the latter instance, rather careful supervision is necessary, because many problems arise which require the information that specialized training in speech correction and clinical psychology makes available.

It is important that the place selected for the speech teaching be divorced as much as possible from the former environment. When possible, the child should be taken out of the home. If this is not convenient, some room should be chosen and changed about so that there are few opportunities in it for self-amusement. We have found that in a clinic room with only a child's table, two chairs, and a few pictures on the walls the child's attention will concentrate on the teacher and make him dependent upon her for his activity. Boredom is one of the best motivations for co-operation, and if the child must depend upon the resources of the teacher, the speech training pro-gresses much more rapidly. The teacher will use many playthings, but she should bring them with her and allow the child to use them only when she thinks it advisable. Some of the more spoiled or more negative children may rebel when this regime is first instituted, but they soon become interested and look forward to the speech periods as the most pleasant parts of their day. One or two half-hour periods each day are usually sufficient, and little progress in terms of actual vocabulary should be expected during the first two or three weeks.

Much swifter progress will be achieved if the groundwork is laid carefully.

As we have indicated, it is essential that the cause of the speech delay be eliminated as soon as possible. Since this usually involves treatment of the parents and the associates of the child, it is best carried out through daily home assignments. For example, in one instance in which the cause was a lack of motivation, the speech-correction teacher sent home daily assignments of which the following are typical:

Collect five instances during the day in which the child used gesture without vocalization in requesting some object, and in which you refused to give it to him until he had grunted or made some speech attempt. Please write up the accounts of these five and send them to me.

Your child likes the red ball. Show it to him with your eyes closed and ask him if he wants it. Report his reaction.

It is usually wise to ask for a written report, since this insures a delegation of some responsibility to the parents and procures much better co-operation. Each day should contain some attempt to minimize or eradicate the condition that caused the speech delay.

Selecting the first words. The next task is that of selecting the words to be taught. The first project should not contain more than five or ten words, and they should begin with the easier sounds, *m, b, p,* or *w* If possible, they should be monosyllabic or should consist of repeated syllables, such as "mama." They should be names of things or activities which the child enjoys. If the child has some distorted speech sounds which he habitually employs for naming favorite objects, it is wise to select new toys or new activities which he has not previously named. When this principle is followed, no unlearning is necessary. Nonsense names can be used if the true names are too difficult or begin with the wrong sounds, since the object of this first training is to teach the child to use speech as a tool and to set up proper speech standards. Later on, the child can be given the more difficult task of unlearning old incorrect names and substituting correct ones for them. The parents and teacher alike must use the nonsense name, however, when referring to the object in the presence of the child. We usually include about two true names among each set of five words used in building the primary vocabulary. Thus, one child was taught the following names in the order given:

1. "Moop" (the name given to an oddly shaped mass of modeling clay which was used in a hiding game). 2. "Wap" (the sound made by the child and teacher in unison as a signal for a Jack-in-the-box to pop out). 3. "Boom" (the name of a toy cannon). 4. "Papa" (the name he used for himself when he pretended to be his father, a physician, engaged in treating the teacher, who pretended to be sick. The boy was given an old medical satchel and tongue depressor and left the room to knock at the door. Whereupon, the teacher asked "Who's there?" and refused to open the door until she knew who was knocking). 5. "Ba" (the name for "ball," or the sound used as the boy bounced it).

After the first set of names has been chosen, the teacher begins to teach the sounds that are used therein. This is done in several ways: (1) by stimulation and other forms of ear training; (2) by combining the sound with some activity; (3) by placement of the organs of speech. The sounds are not incorporated within words but are taught by themselves in isolation, or in short nonsense syllables such as *pa* or *woo*.

Ear training for delayed-speech cases. Some typical methods used in teaching the child to hear the primary speech sounds may be illustrated by the following teacher's report:

Today I had my first session with Tommy. He evidently had created quite a scene at home and both he and his mother were in tears when they entered the room. As we had planned, the mother left immediately, locking the door behind her. I said, "Hello, Tommy," and paid no further attention to him, being busily engaged in filling typewritten O's on a page in front of me with red penciling. Whenever I finished one, I said *p-p-poo*, and went on to the next.

Tommy clung to the door for about three minutes but stopped crying. He then made an exploration of the room, finally stopping beside me to watch what I was doing. He became very interested and I noticed that whenever I completed an O he would form the *p* sound with his lips as I was saying it. Finally he made gestures requesting the red pencil and paper, but I refused with a nod, explaining that I was almost through and that perhaps he could do it some other day.

Having finished, I put the paper and pencil away in the desk, and took out the medicine bottle of water and the cup. Then I said to Tommy, "Listen now, and you'll hear what the bottle says to the cup. It says *puh-puh-puh*." Then I began to pour the water into the cup and he listened with great interest, nodding his head. He reached for the bottle and I let him pour, as I said the bottle sound. I then put the cup and bottle away and said, "Let's you and I play the bottle game. You be the cup and I'll be the bottle." He nodded agreement with great enthusiasm, and I turned him around so that his ear was near my lips and said into it a series of "puh-puhs."

As soon as his interest waned a little, I blindfolded myself and told him to try to prevent my pouring into his ear-cup. We had a great time and he almost wore me out chasing him, but he heard a lot of the bottle sound, and had identified it as such.

I then brought out a little bell and told him to ring it whenever I made the bottle sound. He was blindfolded during this game. I tried to mix him up by using other sounds such as *kuh* and *muh* but only caught him up once. Before we knew it, his mother had returned, and Tommy wept again at having to leave such an interesting place so soon.

The production of speech sounds. The purposes of ear-training techniques are to stimulate the child with the isolated sound, to teach him to identify the characteristics of the sound, and to train him to discriminate between it and other sounds. It is usually unwise to ask the child to make the sound during the first few speech sessions. He should merely listen and signal his awareness through some form of pleasant activity. The teacher makes the sound; the child reacts to it. Many varieties of games and activities should be invented to carry out these purposes, and the teacher needs the quality of inventiveness if she is to be successful.

After four or five sessions of ear training, the teacher should try to get the child to associate the sound with some activity. With most of these children, negativism and refusal will result from a direct request for speech attempt. But when speech is merely a part of a general body activity and the attention is focused on the latter, no difficulty is experienced. For example, one child would gladly make the *mmmmmm* sound whenever he turned the crank of a musical toy, although he had previously refused to attempt it in imitation of his teacher. It is usually well to explain to the child that the activity can be performed only if the sound is made at the same time, and if the teacher illustrates this principle and speaks the sound in unison with the child's activity, the child will co-operate. Occasionally, the association becomes too specific, and the child insists upon cranking the toy whenever the sound is made. This tendency can be eliminated by a joint activity of teacher and pupil, in which the one does the cranking while the other makes the sound. Other techniques will suggest themselves to any ingenious teacher. One of the most successful methods takes advantage of the child's natural urge to identify himself with what he perceives. In the case of the child in the last-mentioned teacher's report, he was told that in place of playing the cup in the blindfold game, he could be the bottle. Immediately he began to pronounce the *p* sound without difficulty or hesitation. The teacher can tell little stories about the objects or things with which the child has identified himself, requesting him to make his sound whenever he hears his name mentioned. Thus a story about a bottle would produce many isolated speech attempts to say the *p* sound.

Stimulation exercises and games. The purpose of such exercises and games is to bombard the child with many of the isolated speech sounds. The child must be stimulated with the sound so thoroughly that it may almost be said to ring in his ears. Every available agency should be used to provide this stimulation. Parents, friends, and classmates can help. Through various devices, the speech defective's attention to the sound must be focused and heightened. He must become aware of it not only in isolation but also as it occurs within spoken words. Always remember to motivate the child by making the stimulation interesting. It is often wise to have the child do something whenever he hears the sound. Below you will find a few sample stimulation exercises. Select those which seem most appropriate for your child and invent others which serve the same purpose.

1. Blindfold the child. Make the sound from several different places in the room. Ask the child to point to where the sound came from or to find you.
2. Pretend that each of you is a certain animal or machine that makes the sound. Have him run around the room with you as you produce the sound.
3. Procure a calendar mailing tube or similar device. Hold one end to the child's ear as he winds a string upon a spool. The moment the teacher stops making the sound, he must stop winding.
4. Certain objects are set aside as demanding the hearing of the correct sound before they can be touched. Such rituals appeal to children and compel attention.
5. Prolong or repeat the sound rhythmically. Ask him to clap his hands or put his fingers in the ear whenever you make it very loudly.
6. Tell the child a story or rhyme and prolong the selected sound whenever it occurs in a word. The important thing is to accent the particular sound you are working on.
7. Tie a rope on the child and tell him to walk back and forth as you pronounce the sound. Whenever you cease making the sound, jerk the rope.

Indirect methods for combining sounds and movements. (Do these first in unison, making the sound a part of the activity.)

1. Snap off the light—say *ow*.
2. Shoot a toy gun—"bang," *ba, boom,* or *pow*.
3. Turn an egg beater—any vowel on which you rhythmically change pitch.

4. Saw a board—*ee-ee* or *ay-ay*, or zzz-zzz.

5. Hit piano or xylophone and sing any vowel.

6. Wind a toy—*mmmm-mmmmm*.

7. Pull the cork out of a bottle—*puh* or *buh*.

8. Pull or push any toy animal and say its sound: Cow—*moo*, dog—*bow-wow*, and so on.

9. Move a zipper: zzz or *sss*.

10. Rock in a chair or bounce—any vowel or consonant.

Direct methods for combining sounds and movements.

1. *For "m."* Have child flip or stroke your lips as you make the *m* sound. Then you stroke his lips as he makes it.

2. *For "puh."* Have child hold his whole hand flat over your closed mouth with cheeks full of air. Ask him suddenly to pull it away as you explode the *puh* sound. Reverse the process.

3. *For "buh."* Hold or have child hold a feather or strip of tissue over your mouth. Then explode the *buh* sound so that the feather or strip moves or falls. Reverse positions.

4. *For "tik."* Cup hands around your mouth and ask the child to look inside and hear the clock. Say *tik-tik-tik*. Then have him be the clock.

5. *For "dee."* By folding a cardboard provide yourself with a series of ten holes each large enough to insert a finger in. Have child hold it in front of himself and as you insert your finger in each hole say *dee*. Then you hold it, refusing to let him hit the hole until he says *dee*.

6. *For "nnnnnn."* Have child place finger on side of your nose as you open your mouth and say *nnnnnn*. Ask him if he feels the little noise. Then ask him to open his mouth so you can feel his little noise (and nose).

7. *For "oo(w)."* Have child watch your rounded lips as you blow into a tube of paper or into a bag or horn. Then have him do it. Then blow the *oo* sound "out loud." Always call this the "blowing sound."

8. *For the "guh."* Call this the "squeezing sound" or the "choking or collar sound." Ask the child to choke you with both hands as you laugh and say *guh-guh-guh*. Reverse, but be gentle.

9. *For the "kuh."* Call it the "coughing sound" and play some sort of a coughing game. For example, put a feather into the mouth and cough it out with *kuh-kuh-kuh-kuh-kuh*.

10. *For the "f."* Call this the "blow on the finger" sound. Hold your finger laterally across the child's lower lip, pushing it inward. Then ask him to blow on your finger to cool it off. Then set his own finger in position and repeat.

11. *For the "v."* Ask him to watch you in the mirror as you "bite your mouth (or lip) and blow out loud." Then ask him to do it.

Other similar exercises were given in the preceding chapter.

Kinesthetic method. There are other ways of teaching a child to produce the isolated speech sounds besides those mentioned above, although most speech correctionists prefer to use the latter first. When

the ear-training and associated-activity methods fail, all speech correctionists turn first to the kinesthetic method. This method may
briefly be described as the teaching of speech movements by relying
upon the "feel" or *kinesthesia* for their identity in the mind of the child.
Thus the *k* sound, to a child taught by this method, is the sound produced by suddenly pulling down the back of his tongue from its former
position in contact with the roof of the mouth. The teacher indicates the part of the tongue and place of contact through touching the
part concerned or through manipulation of the speech organ itself.
Stroking in certain directions can indicate direction of position change.
Mouth openings and lip positions are produced by viewing them in the
mirror, by watching a model, or by manipulation. Nasalization is
suggested by pointing to the nose or by a signal indicating complete
mouth closure. Voiced consonants may be indicated by stroking the
larynx. In the hands of a clever speech correctionist, these methods
are very effective and may produce almost miraculous results. They
are vital to the success of the deaf child, and many children who have
a short auditory memory span make much more rapid progress through
the kinesthetic method than they do through those involving ear training. The kinesthetic method is always used as a supplementary aid
when the child with delayed speech is spastic or possesses a sluggish
jaw, tongue, or palate. A detailed description of the kinesthetic
method will be found in *Children with Delayed or Defective Speech*, by
Stinchfield and Young, a reference which may be found at the end of
the chapter.

Word production. After the child has been taught to make the
sounds that are included in the five or ten words previously selected,
the teacher's next task is to teach him to combine those sounds to form
words. There are two major ways of accomplishing this: by teaching
whole words and by teaching sound sequences. Both methods should
be used for almost all cases of delayed speech, and, for both, ear training should precede actual performance. Generally speaking, the
whole-word method should be used for simple monosyllabic words,
whereas the sound-sequence method should be used for those of more
than one syllable.

In one case, the word *mop* was among the first five words to be
taught. After the child had been given ear training in saying the *m*
and *p* sounds by themselves, the teacher began the ear training necessary to the production of the whole word. She left the room in a very
mysterious manner, returning with a bottle of colored water and a mop.

As soon as she entered the room, she went solemnly to each corner and said *mop, mop, mop*. Then she made another circuit of the room with the child, and in each corner she said the word *mop* into the ear of the child. On her third circuit, she spilled a little water in each corner, uttering the same word three times, prolonging the *m* slightly and emphasizing the *p*. On her fourth circuit, she took the mop itself and wiped up the water with it, saying the word rhythmically as she worked. She motioned to the child to help her, and as he took hold of the handle he began to say the word in unison with her, somewhat to her surprise. In this case, the vivid stimulation and identification with an activity were sufficient to produce the spontaneous response.

When the sound-sequence method is used, the word should not be broken into all of its component sounds, for the vowel should always be spoken in connection with the consonants that precede or follow it in the syllable. Thus the word *wipe* should be sounded as *wi-p*, and the word *cookie* as *kooh-kee*, never as *w-i-p* or *k-oo-k-ee*. The reason for this is that consonants vary in their formation according to the sounds that follow or precede them, and the child must not be asked to break up words into any finer elements than necessity demands.

Sound-combination games. The purpose of these exercises is to lay the foundation for the speaking of whole and correct words by teaching the child the trick of blending sounds together. One reason why so many children develop a jargon or gibberish is that they fail to realize that a word is made up of a series of sounds blended together. They hear the word as a whole and pronounce some sound which bears a certain likeness to it. Some children can be taught some real words immediately by these sound-sequence games. The majority, however, need much practice in "vocal phonics," in combining and blending sounds without regard to meaning, before true words are taught. Most successful teachers of delayed-speech cases first teach blending sounds as an interesting game and skill; then they teach sound combinations which they call nonsense names; then, finally, real familiar words.

1. Let the teacher perform two of the previously practiced movement-sound combinations then ask the child to imitate her. If this is too difficult, alternate before combining.

2. Let the child perform the activities while the teacher makes the sound, then reverse.

3. Trace a circle to form syllables. Have top arc of circle represent one sound, bottom part another. Trace slowly first, faster gradually for advancement, and divide circle into more parts and sides and sounds.

4. Have squares on floor for certain sounds. Say these sounds while stepping in squares. Form words or syllables.

5. Use different notes on the piano for different sounds.

6. Mount two or more cardboard bells on a piece of tag board so that they can be moved when strings are pulled. Color differently and let each represent a sound. Have child pull the strings as you make the sounds. Then exchange places.

7. Cut shapes of paper for various sounds. Arrange two or three in a row on the table for child to sound out after he learns the sounds for them.

8. Roll a ball across the room, having child say the sounds as the ball moves in the various spaces.

Exercises for sound sequences.

1. Select short one-syllable words, which begin with the continuant sounds: *m, n, w, y,* or *v,* or any vowel. (*Examples: nose, yell, neck, man, way, egg.*) Prolong the first sound, pause, then say the rest of the word, asking child to point to object, or indicate by pantomime, what was spoken. Then prolong the pause for several seconds and try the same procedure except for this variation. Next, separate the vowel from the final sound also and repeat exercise. Then increase number of sounds in the words used, allowing child to guess the word. If difficulty is experienced, repeat sounds more swiftly and with shorter pauses between sounds.

2. Show the child some pictures which include a number of objects. Sound out one of them.

3. Select some simple word, sound it out, ask child to help, and then sound it in unison. Ask for identification of word sounded out.

4. With chalk, divide the floor into sections, a sound for each. As child walks across the room saying each sound, ask what word is formed.

5. Sound out words and have child listen to see if he can count the sounds.

6. Tell child to say some nonsense syllables such as *an* just after teacher has pronounced another sound. (*Example.* Teacher says *mmmmm,* child says *an.* Teacher asks child what word they have spoken together. Child should guess *man.*) Then use other combinations, *puh-an, pan, can,* and so on.

7. Sound out, in the fashion indicated, direction which the child must carry out. (*Example:* "Sh-uh-t th-uh doh-r.")

8. Give each finger the name of a sound. Child says each sound as he lifts (or teacher lifts) the appropriate finger.

As soon as the child has mastered a few words, have him use them in as many meaningful ways as you can invent. Review frequently. Draw pictures of them. Send them home or to the regular teacher to practice. Have the child play games with them, perhaps combining them with activities. Make the child realize that the words are useful in these games and give him great praise for their acquisition.

Building a correct basic vocabulary. As soon as the child has had some experience in making words, you should begin the building of a group of words which can serve as a foundation for good acceptable speech. Scrapbooks of pictures clipped from magazines and catalogues, and certain comic strips or cartoons, carefully selected so as to produce certain words, are useful devices to review and "set" this basic vocabulary. Try to get the child to speak these words as spontaneously as possible. Work them into his contacts with other children and adults, into his errands as well as his play. Drill is much less important than use in real life situations. Provide them.

Useful words for a basic vocabulary. The following words employ the easiest sounds and are most frequently used in children's speech. However, if a child prefers others or seems interested in learning others, always follow his desire.

The words that are the easiest to say are: *baby, bacon, bee* or *be, bib, big, bite, boat, book, bow, boy, buggy, cake, can, coat, comb, come, cookies, cow, cup, dig, eat, egg, eye, go, got, gum, gun, hat, home, hot, ink, keep, keys, kitty, man, me, meat, neck, pig, pin, no, talk, tie, top, two, wagon, walk, window,* and *wood.*

Those not quite so easy to say are: *bag, bone, can, cap, come, daddy, deep, do, door, egg, fat, game, gate, hand, he, make, mama, milk, money, moon, night, open, point, pound, put, talk, top, wait, walk, want, we,* and *you.*

Those that are the least easy to say are: *bad, ball, banana, big, book, car, cold, corn, dinner, dog, farm, fight, goat, good, hide, monkey, nose, O.K., paint, paper, pen, potato, take, tongue, water, wind, wing,* and *yes.*

Other suggestions:

1. Keep a list or notebook dictionary of all words correctly spoken without help. Make the child feel that each new word is a wonderful accomplishment.

2. Reward the child for each new word acquired.

3. Tell a story but omit the new word whenever it occurs. The child must say it. Also use the word to end a rhyme.

4. Hide objects or pictures representing the new words then cover your eyes. The child must hunt and tell what he finds.

5. Make a phone call and ask the child to say a word for you. (Use this method in ordering groceries.)

6. Send the child home, or to a friend's house, with the picture and word to "show off" how well he can talk.

7. Whenever the child masters a new word, his mother must write in one of the squares of a large calendar. He should "read" these every day.

8. Pin a picture to the door of a room or to a favorite chair. Child must say its name whenever he sees it.

Penalizing and correcting errors. Once the child has learned to
speak a word correctly he must be helped to remember not to be careless. Yet, since we must be careful not to make him resent or hate his
speech word, this reminding must *never approach nagging*. He must
never be penalized unpleasantly. Occasionally a good-humored but
vivid remark may help. Praise success and ignore error except in
certain "good speech" situations such as a certain room, a certain person, a certain chair, a certain topic of conversation, or a certain meal.
In these "nucleus" situations, insist upon the correct speaking of each
word he has mastered. Finally, tell everyone how well he is learning
to talk and fill his cup to overflowing with surprised praise and appre-
ciation.

CASE PRESENTATION

Barbara .

This child was brought to the clinic for examination when she was
three years and eleven months old. She had made no effort to talk since
a hospitalization experience at fifteen months, although prior to this her
speech development had been normal and she had used consistently and
meaningfully eight or nine modified "babble" words such as *Daddy, Mamma*
and *bye-bye*. The girl had eaten some poisonous mushrooms and "almost
died. We had to rush her to a hospital and she was there three days.
She recovered all right but she hasn't talked since." The parents also
suspected that "the experience of being left alone in the strange place,
with, perhaps, some nasty nurse who had tried to make her talk or whipped
her or something" had caused the girl's refusal to speak. "After she came
back from the hospital she refused to do lots of things she had previously
done without objection. Before, she was always so sweet and nice. Something certainly must have happened there."

Hearing, intelligence, and muscular co-ordination were tested and the
child reacted normally. She had a history of early and consistent right
handedness. There had been no birth injuries of any kind. Physical
growth had been uneventful. There had been no serious illnesses. She
had no child playmates but was said to "play well alone."

The parents were seemingly well-adjusted individuals of superior intelligence and education. They had consulted their family physician and he
had examined the girl at the time of her third birthday, assuring them that
her "speech organs" were perfect and that she would soon begin to speak
of her own accord. Six months later he re-examined the child, and at that
time discovered that "she comprehended adult speech very well." He there-
upon advised the parents to insist that the girl speak the name of any food
she desired or be deprived of it. "He told us to make her say the word
very clearly or go without any food."

The parents did their best to carry out the physician's advice. The child "seemed hurt and confused and bewildered. She would point and grunt and hold her stomach or point to her mouth and cry until we couldn't bear it. We couldn't eat either." After two days of this starvation speech correction, the parents gave up and went back to their interpretation of the girl's pantomime.

During the first clinic interview the child and her parents were observed visually and auditorily without their knowledge as they waited in the play-room for their appointment. Except for some slight parental overconcern about stray wisps of hair and ribbons, their attitude toward the child and toward each other seemed perfectly normal. They did, however, attempt to get her to talk. They said, "See the little telephone, Barbara?" (Barbara looked at it immediately although the parents had not gestured toward the toy.) "Say 'telephone,' Barbara." The girl shook her head and began to play with a toy truck. "Say 'truck,' Barbara." She threw the truck down and faced the wall with her hands in her lap.

Then the child was left alone in the playroom after being assured that her parents would soon return and that she could come in and see them whenever she wished. She dropped her passivity at once and played with all the toys, making a good many noises as she did so. She even used some jargon vocalization as she talked into the toy telephone.

A clinician then entered the playroom, said "hello" casually, erased the blackboard and then began to assemble a swinging toy, ignoring the girl's evident interest. Barbara soon began to express through pantomime her desire to play with the toy. The clinician told her to hold one piece of the toy and she fixed another part to it. This she did very willingly. From this beginning, the progress was rapid. First they manipulated the toy in unison; then Barbara imitated her clinician; then they made sounds to-gether as the toy was swung back and forth. Other toys and activities were explored in the same way, and by incorporating the sounds as part of the interesting activities, the child produced every speech sound per-fectly except the *ch* (tʃ) and *r* (ɚ) sounds. She also said "Band!" as she "shot out" the room lights and "whee!" as a monkey slid down a slide.

Meanwhile, the parents were testifying that the only sound the girl had ever made since the hospital experience was a grunt. This she used to attract attention to her gestures. We led the parents to the observation room where they heard and saw their child making the sounds we have described above. We then outlined and demonstrated the following pro-gram of home therapy:

1. Imitate the child's rhythmic movements so that she will imitate you. Do this at every opportunity. Teach imitation in every way.

2. Never ask the child to speak or to tell you the names of objects or people. Record every time you catch yourself in this error.

3. Play with isolated speech sounds by making them a part of some interesting activity or movement sequence. Let her share this activity only if she wishes. Ignore her and pretend to be fascinated by your vocal and manual performance.

4. Five times a day, pretend to be unable to understand her gestures. Pretend to want to understand.

5. Stop talking to the girl except for important communication and then speak in one- or two-word phrases or sentences. Label the following objects or activities every time the girl desires them or is playing with them: doll; book; ball; buggy; bye-bye. Merely say the word several times, and without a request for repetition from Barbara.

6. Repeat any words the child does use meaningfully with obvious delight, affection, and praise.

7. Accompany your own rhythmic movements (as in egg-beating, knitting, and so on) by repetitive words or phrases explaining the activity. Sing to the child.

8. Try to give Barbara some playtime with another child of her age as often as possible and let them play alone.

9. Each night write down a report of the day's activities and send them to us each week. Record your failures as well as your successes. Plan to return to the clinic once a month to check progress.

The mother was very conscientious and within two weeks we had the following report from her:

Tuesday. We played the peekaboo doll game, shouting "Here doll!" whenever her head popped out of the hole in the box. She said "here da" once and we ignored it, being afraid to make too much of it. I sang the numbers as I counted the cups of water as I poured them into the coffee pot, and saw her lips following me. Not any of us said "say this, say that" all day. We didn't talk much to her and we both have tried hard to do the rhythmic speech and movements. Bob sawed aloud for half an hour.

Thursday. We ironed out loud today and she made a lot of sounds after me, and even said something like "iron too hot." She also began to jabber a lot when Bob and I were talking to each other at dinner. I pretended I didn't know what she wanted when she wanted a drink, and she said "uh- uh- wah-pee." I think it meant water please.

Friday. She was out of doors today and every time I came out, I came out suddenly and said "Here ma!" just like the doll game, and she said "Hi ma!" twice, and "Mamma" once. We've been shaking our heads up and down and sidewise very energetically for yes and no, and we repeat them about five times whenever we do. She said "na" and shook her head once. I praised her.

Saturday. We were getting ready to go away. I kept saying "go bye" all the time I was dressing her. Then I said "Where are you going, Barby?" and she said, "Go boye-bye." Then she put her hand over her mouth. Later in the afternoon we were playing outdoors with the swing. Every time I gave her a push I would say "Whee" and she got so she was doing it every time. She would not play with the sounds and movements today. Bob says I asked her to say things three times. I'll try to do better tomorrow.

Monday. We had several small children over today and she did a lot of jabbering to them. This is the first time she has ever played with strange children and the first time strangers have ever heard her make a noise. We all played dog on all fours and said "bow-wow." She imitated both the action and the words. She laughed a lot. Said, "Hi, 'cama" when her grandmother suddenly surprised her. I went through all kinds of motions with her and she followed perfectly. I then tried it with sounds and she followed me for one or two but then just said "na na" and kept shaking her head. I imitated her jabber once today and she laughed and then imitated me right back. I was putting on her stocking at the time and went right from the jabber into the word "stocking" and she said "stocky" right after me. I praised her and hugged her and she kept saying it over and over, pulling it up every time.

Six months later, the girl was speaking with a marked articulation defect but intelligibly in all situations. She was neither negative nor shy. She accepted correction without emotional response. She was expressing three- and four-word sentences and the prognosis was excellent.

References

1. Beckey, R. E., "A Study of Certain Factors Related to Retardation of Speech," *Journal of Speech Disorders*, 1942, Vol. 7, pages 223–249.
Case history material from 50 cases of delayed speech is analyzed.

2. Davidson, L. D., "Methods for Treatment of Disorders of Speech Due to Birth Injury," *Quarterly Journal of Speech*, 1936, Vol. 22, pages 404–412.
Methods for teaching the poorly co-ordinated in speech better articulation, rhythm, and voice, with suggestions for delayed-speech cases.

3. Davis, E. A., "The Development of Linguistic Skill in Twins, Singletons with Siblings, and Only Children from Age Five to Ten Years," *University of Minnesota Child Welfare Monographs*, Series No. 14, 1937.
Twins are much retarded in speech development. Reasons are discussed.

4. Day, E. J., "The Development of Language in Twins. I. A Comparison of Twins and Single Children," *Child Development*, 1932, Vol. 3, pages 46–52.
An experimental study of language development in twins showing marked retardation, presumably due to the use of the other twin as a language model or as a social substitute for language need.

5. Fröschels, E., *Psychological Elements in Speech*, pages 72–86, Boston, Expression Co., 1932.
An excellent description of the treatment of a speechless child who seemed to be aphasic. The author also mentions the prevalence of behavior problems as a consequence of the inability to express oneself.

6. Gesell, A., Amatruda, C. S., Castner, B. M., and Thompson, H., *Biographies of Child Development*, New York, Hoeber, 1939, pages 129–146.
Two case histories of delayed speech are analyzed in terms of their developmental causes and treatment.

7. Hawk, S. S., "Auditory Deficiency and Delayed Speech," *Proceedings of the American Speech Correction Association*, 1934, Vol. 5, pages 10–21.
The audiograms of a group of delayed-speech cases are analyzed in terms of their effect on speech learning.

8. Hawk, S. S., "Moto-kinesthetic Training for Children with Speech Handicaps," *Journal of Speech Disorders*, 1942, Vol. 7, pages 357–360.

A description of moto-kinesthetic methods for teaching correct speech.

9. Hurlock, E. B., *Child Development*, New York, McGraw-Hill, 1942, pages 183–186.
The causes of delayed speech are listed and discussed.

10. Kanner, L., *Child Psychiatry*, Springfield, Thomas, 1937, pages 183–186.
Some cases of delayed speech are described.

11. Karlin, I. and Kennedy, L., "Delay in the Development of Speech," *American Journal of Diseases of Children*, 1936, Vol. 51, pages 1138–1149.
Influence of diseases, birth injuries, and other trauma in producing delayed speech.

12. Mason, M. K., "Learning to Speak after Six and One Half Years of Silence," *Journal of Speech Disorders*, 1942, Vol. 7, pages 295–304.
A detailed description of methods used in treating a delayed-speech case together with notations as to progress.

13. Orton, S., *Reading, Writing, and Speech Problems in Children*, New York, W. W. Norton and Co., 1937, pages 13–20.
This author expresses the concept of speech readiness in terms of neurological maturation. Children who are delayed in speech are prone to use more crying and other forms of emotional expression.

14. Peppard, H., *The Correction of Speech Defects*, New York, The Macmillan Co., 1925, pages 93–112.
Differentiates between those cases of delayed speech in which the child has no "speech images" and is mute and those cases in which there is much vocalization but no concept of speech-sound sequences. Treatment for each type is described.

15. Rigby, M., "A Case of Lack of Speech Due to Negativism," *Psychological Clinic*, 1929, Vol. 18, pages 156–162.
A general discussion of some of the causes for delayed speech is followed by a very detailed case study of the case mentioned in the title.

16. Rigg, M., "A Superior Child Who Would Not Talk," *Child Development*, 1938, Vol. 9, pages 361–362.
Emotional conflict as a cause of delayed speech.

17. Russell, C. M., "Three Hours a Week with a Word Deaf Child," *American Journal of Mental Deficiency*, 1943, Vol. 47, pages 456–461.
An account of the treatment of a delayed-speech case, due probably to aphasia.

18. Stinchfield, S. M. and Young, E. H., *Children with Delayed or Defective Speech*, Stanford University Press, 1938.
Topics discussed in this monograph are: characteristics of normal and delayed-speech development; results of speech, mental, hearing, and physical examinations given to a large number of delayed-speech cases; a detailed description of the kinesthetic method for teaching new speech sounds.

19. Werner, L. S., "Treatment of a Child with Delayed Speech," *Journal of Speech Disorders*, 1945, Vol. 10, pages 329–334.
An interesting account of the treatment of a delayed-speech case by indirect means, games, play, and so on.

VII

Methods for Diagnosing and Analyzing
Articulation Disorders

The articulatory disorders (dyslalia) consist primarily of the abnormal substitution, distortion, insertion, or omission of the speech sounds. They present a wide variety of symptoms and they may range in severity from an intermittent lisp to a host of defective consonants. The causes of the articulation disorders are many. Often the original cause is lost in the mists of speech development. Frequently several factors may be found, each of which could help to create or perpetuate the defective sounds. At times the defective consonant is merely the product of bad teaching, and its continued presence is due to habit alone. In view of this picture of a wide range of symptoms and causes, we have felt it advisable to devote an entire chapter to the genesis and analysis of articulation errors.

Some teachers who would investigate the background of a stutterer with great care seem prone to disregard the etiology of articulatory disorders. They merely notice, for example, that their victim mispronounces (among a good many sounds) the consonant *s*, and so they start "correcting" this consonant without further ado. Such a teacher may be occasionally successful, but she will fail with the cases who most need her help. The professional speech correctionist never slights his diagnostic methodology.

The Causes of Articulation Disorders

The causes of the various articulatory disorders may be discussed in terms of organic abnormalities, motor in-co-ordinations, emotional conflicts, developmental retardation, and perceptual deficiencies.

Organic causes. Most parents are anxious to discover an organic cause for a child's articulatory disorder: a tongue-tie, a sluggish velum, an abnormally high arched palate, spaced or missing teeth.

127

Yet many persons with perfectly normal speech can be shown to possess these abnormalities, and many articulation cases have perfectly normal articulatory organs. We must be careful that we do not miss significant functional factors in our search for something organic. Fröschels [1] declares that missing front teeth are not the cause of frontal lisps:

Of some 800 cases who passed under our observation we found only three who used the opening formed by the abnormal teeth for protruding the tongue. All other cases lowered the jaw to make room.

He also suggests the hypothesis that the dental abnormality may have been caused by the speech defect:

The pressure of the tongue against the teeth, namely against the incisors . . . or against the lateral teeth, is the cause of the abnormal position of the teeth.

There have been several cases reported in which a person whose tongue had been amputated was subsequently able to achieve intelligible speech.

Nevertheless, the presence of a badly overshot jaw, or an excessively long tongue, or any other of the many organic abnormalities which we look for in examining the speech defective must certainly be a handicap in achieving normal pronunciation. Bright children from homes with high speech standards, who are badly tongue-tied, will no doubt be able to learn other compensatory ways of making their sounds, but less intelligent children whose parents show little interest in their speech improvement will continue to lall. We must not exaggerate the importance of organic factors, but we must not ignore them either. We have been able to teach a good many children with very marked dental, palatal, or lingual abnormalities perfect speech sounds, but we usually find tnat the organic anomaly makes our work more difficult. In some cases, the organic peculiarity is interpreted by the case as a sign of hopelessness so far as good speech is concerned. Backus (8) cites the case of a ten-year-old boy whose tonguetip had been cut off. She says, "There was no organic reason why he could not make the back-tongue sounds (k, g, ŋ), yet the fact remained that

---

[1] Fröschels, E. and Jellinek, A., *Practice of Voice and Speech Therapy*, Boston, Expression Co., 1941, pages 162–163.

he did not make them, nor did he use the tongue much even for vegetative purposes." Later, he was taught to make these sounds as well as all others. We once worked with an adult who mistakenly believed that he had an extremely large tongue, and who did not progress in his speech correction efforts until convinced that his tongue was of normal proportions. It may be that many organic causes are of this order.

As we shall see when we come to our discussion of the treatment of articulation disorders, it is often necessary to teach compensatory or nonstandard ways of producing a given speech sound when dealing with a child who shows a marked organic abnormality. A soldier with a one-sided paralysis of the tongue can be taught to make an excellent *l* sound, but it will seldom be made with the tonguetip against the midline of the upper gum ridge.

The presence of organic defects is therefore important and must be taken in account both in diagnosis and therapy. However, the presence of some organic abnormality need not discourage the speech correctionist even when it cannot be eliminated or changed.

Examination for organic defects. It is wise to make a special examination of the mouth, nose, and throat of every speech case, but such an examination is needed especially for voice and articulatory disorders. While it is true that many normal speakers have organic defects in these speech structures and that such defects therefore cannot be termed essential causes of the speech defect, nevertheless the presence of an overshot jaw or of an excessively long tongue must certainly be a handicapping factor in speech development. Some of us can compensate for these defects because of either training or natural desire for speech perfection, but many others cannot. Hence the presence of these defects is important and must be taken into account in both the diagnosis and the treatment. However, the presence of some anatomical abnormality is of no importance in itself unless it stands in functional relation to defective speech sounds. For example, the presence of a harelip in a child whose sole speech error is an inability to produce the *k* sound is of no causal significance. It is also necessary to caution the inexperienced teacher not to make a hasty diagnosis. Other causal factors may be of far greater importance than the organic defect.

Although a head mirror or laryngoscope is more convenient, an adequate examination may be made by placing the subject slightly to one side of a flashlight or a window and reflecting this light, by means of a little mirror, into his mouth. Tongue depressors, probes, and tooth props are tools easily procured.   The examiner should develop a systematic routine involving quick, sure movements and requests. He should examine each structure, not only in quiescence, but also in its relation to the appropriate speech sounds.   He must record all evidence of handicapping abnormality, together with a notation as to any evidence of compensatory movements in the production of speech. A convenient sequence for the examination is as follows:

1. Examine lips for presence of scar tissue or harelip.   Examine during performance of *p*, *b*, and *m*.

2. Examine jaws in relaxed occlusion to note overshot, undershot, or asymmetrical jaw formation.   Examine during performance of *f*, *v*, and *th*, and note whether tongue movement is compensatory during performance of *s*, *l*, and *r* due to the relative displacement of tongue with respect to the upper teeth.

3. Examine teeth to note malocclusion.   Record whether it is due to the upper, lower, or both sets of teeth.   Record also whether it is on the right, left, or both sides.   Note spaced or missing teeth according to a similar scheme.   Note whether tongue habitually plugs gaps in silence or in making the following sounds: *s, z, sh, ch, j, zh*.   Note relation of teeth to jaws and lips.

4. Note tongue to determine gross abnormality of width and length. Have subject lap tongue several times, finally leaving it out.   Note any evidence of atrophy, in terms of area on both sides of midline, and of wrinkling.   Have subject touch right and left corners of mouth alternately to determine possibility of unilateral sluggishness or paralysis.   Note proximity of frenum to tonguetip.   Can subject lick above upper margin of upper lip without showing bowing effect of frenum?   Is there evidence of past tongue-tie?   Can subject groove tongue at will?   Can subject touch hard palate with tonguetip easily?   Have subject touch tongue depressor held one inch out from the teeth as you count rhythmically at a rate of three counts per second for five seconds.   Note action of tongue in making *th, s, l, r, d, t, k, g*.

5. Examine roof of mouth to note gross abnormality in height and width of hard palate.   Note tongue placement for *r* and *l*, *k* and *g*, to determine compensatory positions.   Note slope of hard palate from alveolar ridge. Note whether any evidence of present or past cleft exists.

6. Examine velum for presence of cleft, shortness, uvular abnormality, atrophy, or asymmetry.   Is uvula pulled to one side?   Is it so long as to stick to back of tongue?   Have subject phonate vowel *a* and note action of velum and pharynx.   (A guttural mirror may help in this part of the examination.)   Is velum too short for good closure?   Note action of velum in producing *k* and *g* sounds.   Determine whether gag reflex exists.   Note size and condition of tonsils and part they play in velar action.   Note injuries or scar tissue on pillars of the fauces.   Note inflammation of the velum and surrounding tissues.   Ask student to swallow a large mouthful

of water. Note if any comes out of the nose. Ask student to blow up a balloon.

7. Examine pharynx as subject nasalizes vowel *a* and as he phonates a normal *a*. Note presence of adenoids, using guttural mirror. Note inflammation and amount of mucosa. Have subject alternate *m* and *ba* sounds as rapidly as possible for 5 seconds. He should be able to average at least 2 per second if a child, and 3 per second if an adult. Note presence and condition of adenoids. Is there a constant nasal drip from the nasopharynx?

In so far as possible it is always wise to examine the articulatory organs (the tongue, lips, teeth, jaws, and soft palate) as the incorrect sounds are being attempted. Occasionally we must insert a tongue depressor between the teeth to observe the action of the tongue or palate. This does not give a normal picture of the manner of sound production, but it does help to identify basically incorrect movements and contacts. Thus, one adult who could not produce a normal *ch* (tʃ) sound was observed beginning this sound from a contact of the tonguetip and the soft palate. A passable *ch* (tʃ) sound can be made in this way but not at conversational speeds. Helping him to locate the normal starting position on the upper teeth or gum ridge soon cleaned up his difficulty. Many cases of lateral lisping will be observed lifting the tonguetip to the contact for an unvoiced *l* as a substitute for the *s*. It is often impossible for these cases to adopt a new correct method of sound production until they can identify the old one. We cannot break an unconscious habit except by bringing it up to consciousness. By studying the action of the articulatory organs as they produce the incorrect sounds, we can plan a much better treatment.

Auditory acuity. The importance of hearing to speech has been discussed elsewhere and need not be emphasized again. However, all speech-correction teachers should familiarize themselves with audiometric technique and the interpretation of audiograms. The use of the proper hearing aid will work wonders with a refractory articulatory case whose acuity is defective in the frequency range of the sounds he cannot pronounce. Not only does a hearing loss affect diagnosis and prognosis, but it also largely determines the type of remedial methods to be used. An excellent discussion of hearing tests will be found in *Speech and Hearing*, by Fletcher, and a very illuminating application of these tests to speech correction is given in *The Rehabilitation of Speech*, by West, Kennedy, and Carr. The results of all articulatory tests and many of the voice tests should be scrutinized carefully to determine whether or not the errors point to defective hearing as a causal factor.

Motor in-co-ordinations. Articulation cases are occasionally seen who could truly be called the "slow of tongue." They can scarcely protrude the tongue even in the expression of impudence without having it lall around and droop over. Sometimes, these poorly co-ordinated movements seem to be localized about the mouth. The tongue, jaw, soft palate, all are sluggish. But in most of these clumsy-mouthed individuals the other co-ordinations are similarly affected.

Patton (23) found a tendency for articulation cases to show less tongue strength and poorer performance on the Oseretzky motor tests. Karlin, Youtz, and Kennedy [2] found them deficient in speed of co-ordination. Bilto [3] showed that the larger motor skills as measured in the Brace tests were deficient. Berry (3) found that three fifths of a group of college students with articulation defects were below average in motor ability. Palmer and Osborn (22) showed that articulation cases had less tongue strength than had normal speakers.

Not all articulation cases are thus poorly co-ordinated, but those who are so handicapped must be given therapy devoted to their needs. In earlier speech correction, tongue exercises had the status of a religious ritual. All speech defectives were given rigorous training in this routine. In modern speech correction, the emphasis on tongue exercises has almost disappeared. Yet for certain of the "clumsy-tongued" individuals with whom we work, modern forms of these exercises are very valuable.

A good many diseases and neuromuscular malconditions reflect themselves not only in muscular inco-ordination but also in distorted speech. The speech correctionist is often able to refer them to the physician they need. The student of speech correction should therefore be able to recognize the general symptoms of paralysis, both flaccid and spastic, and pronounced neuromuscular in-co-ordinations. Besides the tests mentioned in the references, other simple activities which may demonstrate poor co-ordination are: walking a straight line; extending arms above head and dropping them sud-

---

[2] Karlin, I. W., Youtz, A. C., and Kennedy, L., "Distorted Speech in Young Children," *American Journal of Diseases of Children*, 1940, Vol. 59, pages 1203–1218.

[3] Bilto, E. W., "Comparative Study of Certain Physical Abilities of Children with Speech Defects and Children with Normal Speech," *Journal of Speech Disorders*, 1941, Vol. 6, pages 187–203.

denly; beginning with hands resting on knees as one sits in a chair, alternately touching nose with forefinger of each hand; standing first on one leg and then on the other, with eyes closed; skipping; standing on tiptoe for five seconds.

It is possible to get an excellent estimate of the sluggishness of the articulation apparatus by measuring the rate of jaw movement. Maximum rates are achieved in about ten seconds, but several short practice sessions should be used to ensure understanding of the task. Demonstrate the opening and closing of the jaw with a clicking of the teeth on the closure. Instruct the case to imitate you as rapidly as possible, and count the number of clicks in five seconds. Be sure not to create fatigue. Jenkins (18) gives the following norms for this diadochokinesis of the jaw in number of jaw closings *per second*:

Age	Number of Jaw Movements per Second	
	Males	*Females*
7	3.5–3.8	3.7–4.0
8	3.6–3.9	3.8–4.0
9	4.0–4.4	4.0–4.3
10	4.1–4.3	4.2–4.3
14	4.9–5.1	5.0–5.2
15	5.1–5.3	5.2–5.4
Adults	5.2–5.4	5.4–5.6

Similar rates of tongue movement may be determined by counting the number of times the subject can say the syllable (tʌ) per second. A series of five-second trials should be used to provide a maximum response. Norms are not available for children, but adults should be able to average seven (tʌ) sounds per second.

Emotional factors. Some of our most difficult articulation cases are those in which the child failed to acquire adult pronunciation because of emotional conflicts.

For over two years we worked with a co-operative girl who had what seemed like a fairly simple frontal lisp. She seemed to do her utmost; she obviously disliked the penalties which it evoked in her college classes, but she consistently failed to master the correct *s* and *z* sounds. We interviewed her at some length but were unable to discover any emotional blocking. Then her father visited us and said: "Dorothy always gets what she wants from me. If I say no, she just crawls up on my lap and puts her arms around me and talks baby talk. I'm a sucker, but she hooks me every time. That lisp of hers cost me $800 last year. Put it into a car she wanted."

The desire to remain a child or to return to childhood security has produced many symptoms of articulation disorders. Speech therapy alone with these cases is useless. Consciously they may desire to overcome their infantile errors, but they will cling to them with a compulsiveness that must be experienced to be understood. West (7) cites numerous cases to show that articulation errors can be due to a sensitivity of one kind or other. He says, "Malocclusions have their greatest effect on speech disorders psychologically" We have had cases whose mumbling, half-articulated syllables were clearly the result of unsightly teeth.

Social penalties upon unconscious habits can often make them very difficult to eliminate. The parent who scolds or ridicules a child for his articulatory errors may make it impossible for the latter ever to attempt to correct himself. We have known lispers to become so emotional over their errors that they could not make an intelligent attempt to produce the *s* sound in a different way. One girl smashed a radio with a mallet upon hearing a "comedy" program in which an articulatory defect was assumed for humorous purposes. Another fainted when she heard a recording of her speech.

Developmental factors. The factor of low intelligence has long been known as having etiological importance in articulatory disorders. Most of the research (9) (29) demonstrates that feeble-minded individuals have more articulatory defects than have those of normal intelligence. The mastery of good speech requires a good brain. However, many adult feeble-minded persons attain mental ages of seven or more, an age when normal children are speaking with few errors, and so the effect of intelligence is probably most important in enhancing the other etiological factors.

The age of onset of speech is important. A child who begins to say his first true words at five, could not be expected to be as free of articulation errors at seven as a child who started to talk at eighteen months. Perhaps we need the concept of "speech age" as well as chronological and mental age to guide us in our treatment of the younger articulation cases. Brander observed that premature babies persisted in their articulation errors longer than did full-term babies. They were also slower in beginning to talk.

Parental attitudes toward the child's speech are of great impor-

tance. Many parents make no effort to teach their children to talk
or to provide them with adult standards of pronunciation. They feel
that their children will outgrow their baby talk, or think it cute. Occasionally overanxious parents will correct too much and too often and
too soon, with the result that the child becomes negative to all correction.

Parental baby talk as a cause of articulation disorders has often
been mentioned as a prime factor. We feel that it is not a very common cause. More important is the presence of other individuals who
have a similar speech defect. Backus (1) mentions a mother of a
lisper who introduced herself as "Mithithmith." We once found
eighteen children in a class of twenty-five who had the same variety of
lisp. Investigation showed that the teacher of that grade had the
same error. In one farm family where the father had cleft-palate
speech and the mother had defective s, l, and r sounds, all seven children had articulatory disorders. Rural families are more likely to
show the effect of this imitation.

Perpetual deficiencies. Deafness or hearing loss is certainly one of
the important causes of articulation defects. It is difficult to produce
a sound that you cannot hear. Many individuals with high-frequency
·hearing losses will confuse the s, th, and f sounds because they do not
hear the components of different pitch which distinguish these sounds
from one another. Other individuals with articulatory defects can
hear very well, but seem to find difficulty in retaining auditory impressions, especially when they occur in sequence. Auditory memory-span tests have shown some articulatory cases to be very poor in
this ability. Other cases have great difficulty in discriminating one
consonant from another, even when their auditory acuity is excellent.
Still other cases find it extremely difficult to analyze the component
sounds within words, or to take a series of sounds and put them together to compose a word. These phenomena may be true perceptual
deficiencies or they may be merely the result of poor training. It is
possible to improve the ability of the articulatory case to discriminate, to remember auditory impressions, and to analyze and synthesize sound sequences, once we know such deficiencies exist. It is
necessary, therefore, to test for these perpetual deficiencies, especially
in those cases whose speech behavior seems to indicate their existence.

Testing auditory memory span. In testing the articulation cases'
auditory memory span, several methods may be used. We may follow the procedure used in intelligence testing and determine how many

digits a child can recall. We may use a series of isolated nonsense syllables with two-second intervals (21), or we may use a series of non-sense words in which the syllables are combined as in "goulabi." Research has not shown any conclusive difference between groups of articulatory cases and groups of normal-speaking individuals on audi-tory memory-span tests, but certain individuals are found whose audi-tory memory spans are so short that this factor must be taken into account during treatment. The purpose of these tests is to discover these individuals.

Some norms for auditory memory-span tests are now given:

I. For repeating digits at one-second intervals (Robbins):

Age	Number of Digits
3	3
4	4
7	5
10	6
14	7
18	8

II. For repeating nonsense syllables (kʌ, pʌ, and so on) (Metraux) at two-second intervals:

Age	Number of Syllables
5	2.0
6	2.3
7	2.6
8	2.6
9	2.8
10	3.0
11	2.9
12	3.1

III. For repeating nonsense words (Beebe [4]):

Age	Number of Syllables per Nonsense Word
4	4
5	3.8
6	4.3
7	4.3
8	4.6

[4] Beebe, H. H., "Auditory Memory Span for Meaningless Syllables," *Journal of Speech Disorders*, 1944, Vol. 9, pages 273–276.

Phonetic discrimination ability. Ordinarily we combine our examination of the case's ability to hear differences among the various speech sounds with the general articulation tests. We do this by determining whether he can tell his errors from the correct sounds when both are produced in random fashion by the examiner. But occasionally we find a case who seems to be especially lacking in phonetic discrimination. In order to be certain that this is indeed an important factor, we administer a more formal type of test. The one which we have found most useful is the modification of the Travis-Rasmus test used by Templin (27). It is simply administered by requiring the case to write down on a sheet of paper his judgment of whether or not the two sounds given by the examiner are the *same* or *different.* A short practice session is given to clarify the task. The series of paired syllables used by Templin in the short form of her test are as follows:

SHORT TEST OF SOUND DISCRIMINATION

Examples:	*Key:* All D Except:
te-de	A. 1, 8
ere-ere	B. 1, 6, 8, 10
os-og	C. 3, 6, 8, 9
	D. 4, 9, 10
	E. 3, 9
	F. 3, 7
	G. 3, 6

A	B	C	D
1. te-te	1. ne-ne	1. fo-θo	1. pe-ke
2. hwe-we	2. dʒe-tʃe	2. vo-ðo	2. tʃo-ʃo
3. ne-me	3. ʃe-tʃe	3. zo-zo	3. ki-ti
4. ðe-de	4. im-iŋ	4. ʃe-ʒe	4. eb-eb
5. fi-vi	5. hwi-wi	5. fi-θi	5. ehwe-ewe
6. he-pe	6. ge-ge	6. ze-ze	6. en-em
7. se-ze	7. dʒi-tʃi	7. mai-nai	7. eð-ed
8. θe-θe	8. fai-fai	8. θe-θe	8. ehe-epe
9. ʒe-dʒe	9. ðe-ve	9. he-he	9. ov-ov
10. vo-bo	10. pe-pe	10. dʒi-ʒi	10. eθ-eθ

E	F	G
1. eʒ-edʒ	1. eð-ev	1. if-iθ
2. ov-ob	2. et-ep	2. aim-ain
3. ed-ed	3. ep-ep	3. eθ-eθ
4. en-en	4. of-oθ	4. ini-iŋi
5. edʒ-etʃ	5. ov-oð	5. ef-ep
6. eʃ-etʃ	6. ed-eg	6. eð-eð

SHORT TEST OF SOUND DISCRIMINATION (*Continued*)

7. imi-iɲi	7. em-em	7. idʒ-iʒ
8. ihwi-iwi	8. eð-ez	8. ep-ek
9. eg-eg	9. airai-aiwai	9. otʃ-oʃ
10. is-iz	10. eʃ-eʒ	10. ez-eð

Our own norms, based on 30 normal-speaking children from each of the grades 2 through 6 are as follows:

Grade	Average Number of Errors
2	14.2
3	11.8
4	10.1
5	10.2
6	10.1

Great care must be taken to ensure attention and to prevent fatigue. From a consideration of the test data, we would not feel justified in considering a person markedly deficient in phonetic discrimination unless he made ten or more errors above the averages given.

Exploring for causal factors. We have given several examination and testing procedures to help us identify the organic, perceptual, and motor factors that could produce or maintain articulatory disorders. But how can we discover the other factors that are so important in articulation? The case history, the interview, and controlled observation and experiment will give us this information. In order that the student may realize some of the possibilities of this type of exploration, we shall now present a few significant facts which proved of importance in the treatment of some of our cases. These bits of information will be organized in terms of the major divisions of the general case history. (See Appendix.)

Parental and Family Influences

Names. If the names of the parents are foreign, the child's consonant errors might possibly be due to imitation of parental brogue, or to the learning of similar consonants belonging to another language. Thus, in one of our cases, the child who substituted *t* for *th* (θ), did so because he imitated his father's pronunciation of *th* words. The father's name (which gave us the first clue) was Molo Zymolaga.

Age. When the age of the parents seems somewhat unusual in terms of the child's age, certain emotional factors may be influencing the latter's speech development. Thus, Peter, aged 7, had parents aged 22 and 24, and (as we found out by following the clue) was an unwanted child, neglected, unstimulated, and untrained. His articulatory errors were easily understood against this background. Or, consider Jane, who astonished her 49-year-old father and 45-year-old mother by being born. Their excessive attention and demand for adult speech standards too early drove the child into a negativism which made her reject their constant corrections and persist in her errors.

Speech defect. Imitation is often a causal factor in articulation, but we must be sure that the symptoms are similar. All five children of a family living on an isolated farm had nasal lisps. Organically, they were perfect specimens, but their mother had a cleft palate. It is often wise to explore to ascertain whether or not the parents had possessed a speech defect in their own childhood, since such an event would affect their attitudes toward the child's difficulty.

Physical defects. If the mother is deaf, we can easily understand how a child's articulatory errors would receive little attention from her. Here are two other items from our case history files which had significance in our understanding of the child's speech problem: a father whose tonguetip had been shot off in a hunting accident; a "nervous" hyperthyroid mother so unstable that she screamed whenever the children made noise or mispronounced a word.

Emotional conflicts. Conflicts between one parent and the other, or between parent and child, can arise in each of the other areas mentioned in the case history: handedness, religion, education, occupation, and so on. Other people living in the home or closely associated with the child may have significant malinfluences on the child's speech development.

Developmental History

Birth history. Severe birth injuries have malformed the mouth cavity and wrecked the alignment of the jaws or teeth. They sometimes produce, through their injury to the brain, not only feeble-mindedness but the unsure, trembling or spastic co-ordinations of cerebral palsy.

Physical development. When we learn that a child was delayed in sitting alone, in feeding himself, in walking, we usually probe to discover whether the speech development was similarly retarded. Almost any factor that retards physical development also retards speech. Many articulation cases with sluggish tongues and palates have histories of slow physical development.

Illnesses. These have importance according to their severity and sequellae. Certain illnesses such as scarlet fever may impair hearing. Others may so lower the child's vitality that he does not have the energy to learn the difficult skills of talking correctly. Prolonged illness may result in parental attitudes of overconcern or of overprotection. The parents may anticipate the child's needs so that he learns to talk relatively late. They find it difficult to "correct" the speech of a sick child. If illness occurred during the first year of life, the child may not have the necessary babbling practice.   Injuries to the tongue may make certain sounds defective.   One child who had burned his tongue started immediately to lall and continued in this articulatory disorder long after the tongue had healed.   Many children lose their speech after a prolonged illness with high fevers and find it difficult to master it again.

Mental and educational factors.   It is often the unpleasant chore of the speech correctionist to help parents face the fact that their child is feeble-minded, and that his general retardation is not solely the consequence of his delayed speech.   When we find such children, we usually postpone speech therapy until they have a mental age (on a nonverbal test) of from five to six years.

Failures in the school subjects, especially in reading, may be a direct consequence of defective articulation, and remedial reading can frequently be combined with remedial speech.   Children who fail in school are likely to be resistant at first to speech correction.   If they have been penalized for their school failure, they may become so emotional over their speech handicap that their tension prevents new muscular adjustments of the articulatory organs.   One of our cases made no progress in his speech until he was transferred to another grade.   The hatred he felt toward his teacher constantly reflected itself in our work with him.

Play.   Children adopt the consonant errors of their playmates as well as their grammatical errors.   In one instance, children from three different families in the neighborhood acquired a lisp by identification and imitation of a dominant older boy.   It is said that *s* and *z* are pronounced as *th* (θ, δ) in Castilian Spanish because a certain king of Spain lisped and his courtiers adopted his pronunciation of the sibilant sounds.   Little tyrants in every child kingdom similarly impose their speech peculiarities upon their subjects.

Home conditions and emotional problems.   A knowledge of the home conditions, the tempo of life lived therein, the attitudes of its inmates, is often vital to the understanding of the articulatory problem.   Parents may bedevil a child for his social blemishes merely because they are sensitive about their own.   An unhappy home can make our speech correction difficult.   The list of emotional problems given in the case history can give us some indication of the child's reaction to his speech defect.   The child who is always fighting, hurting pets, setting fires, or performing similar aggressive acts must be handled much differently from one who withdraws from the challenges or existence.   Articulatory disorders, like stuttering, can be primary or secondary, according to the manner in which the child regards his difficulty.   We have known lispers to substitute easier words for those which included sibilant sounds.   One boy's speech was so halting that he was referred to us as a stutterer.   Extremely maladjusted and antagonistic, he avoided speech whenever he could.   Asked to recite in school, he would growl, "I don't know and I don't care."   Investigation showed that he had been penalized severely by his classmates for his lisp. His breaks in fluency and his behavior problem disappeared simultaneously with his lisp.

Language development. The chapters of this book on learning to talk and on delayed speech have provided many instances of the factors which can cause articulation errors to persist. By and large, poor teaching methods are no doubt responsible for more defective articulation than is any other factor. We always try to interview the parent of a young articulatory case to determine how they attempt to correct his errors. Observation of this parental correction at work will often demonstrate penalties, confusions, and impatience as well as ignorance.

Although the case history gives us much information about the causes and development of a speech disorder, it tells us little of what we need to know about the actual symptoms. To discover these, we use systematic methods of speech analysis. As we have previously implied, it is seldom sufficient in speech correction to discover and remove the original causes of the disorder. Frequently they no longer exist at the time the patient applies for treatment, but they have lasted long enough to set up bad speech habits which can perpetuate themselves. As we have said, speech correction is re-education, and therefore implies error-analysis, the tearing down of defective speech habits, the substitution of correct speech habits, the removal of etiological factors, and the formation of adequate reactions to speech situations.

Articulation Tests

Articulatory disorders, as we have defined them, are characterized by errors of sound substitution, addition, omission, and distortion. Each speech correctionist devises his own procedure for giving the articulatory examination. Even when students have been trained according to one standard technique, they find it necessary to make modifications to fit the individuality of each case they examine. For this reason, we have described various procedures under each of the types of articulation tests and have provided word lists, sentences, and reading passages which the student may use as he sees fit. His task is to determine the nature, number, and characteristics of the articulatory errors as they occur in the case's speech.

Spontaneous production of a speech sound may be tested in several ways, two of which are most commonly used. These are the naming of pictures and the answering of question riddles. For both, a common set of objects or activities is used, the names of which include all the speech sounds in all three word positions. Such a list, with the sounds classified according to manner of articulation, is given at the end of this section. The words are chosen from the lists given in *A*

Reading Vocabulary for the Primary Grades, by A. I. Gates, and therefore are suited to small children as well as to adults. The technique of administering this test is simple. After gaining rapport, the teacher points to the picture and asks the child to name it. Or, for example, when using the question riddle to get the sound of voiceless *th* in the

Fig. 3. Typical sets of articulation test pictures. Note the arrangement according to initial, medial, and final positions of given sounds. In the lower part of the illustration is a metal shield with an exposure window.

final position, she says, "Watch me bite my finger. What did I bite my finger with?" Pictures representing the words in the test list may be cut from old magazines, and every teacher should have such a scrapbook.

The same word list may be used in administering the part of the articulatory analysis which requires the subject to repeat after a model provided by the teacher. The teacher merely asks the child to listen carefully, to wait a moment until the teacher lifts her finger as a signal, and then to repeat what the teacher has said. In addition to the word lists, it is often wise to use nonsense material such as "tho, otho, oth" to determine if a child can follow a model when the effects of training

TEST FOR ARTICULATION

WESTERN MICHIGAN COLLEGE OF EDUCATION

FRANK ROBINSON

With Drawings by H. J. McCook

Kalamazoo, Michigan

I would like to have you help me read a picture letter just like one that you may get some day. It has some words and some pictures in it. I'll read the words and I want you to read the pictures. It goes like this:

There was a big white — — — →

in front of the ↓

That's all there is to it. Now you turn the page and we'll read.

Dear . . . . .

I want to tell you about last Saturday when my mother and I went down-town. We really had a wonderful time. I got up early and went out to feed my — — →

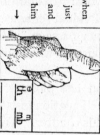

d ___ g

and my bunny — — →

r — b — t

The last time you were here I just had a rabbit. Now I have two pets. They each have a little house of their own out in the back — — →

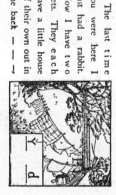

Y ___ d

Remember when the rabbit was just a little bunny and I would let him suck on my →

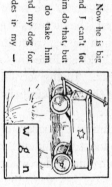

th ___ mb

Now he is big and I can't let him do that, but I do take him and my dog for rides in my →

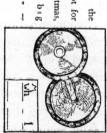

w ___ g ___ n

That's the one I got for Christmas, with the big red · · · →

wh ___ l

Fig. 4.

143

are minimized. Nonsense pictures may be drawn and named with nonsense words containing the sound to be tested. The speech correctionist may also ask the child to repeat "monkey-talk" words.

Both the spontaneous production of the various speech sounds and the student's ability to repeat them after stimulation can be tested by having the student read material that has been organized to include all the speech sounds in all three positions within the word. In addition to the word lists given, the reader will also find individual sentences, one for each of the speech sounds. A continuous passage, "My Grandfather" (see page 147) may be used for this purpose when only a little time is available.

An especially excellent collection of articulation test pictures is provided by Bryngelson and Glaspey (33). Other articulation testing material is provided in the references at the end of this chapter. Two other methods for evoking the spontaneous production of the various speech sounds for children who cannot read the sentences we have listed in this chapter are often employed. In the first, the pictures are drawn, or pasted on a continuous strip of paper which passes through guides behind a window in a cardboard shield. Children love these "movies" and will readily name them as they appear. In the second method, a picture letter is used, the teacher reading the words and the child naming the pictures which fit into the context.

In analyzing the articulatory errors prior to outlining a program of remedial work, we have three essential tasks: (1) to locate and identify the speech sounds which are defective; (2) to determine under what conditions these errors occur; and (3) to analyze these errors according to their manner of production.

Locating the errors. The majority of articulation cases have more than one defective consonant sound. One of our adult cases had only four standard consonants, the *p, g, m,* and *t.* For "Give me a strawberry soda" he said "tɪmɪ tabɛti toʊtə." We often find individuals who use consonants interchangeably. One of them said "thoup" for "soup" and "sum" for "thumb." Many individuals will use a consonant correctly at the beginning of a word but always mispronounce it in the final position. One of our cases substituted a *w* for the *l* sound at the beginning of a word and a *y* (j) for the same sound when it was found in the middle position. Since we prefer to work on only one sound at a time and with the easiest sound, it is necessary to locate and define these errors.

Recording results of articulation tests. The words in which errors occurred may be written in phonetic transcription, or the errors themselves may be listed and described according to the substitutions, omissions, additions, or distortions that occurred. The position of the error within the word should also be indicated, since it is important in certain retraining methods. Thus, when the lisper says "*th*aw" for "saw," the error is recorded as *th/s* (*I*). The substitution is always given first. The letter *I* in the parentheses refers to the fact that the substitution occurred in the initial position of the word. The letters *M* and *F* refer to the medial and final positions. Omissions and additions are indicated by minus and plus signs, respectively. Distortions are described by adjectives.

Articulatory Test Material

Lip sounds: *P*—pie, apple, cup; *B*—boy, rabbit, bib; *M*—mouse, hammer, drum; *WH*—wheel, whistle; *W*—window, sidewalk, sandwich; *F*—fork, telephone, knife; *V*—valentine, river, stove.

Tonguetip sounds: *TH* (*unvoiced*)—thumb, bathtub, teeth; *TH* (*voiced*) —the, feather, smooth; *T*—top, potato, cat; *D*—dog, Indian, bird; *N*—nose, banana, man.

Back of tongue: *K*—cup, basket, clock; *G*—girl, wagon, flag; *NG*—monkey, swing; *H*—house, schoolhouse.

Complicated tonguetip sounds: *L*—leaves, balloon, ball; *R*—rug, orange, chair; *S*—Santa Claus, bicycle, glass; *Z*—zebra, scissors, eyes; *SH*—shoe, dishes, fish; *ZH*—pleasure, treasure; *CH*—chicken, pitcher, peach; *J*—jelly, soldier, bridge; *Y*—yellow, onion.

Blends: *TW*—twenty, between; *DW*—dwarf; *BL*—black, bubble; *CL*—clown, declare; *FL*—flag, snowflake; *GL*—glass; *PL*—please, airplane; *SL*—slim, asleep; *SPL*—split, splashed; -*DL*—cradle; -*TL*—turtle; -*ZL*—puzzle; *BR*—bring, umbrella; *CR*—cry, across; *DR*—drop, children; *FR*—friend, afraid; *GR*—grandma, angry; *PR*—prize, surprise; *SCR*—screw, describe; *SHR*—shrub; *SPR*—spring; *STR*—string, destroy; *TR*—trip, country; *THR*—thread, three; *SK*—school, asking, desk; *SM*—smell, smoke; *SN*—snow, speak; *SP*—spool, whisper, clasp; *ST*—stop, upstairs, nest; *SW*—swing, swim; *FS*—laughs; -*LS*—else; *NS*—once, bounce; -*PS*—cups, pups; -*TS*—cats, puts; -*STS*—vests, tests; -*THS*—months; -*BZ*—tubs, bibs; -*DZ*—birds, reads; -*LZ*—girls, balls; -*MZ*—drums, homes; -*NZ*—pans, runs, rains; -*NGZ*—songs, rings; -*THZ*—clothes, breathes; -*VZ*—lives, moves; -*LK*—milk, milking, silk; *KW*—queen, require; *SKW*—squirrel; -*KS*—packs, except; -*GZ*—eggs, rugs; -*NG*—sing, hang, wrong.

Vowels: i—eat, meat, tree; ɪ—it, pig; ɛ—egg, bread; ɛɚ—bear, pear; æ—at, cat; ʌ—up, cup; ɚ—turkey, mother; ə—away, banana; u—moon, shoe; ʊ—book, cooky; ɔ—all; a—arm, star; eɪ—age, cake, day; aɪ—ice, kite, pie; oʊ—old, boat, snow; aʊ—owl, house, cow; ɔɪ—oil, noise, boy.

Reading Sentences

Lip sounds: 1. *P*—The pig ate his supper with the sheep. 2. *B*—
The baby robin is in the tub. 3. *M*—The man hammered his thumb.
4. *WH*—Why is the wheel off? 5. *W*—We found a wagon. 6. *F*—The
farmer drank coffee with his wife. 7. *V*—His vest is over by the stove.

Tonguetip sounds: 1. *TH* (*voiceless*)—I think the baby needs a birth-
day bath. 2. *TH* (*voiced*)—The baby's mother will bathe him. 3. *T*—
Take the pretty coat to her. 4. *D*—Get the doll ready for bed. 5. *N*—
At night through the window we see the moon.

Back-tongue sounds: 1. *K*—Come and get your broken kite. 2. *G*—
Let's go again and find a frog. 3. *NG*—She sang as she was dancing.
4. *H*—He likes horses.

Complicated tonguetip sounds: 1. *L*—Let me bring a tulip and an apple.
2. *R*—The rabbit likes four carrots. 3. *S*—We saw a seesaw on the grass.
4. *Z*—The zoo is the home for bears. 5. *SH*—She washes every dish.
6. *ZH*—It is a pleasure to have a treasure hunt. 7. *CH*—The child went
to the kitchen for a peach. 8. *J*—Jack saw a pigeon under the bridge.
9. *Y*—Your dog ran into the barnyard.

Blends: 1. *TW*—The twin stood between the others. 2. *DW*—The
dwarf is a little man. 3. *BL*—He blew a bubble from a black pipe. 4. *CL*
—The clown climbed a tree to declare he was king. 5. *FL*—The flag flew
in the snowflakes. 6. *GL*—He broke the big glass. 7. *PL*—Please let me
have an airplane ride. 8. *SL*—The slim little boy fell asleep. 9. *SPL*—
I will splash some water on you. 10. *-DL*—Put the baby in the cradle.
11. *-TL*—See the little turtle. 12. *-ZL*—I like a puzzle. 13. *BR*—Bring
me a brown umbrella. 14. *CR*—You could hear him cry across the room.
15. *DR*—The children dropped their balls. 16. *FR*—My friend is afraid
of the dark. 17. *GR*—Grandma was angry with me. 18. *PR*—Won't the
prize surprise her? 19. *SCR*—The screw is described in the book. 20.
SHR—There is a shrub by our barn. 21. *SPR*—Spring is coming. 22.
STR—The string has been destroyed. 23. *TR*—A trip to the country
will be nice. 24. *THR*—She has three spools of thread. 25. *SK*—I am
asking for a new desk at school. 26. *SM*—Do you smell smoke? 27. *SN*
—Let's sneak out and play in the snow. 28. *SP*—They whisper about the
lost spool. 29. *ST*—Stop upstairs and see the robin's nest. 30. *SW*—
We will swim over to the dock. 31. *-FS*—She laughs at all the jokes.
32. *-LS*—Give me something else. 33. *NS*—You can bounce my ball
once. 34. *-PS*—The little pups can drink out of cups. 35. *-TS*—She
puts the cats to bed in the barn. 36. *-STS*—He slipped the tests in one
of his father's vests. 37. *-THS*—It took him two months to read the
book. 38. *-BZ*—Mother washed the bibs in the tubs. 39. *-DZ*—He reads
about birds every day. 40. *-LZ*—The girls took our balls away. 41. *-MZ*
—They have drums in all the children's homes. 42. *-NZ*—The water runs
over the pans when it rains. 43. *-NGZ*—Teacher rings the bell for us to
sing more songs. 44. *-THZ*—I have some new clothes. 45. *-VZ*—The
fish lives and moves in water. 46. *-LK*—Don't wear a silk dress when

you are milking a cow.   47. *KW*—The queen requires that we obey her.
48. *SKW*—That squirrel has a bushy tail.   49. -*KS*—Bring all the packs
except one.   50. -*GZ*—Mary dropped the eggs on the rugs.   51. -*NG*—
We all sang the wrong song.

Vowels: 1. i—The dog can eat his meat under the tree.   2. ɪ—Give
the rest of it to the pig.   3. ɛ—Let's eat an egg with the bread.   4. ɛɚ—
That bear went up our pear tree.   5. æ—Don't throw a tin can at the cat.
6. ʌ—Take the cup up from the table.   7. ɝ—Mother put the turkey on
the platter.   8. ə—Throw away that banana skin.   9. u—Can you look
in the moon and see a shoe?   10. ʊ—I like to eat a cooky when I read a
book.   11. ɔ—All of us like corn.   12. *a*—Point your arm up at the biggest
star.   13. eɪ—At the age of ten I will have a cake on my birthday.   14. aɪ
—If the ice doesn't freeze over night, I will make you a pie.   15. oʊ—The
old boat was lost in the snow.   16. aʊ—The owl hooted from the house
and the cow was afraid.   17. ɔɪ—The oil lamp made so much noise that
the boy couldn't sleep.

The following passage may be used for a quick survey of the student's ability to produce correct speech sounds.   It includes all of
the speech sounds, and may either be read by the student or be repeated phrase by phrase after the examiner.

My Grandfather

You wished to know all about my grandfather. Well, he is nearly
ninety-three years old; he dresses himself in an ancient black frock coat,
usually minus several buttons; yet he still thinks as swiftly as ever. A
long, flowing beard clings to his chin, giving those who observe him a pronounced feeling of the utmost respect. When he speaks, his voice is just
a bit cracked and quivers a trifle. Twice each day he plays skillfully and
with zest upon our small organ. Except in the winter when the ooze or
snow or ice prevents, he slowly takes a short walk in the open air each day.
We have often urged him to walk more and smoke less, but he always
answers, "Banana oil!" Grandfather likes to be modern in his language.

Determining under what conditions the errors occur.   A college professor came to the speech clinic for assistance in eradicating his lisp.
We administered a careful articulation test but were unable to hear
any errors of any kind. He made the sibilant sounds perfectly, in
isolation, in nonsense syllables, in words, phrases, and sentences. He
spoke them correctly even in swift unguarded conversation. He could
even alternate pairs of syllables such as *see-thee* at very fast rates of
speed. In answering our skepticism he said, "I have no difficulty in
ordinary conversation, but when I become emotional I lisp as badly
as I did when I was a child."

Many parents consider their children stubborn because they can pronounce a consonant correctly when shown a model by the parent and yet continue to make the same errors. Many cases can make the defective sounds correctly in isolation but fail when they use them in consonants. It is necessary therefore to do more than identify the errors. We must determine under what conditions they occur.

For convenience we have divided the conquest of a defective sound into nine stages:

1. Cannot make the sound nor discriminate it from its error even when the word pairs (*soup-thoup*) are pronounced by another individual so as to exaggerate the characteristics of the sound in question.

2. Cannot make the sound but can hear the error in another's speech.

3. Can make the sound in isolation (*ssss* or *kuh*) but only after strong stimulation by the teacher.

4. Can make the sound in isolation (or with the schwa [ə] vowel) without requiring stimulation.

5. Can use the sound in nonsense syllables in all positions (*soo, oos, oosoo*).

6. Can use the sound in isolated words when careful.

7. Can use the sound in careful speaking of prepared sentences.

8. Can use the sound habitually in swift nonemotional speech.

9. Can use the sound habitually in swift emotional speech.

These stages are not exact divisions of the learning process, of course, and many substages could be mentioned, but they help to indicate the influence of environmental factors on articulatory errors.

Most articulation cases are not at the bottom of this nine-rung ladder when they come to us. Nor are all of their defective sounds at the same level of mastery. If we are to know with which sound to begin our therapy we should have some means of analyzing the errors to indicate which sounds are closest to mastery. By checking the various errors against this nine-stage table, we can get a crude basal level for each of the errors. Thus, if a child had three defective sounds and their basal levels of mastery were represented thus: t/k $(I, M, F.)$ Level 6; d/g $(I, M, F.)$ Level 4; p/v $(I, M, F.)$ Level 7, we would have some basis for determining with which error to work first. If a simpler procedure were desired, we could merely record the error: (t for k, I, M, F, but makes the sound correctly in isolation and nonsense syllables when strongly stimulated).

For a more exact and revealing analysis—and one which can be used as a measure of improvement—the factors of speed, stimulation, and discrimination should be explored and recorded. *Speed* of production is important. If a child can only produce the correct sound at slow speeds, he will never use it in conversation. We prefer to teach our articulatory cases to master each level at fast speeds before going on to the more difficult material.

The factor of *stimulation* is vital in determining which sounds will be easily mastered. While the developmental sequence of labials to blends usually indicates which of a number of defective consonants should be treated first, it does not always do so. If the child mispronounces the *k*, *l*, and *r* sounds, can make the *l* sound immediately after stimulation by the speech correctionist, yet cannot even hear his errors on the other two sounds, we would start working with the *l* sound first. This stimulation is usually done by merely pronouncing the sound, syllable, or word in such a way as to emphasize the sound. After hearing it repeatedly, the case is asked to speak it in unison or in echo fashion.

The factor of *discrimination* is also important. Some children can hear their own errors. Others are incapable of so doing, even at very slow speeds. The nearer the case approaches complete mastery of a sound, the more important is this recognition of errors, if the casual errors are to be eliminated. We repeatedly test for this discrimination ability throughout the treatment as well as during the initial examination. It gives us an excellent ideal of progress as well as prognosis.

The two charts that follow show the progress that was made by our cases who had received help for two weeks in the effort to eliminate a defective *ch* (t∫) sound. The first chart represents the results of the initial articulation test for this sound. The small letters in the corners of the squares indicate whether the error occurred only in the initial, medial, or final position of the word.

Determining the nature of the error. One of our cases had what are known as "cognate" or "sonancy" errors. He substituted the unvoiced sound for its voiced equivalent: *k/g*; *t/d*; *f/v* and *s/z*. He mastered all of these errors at once by realizing that there were pairs of sounds articulated in much the same way but differing in the presence or absence of vocal-cord vibration. He got this insight by feeling both his own and his clinician's throat as the pairs of sounds were produced and, later, by making them with his fingers in his ears. In this latter activity the vibration of the voiced sounds (*d*, *g*, *v*, and *z*) was so unmistakable that he improved immediately. From this example it is clear that knowledge of the nature of the error is very important in working with the articulatory case. Much time and labor

CHART I

ERROR ANALYSIS

Name............ Type of error *t/k* (*I, M, F*) Date 4/16/ Clinician............

TYPE OF SPEECH ACTIVITY	CAREFUL STIMULATION		SPONTANEOUS SPEECH		ABILITY TO HEAR ERRORS	
	Slow	*Fast*	*Slow*	*Fast*	*Slow*	*Fast*
Emotional unguarded speech	X I, M, F		X I, M, F	X I, M, F	X I, M, F	X I, M, F
Nonemotional conversation	X M	X I, M, F	X I, M, F	X I, M, F	X F	X M, F
Rehearsed sentences		X I, M, F				X F
Isolated words		X I, F	X M, F	X M, F		
Nonsense syllables		X M				
Isolated sounds						

150

CHART II
ERROR ANALYSIS

Name.................... Type of error t/k (I, M, F)   Date 4/30/   Clinician....................

TYPE OF SPEECH ACTIVITY	CAREFUL STIMULATION		SPONTANEOUS SPEECH		ABILITY TO HEAR ERRORS	
	Slow	*Fast*	*Slow*	*Fast*	*Slow*	*Fast*
Emotional unguarded speech				X I, M, F		
Nonemotional conversation		X M, F	X F	X M, F		
Rehearsed sentences		X M				
Isolated words						
Nonsense syllables						
Isolated sounds						

151

may be saved by discovering just what the case is doing when he is producing the error. We should determine not only what the errors are and under what conditions they occur, but their nature as well.

Generally speaking, the most frequently mispronounced consonants are the s and z; the two th sounds (θ) and (ð); the various r (r) (ɔ˞) (ʒ) sounds; and the (l) sounds. Errors on the j (dʒ) and ch (tʃ); sh (ʃ), f, and v are also common. In younger children the substitutions of t for k, and d for g are often heard.

In terms of type of error, substitutions are most frequent, then distortions, then omissions and insertions. Errors occur most frequently in the final position of the word and least frequently at the beginning. In substituting one sound for another, the child replaces the correct sound with one which is simpler, easier, more visible, more familiar, developmentally earlier, acoustically similar, or kinesthetically similar. They substitute consonants which sound alike (th/s) or are produced in a similar fashion (t/k). Distortions follow the same principles of replacement. Omissions are due to poor vocal phonics, defective hearing, inability to produce, or to unstressing.

Each of the speech sounds can be incorrectly produced in several ways. The most frequent error of such *stop-plosives* as k and g seems to be due to (1) the wrong location of the tongue contact. Other errors include (2) the wrong speed in forming the contacts; (3) the wrong structures used in contacts; (4) the wrong force or tension of the contacts; (5) too short a duration of the contacts; (6) too slow a release from contacts; (7) the wrong mode or direction of release; (8) the wrong direction of the air stream; and finally (9) sonancy errors in which voiced and unvoiced consonants are interchanged. Examples of these errors are now given for illustration:

1. The child who says "tandy" for "candy" is using a tongue-palatal contact, but it is too far forward.
2. A breathy k sound (xki) for (ki), results when the contact is formed so slowly that fricative noises are produced prior to the air puff.
3. A glottal catch or throat click (ʔæt) for (kæt) is often found in cleft-palate cases. They make a contact, but with the wrong structures.
4. Insufficient tension of the lips can result in the substitution of a sound similar to the Spanish v (φ) for the standard English b sound.
5. When the duration of the contact is too short, it often seems to be omitted entirely. Thus the final k in the word *sick* (sɪk) may be formed so briefly that acoustically it seems omitted (sɪ).
6. Too slow a release from the contact may give an aspirate quality

to the utterance. "Kuheep the cuhandy" (kʰip ðə kʰændɪ) is an example of this.

7. The lowering of the tonguetip prior to recall of the tongue-as-a-whole can produce such an error as "tsen" for "ten" (tsɛn) for (tɛn). In this error the case is not inserting an *s* so much as releasing the tongue from its contact in a peculiar fashion.

8. Occasionally the direction of the air stream is reversed and the plosion occurs on inhalation. Try saying "sick" with the *k* sound produced during inhalation, and you will understand this error.

9. The person who says "back" for "bag" illustrates a sonancy error.

Most of the errors in making the *continuant* sounds are caused by: (1) use of the wrong channel for the air stream (using an unvoiced *l* for the *s*); (2) use of the wrong construction or constriction ("foop" for "soup"); (3) use of the wrong aperture (a lateral lisp); (4) use of the wrong direction of the air stream (nasal lisp; inhaled *s*); (5) too weak an air pressure (acoustically omitted *s*); (6) the presence of nonessential movements or contacts (*t* for *s*, occluded lisp); and (7) cognate errors (*z* for *s*, or vice versa).

Most of the errors in making the *glide* sounds are produced by combining the types of errors sketched above. They may be generally classed as movement errors. They include: (1) use of the wrong beginning position or contact ("yake" for "lake"); (2) use of the wrong ending position (fɪʊ) for (fɪɚ); (3) use of the wrong transitional movement in terms of speed, strength, or direction (rweɪd) for (reɪd); (4) the presence of nonessential contacts or positions (tjɛloʊ) for (jɛloʊ); (5) cognate errors (wɛn) for (hwɛn).

It is necessary to analyze any given articulation error according to the above scheme so as to understand its nature. It is not sufficient merely to start teaching the correct sound. We must also break the old habit. Many of our most difficult articulatory cases will make rapid progress as soon as they understand clearly what they are doing wrongly. Insight into error is fundamental to efficient speech correction.

A TYPICAL ARTICULATION TEST REPORT

Name of Case: *Examiner:*   *Date:*

Summary of errors: t/k (I, M, F) Except in slow nonsense syllables repeated after examiner. Wrong location of contact.

A Typical Articulation Test Report (*Continued*)

d/g (*I, M, F*)　Same as above, but said "go" correctly. The case can hear these errors when imitated by examiner at both slow and fast speeds, but cannot hear his own errors except in slowly spoken nonsense syllables.

t/s (*I, M*)　Except in slow production of isolated sound after strong stimulation by examiner. Can always hear own error except in fast conversation. Doesn't realize no contact is needed.

-s (*F*)　Makes no attempt to produce it. Evidently does not hear it as a part of the word when it comes in the final position.

Organic factors:　High narrow palatal arch, but teeth are normally placed and tongue assumes good lateral contact with the teeth in making the z sounds. Makes the contacts for defective k and g sounds too far forward and with blade of tongue. When he tries to produce a genuine t or d he uses the tonguetip against the upper teeth.

Motor co-ordinations:　Excellent in every respect.

Emotional factors:　Not particularly sensitive. Will try persistently to follow instructions even when failing. Mother says he will try to say a word correctly for his father but not for her. "I'm too impatient, I guess." Boy seems to be mature for his age.

Developmental factors:　Had been seriously ill the majority of his first year and a half. Onset of speech at 32 months.

Perceptual deficiencies:　Very poor phonetic discrimination except for isolated sounds. Auditory memory span O.K. Poor ability to analyze component sounds of words. Could not recognize "mouth," "shirt," or "nose" when they were sounded out phonically.

Prognosis:　Good.

References

Nature of Articulatory Defects

1. Backus, O. L., *Speech in Education*, New York, Longmans Green, 1943, pages 133–156.
This reference cites causes, case load, order of teaching sounds, and general procedures to be followed.

2. Bender, J. F. and Kleinfeld, V. M., *Principles and Practices of Speech*, New York, Crofts, 1938.
The description of the organic examination is perhaps the outstanding feature of this book.

3. Berry, M. and Eisenson, J., *The Defective in Speech*, Crofts, New York, 1942, pages 74–75.
A discussion of the causes of articulatory defects with frequent citations from the literature.

4. Fairbanks, G., *Voice and Articulation Drill Book*, New York, Harper, 1940.
The common errors for each of the consonant sounds are given, and a general discussion of the nature of articulatory defects is provided.

5. Ogilvie, M., *Terminology and Definitions of Speech Defects*. New York, Teachers College, *Columbia University Contributions to Education*, Number 859, 1942.
This monograph helps to clear up some of the confusion between the various terms used to designate the same articulatory disorder. It also provides a valuable bibliography for articles written prior to 1938.

6. Seth, G. and Guthrie, D., *Speech in Childhood*, London, Oxford University Press, 1935.
A general discussion of articulation problems, especially from the developmental point of view.

7. West, R., Kennedy, L., and Carr, A., *The Rehabilitation of Speech*, New York, Harper, 1937, pages 36–37.
An illustration of the main differences in the educational techniques used to teach normal children and speech defectives acceptable sounds—"training vs. retraining."

Causes of Articulatory Defects

8. Backus, O. L., "Speech Rehabilitation Following Excision of the Tip of the Tongue," *American Journal of Diseases of Children*, 1940, Vol. 60, pages 368–370.
Not only the sounds made with the tonguetip were defective but other sounds as well, and remedial speech work was successful despite the injury.

9. Bangs, J. L., "A Clinical Analysis of the Articulatory Defects of the Feebleminded," *Journal of Speech Disorders*, 1942, Vol. 7, 343–356.
An analysis of the articulatory errors of feeble-minded children in terms of the characteristic types of substitutions, omissions, and insertions.

10. Beckey, R. E., "A Study of Certain Factors Related to Retardation of Speech," *Journal of Speech Disorders*, 1942, Vol. 7, pages 223–249.
This reference is important in stressing the relation between articulatory defects and the conditions surrounding the learning of speech. Illnesses, economic status, birth injury, parental coddling, and parental anxiety are listed as among the causes.

11. Chess, S., "Developmental Language Disability as a Factor in Personality Distortion in Childhood," *American Journal of Orthopsychiatry*, 1944, Vol. 14, pages 483–490.

The effect of defective speech on personality development is sketched. Behavior problems must be solved before therapy will be successful.

12. Carrell, J. A., "A Comparative Study of Speech Defective Children," *Archives of Speech*, 1936, Vol. I, pages 179–204.
Gives the relative percentages of different types of articulatory errors and the most common sound substitutions as well as listing causes.

13. Fymbo, L., "The Relation of Malocclusion of the Teeth to Defects of Speech," *Archives of Speech*, 1936, Vol. 1, pages 204–217.
A study of the oral and speech examinations given to 410 students, showing that 87 per cent of the defective speech cases, 62 per cent of the average speech cases, and 35 per cent of the superior speakers had malocclusion of the teeth. Other conclusions are also noted.

14. Goldstein, M., "Practical Aspects of Speech Correction," *Journal of Speech Disorders*, 1939, Vol. 4, pages 99–102.
This reference describes several cases of individuals without tongues who nevertheless had intelligible speech.

15. Hall, M., "Auditory Factors in Functional Articulatory Speech Defects," *Journal of Experimental Education*, December, 1938, pages 110–132.
This study was carried out with a group of functional articulatory speech defectives, who were matched with a group of normal speakers. Among the conclusions, we find: no significant differences in the two groups in their ability to discriminate between pairs of speech sounds; articulation rating had a zero correlation with all four auditory measures used; and the experimental group had more low ratings on voice than the control group exhibited.

16. Hansen, F. M., "Application of Sound Discrimination Tests to Functional Articulatory Speech Defects," *Journal of Speech Disorders*, 1944, Vol. 9, pages 347–355.
Three tests of sound discrimination were given to adult articulatory and normal-speaking subjects. A vowel discrimination test is described.

17. Henry, J. and Henry, Z., "Speech Disturbances among Pilagra Indian Children," *American Journal of Orthopsychiatry*, 1940, Vol. 4, pages 99–102.
They talk baby talk until they are seven years old, and substitute easier sounds for the more difficult ones in terms of co-ordination.

18. Jenkins, R. L., "The Rate of Diadochokinetic Movement of the Jaw at the Ages of Seven to Maturity," *Journal of Speech Disorders*, 1940, Vol. 6, pages 13–22.
Summarizes other studies of the speed of jaw activity and presents original data to show that it increases with age up to 17 years. Females can move their jaws faster than males, a not surprising conclusion, if we may say so.

19. Keaster, J., "Studies in the Anatomy and Physiology of the Tongue," *Laryngoscope*, 1940, Vol. 50, pages 222–257.
Cites cases to show that speech in tongueless patients is much less interfered with than chewing and swallowing.

20. McDowell, E., "The Role of Speech Training in a Program of Orthodontic Treatment," *International Journal of Orthodontia and Oral Surgery*, 1936, Vol. 22, pages 105–113.

Dental and jaw defects are discussed in relation to defective speech sounds. A discussion of the paper by Raubicheck includes a statement that speech correction is possible despite marked organic abnormality. Research is given to support this view.

21. Metraux, R., "Auditory Memory Span for Speech Sounds of Speech Defective Children Compared with Normal Children," *Journal of Speech Disorders*, 1942, Vol. 7, pages 33–36.
No important differences were found. Auditory acuity and auditory memory span are different functions.

22. Palmer, M. F. and Osborn, C., "A Study of the Tongue Pressures of Speech Defective and Normal Speaking Individuals," *Journal of Speech Disorders*, 1940, Vol. 5, pages 133–141.
Articulatory speech defectives are especially poor in tongue strength.

23. Patton, F. M., "A Comparison of the Kinesthetic Sensibility of Speech Defective and Normal Speaking Children," *Journal of Speech Disorders*, 1942, Vol. 7, pages 305–310.
Articulatory cases are inferior to normal speakers in the kinesthetic perception ability as measured by Starling's tests.

24. Robbins, S. D., "Importance of Sensory Training in Speech Therapy," *Journal of Speech Disorders*, 1942, Vol. 7, pages 183–188.
Discusses the auditory memory span for digits with norms, and shows the importance of defective auditory memory span in dyslalia.

25. Roe, V. and Milisen, R., "The Effect of Maturation upon Defective Articulation in the Elementary Grades," *Journal of Speech Disorders*, 1942, Vol. 7, pages 37–50.
A modification of the Detroit Articulation Test was given to a large number of unselected primary pupils. Results are analyzed in terms of types of errors.

26. Sullivan, E. M., "Auditory Acuity and Its Relation to Defective Speech," *Journal of Speech Disorders*, 1944, Vol. 9, pages 127–130.
Articulation cases had more hearing loss than did the normal population.

27. Templin, M., "A Study of the Sound Discrimination Ability of Elementary School Pupils," *Journal of Speech Disorders*, 1943, Vol. 8, pages 127–132.
A short test of speech-sound discrimination is described and compared with the Travis-Rasmus Test.

28. Voegelin, C. V. and Adams, S., "A Phonetic Study of Young Children's Speech," *Journal of Experimental Education*, 1941, Vol. 3, pages 107–116.
Children are inconsistent in their articulatory errors. The sounds used for substitution are listed. The most difficult sound is the *l*.

29. Voelker, C., "Dyslogia in Mongolism," *Proceedings of the American Speech Correction Association*, 1934, Vol. 4, pages 31–34.
A description of Mongolism and the features which produce speech defects. A brief description of treatment is given.

30. Williams, H. M., *A Qualitative Analysis of the Erroneous Speech Sound Substitutions of Pre-school Children, University of Iowa Studies in Child Welfare*, 1937, Vol. 13, No. 2, pages 19–32.

The articulation errors are analyzed with regard to type and difficulty.

31. Wolf, I. J., "The Relation of Mal-occlusion to Sigmatism," *American Journal of Diseases of Children*, 1944, Vol. 68, pages 250–252.
Types of malocclusion and their effect on speech are presented.

Articulation Testing

32. Arnold, G., Articulation Testing Material, Expression Co., Boston.
A set of cards with pictures suitable for evoking speech sounds in a systematic way.

33. Bryngelson, B., and Glaspey, E., *Speech Improvement Cards*, Chicago, Scott Foresman, 1941.
A set of cards with pictures used for testing and remedial work, together with a manual describing procedures.

34. Backus, O. L., *Speech in Education*, New York, Longmans Green, 1943, pages 61–65.
A description of testing procedures with the variations required by individuals of different ages and severity of defect.

35. Curry, R., Kennedy, L., Wagner, L., and Wilke, W., "A Phonographic Scale for the Measurement of Defective Articulation," *Journal of Speech Disorders*, 1940, Vol. 8, pages 123–126.
A series of phonographically recorded samples of defective articulation, graduated according to degree of severity.

36. Du Cles, H., "The Play Approach to Testing the Speech of Children," *Proceedings of the American Speech Correction Association*, 1936, Vol. 6, pages 32–38.
Criticisms of existing articulation tests. Recommends flash cards with a single picture on each card. Words of her test are chosen from the Horn lists of words used by children.

37. Fairbanks, G., "*Voice and Articulation Drill Book*," New York, Harper, 1940.
Testing procedures are outlined and sentence material is provided.

38. Henderson, F. M., "Accuracy in Testing the Articulation of Speech Sounds," *Journal of Educational Research*, 1938, Vol. 31, pages 348–356.
A study of the accuracy and reliability of the judgments of examiners doing articulation testing.

39. Milisen, R., "Principles and Methods of Articulation Testing," *Speech and Hearing Therapist*, 1945, Indiana University Speech and Hearing Clinic, Bloomington, Indiana, February, pages 6–10.
One of the best articles on articulation testing ever written.

VIII

Treatment of Articulatory Disorders

Many speech correctionists ignore the fact that more than 70 per cent of all the speech defects are articulatory, and, if they treat them at all, they do so superficially and haphazardly. It should again be emphasized that children do not outgrow speech defects. Some of them overcome their difficulties through blundering methods of self-help, but many others do not. They require treatment which is carefully planned and carried out. Since most of the texts in speech correction give a host of drill material for the various speech sounds, this text will ignore such drill and will concentrate upon techniques and policies.

General principles of treatment. With the exception of neurotic lisping and neurotic baby talk, the treatment for all of the articulatory disorders follows the same general plan. Many variations must be made for individual problems, but these will be provided for within our discussion. Lalling, lisping, baby talk, oral inaccuracy, foreign speech, sound substitutions, omissions, and distortions of all kinds may be eradicated in much the same way. The neurotic disorders seldom respond to such treatment and require emotional retraining and adjustment prior to actual speech correction.

The course of treatment for the majority of articulation cases may now be outlined. (1) The speech defective must be convinced that he has errors which he must eradicate. (2) The causes of the disorder, if still existent, must be eliminated. If those causes are no longer present, their influence must be counteracted. (3) Through intensive ear training, the old word configurations are broken down so that the correct sound and the error may be *isolated, recognized, identified,* and *discriminated.* (4) Through various methods, the speech defective must be taught to produce the correct sound in isolation and at will (5) The new and correct sound must be strengthened. (6) The new sound must be incorporated within familiar words, and the transition

159

to normal speech must be accomplished.   (7) The use of the correct sound must be made habitual, and the error must be eliminated.

In cases where the person makes more than one error, it is well to work with the sounds according to their usual developmental order: first the lip sounds, then the dentals, then the gutturals, then the complicated tongue sounds, and, finally, the blends.   It is usually wise to work with the sound first in the initial position, then in the final position, and, finally, in the medial position.   One should continue working with one sound until the person can make it alone at will, can use it in all three word positions when he watches himself, and uses it habitually on about ten common words.   Then we may rely on parental and teacher co-operation to do the rest.

Convincing the Student That He Makes Speech Errors

The child must be convinced that he has a problem which he must solve. This is not so easily done.   Owing to sheltered environments and the tolerance of associates who have become accustomed to the speech difference, many speech defectives grow to adulthood without ever having been made aware of their speech disorder, although it may be so noticeable that it shrieks its presence whenever its possessor opens his mouth.   If friends and acquaintances will not mention it, certainly the average stranger will not.   We seldom hear ourselves speak.   Instead, we listen to our vocalized thinking.   And so the speech defective himself has little chance of becoming fully aware of the nature or frequency of his errors.

Although many articulatory cases are thoroughly aware of their speech disorder, they do not seem to recognize all of their errors; and there are other cases who seem totally unaware of any speech difficulty. Small children, especially, need to be convinced that they have sound substitutions, additions, omissions, or distortions before they will co-operate or respond to treatment.   The older ones must learn to recognize error whenever it occurs.   A vague, generalized feeling that something is wrong with the speech will not provide sufficient motivation for the type of retraining that is necessary.

Teachers frequently ask whether or not it is advisable to work upon the child's speech in view of the self-consciousness and embarrassment which might be produced.   The answer to this question is that the quickest way of getting rid of these errors is to make the child aware of them. The habits should be broken before they become fixed. Moreover, it is perfectly possible to work on a speech defect without shame, and if the teacher makes the child understand that a certain skill is to be learned and a problem is to be solved, no insecurity will be created. If she adopts a calm, unemotional attitude herself, empathic response will ensure a similar attitude in the child.

There are various ways of teaching an articulatory speech defective to recognize his errors, and some of them are given in the next paragraphs. One mother patiently corrected her child on every mispronounced word for three successive days, and he responded by refusing to talk at all for a week. With small children, no such nagging is necessary or advisable. The teacher should select five or six common words in which the child uses the error and should try to create in the child the feeling that in these words he is doing something incorrectly. She may tell him that there are other troublesome words, but she should set up as the first definite project the correction of these five or six. By narrowing the disorder to such a slender nucleus, the task is made easier and specific. The child must learn to recognize these words as "wrong words" and must come to realize that in these words he is likely to use "wrong sounds."

Sample exercises for teaching the child to recognize his errors:

1. The teacher reads a story to the child in which the five or six error words are used many times. The first time she reads it, she imitates the child's errors, cupping her ear every time she does so. The child is asked to do the same thing. The second time, the teacher reads it correctly except for one word. The child is asked to cup his ear when he hears the one error.

2. The teacher reads a list of words among which are included the error words. The child repeats all but the error words after the teacher, who pronounces the error words twice, first correctly, then incorrectly.

3. The child tells a story or recounts some experience and the teacher rings a bell whenever she hears the child mispronounce one of the error words.

4. One of the error words that is the name of a certain object is selected. The teacher draws two pictures of the object and asks the child to scribble over one of them. The teacher then names the two pictures, pronouncing the scribbled one with the child's error, and pronouncing the other one correctly. She then tells the child a story, sometimes using the word correctly and sometimes incorrectly. The child is asked to hold up the appropriate picture. The child then tells a story while the teacher holds up one picture, usually the scribbled one.

Sample exercises for teaching the older child or adult to recognize errors:

1. The student silently reads prepared material which illustrates the error: Thus: He thaw/saw the bird fly to the netht/nest. The teacher then reads it aloud.

2. Have the student write from dictation, putting down in phonetic spelling the errors which the teacher purposely makes.

3. Teacher speaks a word five times, once with error. Student signals when error occurs. The same assignment can be made but with the teacher saying the word correctly only once out of five trials.

4. Same as above but with student immediately imitating teacher's error. (*Note.* Speech penalties are more effective than any other penalty.)

5. Using material with *s* words (or other error-sound words) underlined, have student (1) make judgment as to error occurrence as he reads; (2) pause after attempt on *s* word while teacher imitates and asks for judgment of right or wrong; (3) pronounce the *s* in three different ways, raising finger for the incorrect pronunciations; (4) repeat each *s* word three times, making judgment as to which attempt was the best; (5) repeat *s* sound five times before proceeding, while teacher makes judgments for each; (6) prolong *s* sound and make judgment.

6. Use the same assignments as above but (1) reading lists of words, one at a time; (2) saying prewritten speech; (3) using conversation.

7. Student uses telephone and teacher interrupts conversation by hanging up immediately upon occurrence of error.

8. Teacher requires student to do something absurd (such as going to mirror, shaking head, and saying "Oh, oh") after each error.

9. Student confesses and points out own errors each time they occur.

10. Student imitates own error whenever it occurs, exaggerating it.

Elimination of the causes of articulation defects. In the preceding chapter we have discussed the various causes of articulatory errors. In this chapter we are primarily interested in the methods available to us for eliminating these causes or canceling their effects. While it is true that often the articulatory errors are habits that can persist long after their original cause has disappeared, there are many cases in which the causes are still potent factors in maintaining the disorder.

Organic abnormalities can certainly act as contributory or maintaining causes. There are two methods for minimizing their influence: (1) reconstruction of defective organic structure through surgery and orthodontia, and (2) the teaching of compensatory movements in speech-sound production.

In recent years, orthodontia has made great strides, and almost unbelievable changes in dental, palatal, and jaw structures have been accomplished.   The speech-correction teacher should refer all children with marked mouth deformities to these specialists and should begin her work after the reconstruction has been carried out.   Unfortunately, such reconstruction is expensive, and many cases cannot be taken care of in this way.   Nevertheless, the speech-correction teacher should acquaint herself with the resources in the orthodontic field so that she will not waste months of effort in teaching compensatory movements to a child whose speech problem can be taken care of through surgery or the displacement of structures.   Similarly, she should realize that palatal abnormalities are frequently associated with those of the jaws, and that orthodontic projection or retraction of the jaw can facilitate tongue contact with the roof of the mouth. Modern surgery also offers a wide variety of repair and reconstruction techniques.   Scar tissue can be excised, and grafts can be made which will provide the necessary mobility.   High palatal arches can be lowered, and the velum can be modified to almost any desired degree. Much of this work should be done early in childhood, and the speech-correction teacher is often responsible for seeing that it is done.   Frequently, parents postpone such remedial work until too late, but they may often be convinced of its necessity by the teacher who points out the social maladjustment which such defects may produce.

Paralyzed structures occasionally can be helped by exercises, and a professional physiotherapist should be consulted in planning a remedial program if the physician's report indicates a possibility of success.   Such remedial work usually consists of recourse to the more biological functions and the tying up of the specialized movement with gross muscular action.   Spaced practice, well motivated by graphs of successes, is advisable.

Hearing disabilities frequently necessitate the use of hearing aids, visualization, phonetic diagrams, and schemes of muscular contractions.   In deaf and blind children, manipulation by the teacher to set the jaws, mouth, and teeth is sometimes required.   In cases of mental deficiency, many articulatory disorders occur, and the speech correctionist is called upon for aid.   Although it is recommended that speech correction be carried out by the regular special-room teacher, the speech specialist should plan the program, fitting the technique to the typical traits of the feeble-minded.

Teaching compensatory movements.   As we have said, many cases showing severe organic defects cannot be helped by the orthodontist or plastic surgeon because of age or financial reasons.   The picture is by no means hopeless, however, since all of the speech sounds may be made in various ways. The art of the ventriloquist demonstrates compensatory activity of the tongue for that of the lips and jaws. Many normal speakers have profound anatomical abnormalities, occasionally so marked as to excite wonder in the speech correctionist

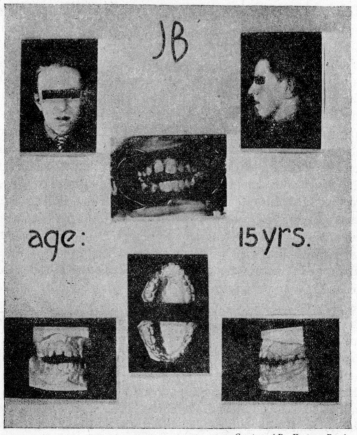

Courtesy of Dr. Kurt von Frouine

Fig. 5. A child in urgent need of orthodontia. This child omitted *f* and *v* sounds and had a lateral lisp.

familiar with the ordinary production of the speech sounds. Perfect *t* and *d* sounds, for example, have been made by individuals so tongue-tied that they were unable to lift the tonguetip to contact the upper teeth. Inmates of prisons frequently learn to talk out of the side of the mouth—the one farthest away from the guard—with but minor jaw movements.

In order to teach compensatory or nonstandard ways of making any speech sound, it is first necessary to make a phonetic analysis in terms of the type of sound to be produced.   For example, the production of an *s* sound requires the propulsion of a narrow stream of air past a cutting edge.   The cutting edge should be placed at about right angles to the air stream in order to produce a clear *s*.   The average person produces this narrow stream of air by placing the sides of the tongue along the side teeth, thereby cutting off all lateral escape of air, and by grooving the center of the tongue so that the air stream is projected directly past the cutting edge of the front incisors.   Lacking these front teeth, or having them widely spaced, the person can get an equally good *s* by directing the air stream past the cuspids or bicuspids on the side of the mouth having the better teeth.   This new mechanics, however, is not quite so simple as the preceding sentence might imply.   The tongue must adjust itself so that on one side it makes a larger occlusion and the groove is diagonal.   The lips must plug the former opening and part at the appropriate side.   Frequently the mandible must be moved sidewise so that the best upper and lower teeth will be brought together.   Thus the teacher must plan the type of compensatory mechanics necessitated by the particular mouth deformities involved.   In this plan, the teacher should take into account or seek to minimize as far as possible the following factors: complexity of performance (the fewer adjustments, the better), ease of transition from other sounds, amount of facial contortion, distinctness of kinesthetic and tactual sensations, and the motivation and co-operation of the subject.

In teaching compensatory mechanics, then, the teacher should follow this general outline.   (1) Note how the student articulates the defective sound.   (2) Make phonetic analysis to determine what the essential mechanics of the sound must be.   (3) Discover what structures the student might possibly use to satisfy these requirements. (4) Give the student a thorough course in ear training, stimulation, and discrimination along the lines of the program sketched in the next section.   (5) Through manipulation, phonetic diagrams, mirror work, imitation, and random activity, try to get the student to produce a sound similar to that made by the instructor.   (6) Once achieved, do not let the student move a muscle of face or body until he prolongs, repeats, and uses it in nonsense syllables many times.   (7) Build up its strength through techniques suggested in the next section.   (8) Do not worry about exaggerated movements used by the student in making the sound. At first, most students will use facilitating movements of other structures as a baby uses gross movements prior to specialization. We frequently encourage head and jaw movements or modifications of smiling, chewing, biting, and swallowing as accessory tools. These extraneous movements drop out as the new performance pattern becomes habitual. (9) Increase the speed with which the new performance pattern can be initiated. No compensatory movements will become habitual if they cannot be used quickly and easily. (10) Be careful to change the transition movements as well, working for new and quick patterns of change from one speech sound to another.

Functional causes. Besides the organic factors previously described, we have a large number of functional causes. The emotional causes of articulation disorders are best remedied by following the procedures outlined in Chapter IV. The case must be given insight into his problems. His social assets must be increased; his liabilities diminished. His habitual reactions of attack or retreat must be altered so that he can be freed from social penalty. He must learn to adopt an objective attitude toward his differences and to carry out a campaign of self-improvement. As he begins to fulfill his potentialities and meets social acceptance, the emotional causes will no longer hamper his efforts to eliminate his speech difference.

The developmental factors which cause articulatory speech defects can best be overcome by following the general methods described in the chapter on delayed speech and the one on the development of speech. The child must become familiar with the major characteristics of the various speech sounds and he must learn the elementary facts of vocal phonics. Activities aimed at these goals can easily be added to the general speech correction procedures to be described later in this chapter. Even as tongue exercises are often a part of the daily sessions used to teach a new sound and eliminate an error, exercises in identifying the isolated speech sounds can also be made an integral part of the program. When the child has developed habitual antagonistic or frustrating attitudes toward any type of correction because of scolding or impatient methods of the parents, we must be careful to follow the child's own interests in devising our assignments or activities. One of our adults felt sure he could never acquire a normal *r* sound and passively resisted every attempt on our part to help him do so until we gave him the task of helping a girl correct her lisp.   He became so interested in the project that his whole attitude toward his own errors changed and he quickly succeeded in eliminating them.

It may be said that anything which puts a great deal of pressure on speech will tend to produce speech defects of all kinds, and, if this pressure is exerted during the development of speech, articulatory disorders frequently occur.   Some of these factors are: fear of interruption, habitual urge to interrupt others, oral confession of guilt, too high speech standards in home or school, public recitation or speaking of pieces, too much excitement, ridicule, fear of punishment or sarcasm, speech when fatigued, bluffing, too great parental or teacher pressure for school progress, speaking while confused, general unhappiness or emotional strain, and constant need for speech to strangers. There are many others, and the average teacher can readily devise ways for eliminating or minimizing these conditions after she discovers what they are.

Imitation and poor environmental speech standards are difficult factors to eliminate, but the best approach seems to be through frank recognition of the problem, the adoption of other models, and the provision for contacts with other environments which have high speech standards.   The teacher should not berate the parents or companions whose speech is not acceptable or ask the child to adopt a speech which is foreign to his environment.   A better policy is to tell the child that he may continue to use the jargon and poor speech of his home and neighborhood while he is there, but that he should learn a different type of speech for other situations.   He should be shown other environments and future opportunities, and the necessity for adequate speech therein.   Without such a horizon, no permanent progress will be made.   Very seldom can the home or neighborhood speech standards be changed, and the speech correctionist may as well face that fact.

Weak auditory memory span.   The factors of poor auditory discrimination and short auditory memory span are usually taken care of in the intensive ear training that is the keynote of modern articulatory therapy.   Many exercises to take care of these factors may be found in later pages of this text, and it is well to give the child a preliminary course in discrimination, recognition, remembrance of sound sequences, and self-hearing.   We have found that most inadequate auditory discrimination or memory span is due to a lack of directed attention and that it will respond to appropriate treatment. Some special techniques for improving one's auditory discrimination or memory span follow.

1. Auditory memory-span drill. Teacher pronounces a series of digits or words. Student repeats them after intervals varying from 1 to 60 seconds. This assignment should be followed by the student's giving himself his own series, waiting the prescribed interval, and then repeating. Errors should be checked, and this procedure should be strongly motivated. The above drills can be carried out through phonograph records, the student being asked to write down the series.

2. Jabber-repetition. This consists, like the above, of stimulation and repetition. The teacher says certain nonsense words (polysyllabic) such as "wahwo-kadda-makeree-samma." The student repeats these after a certain interval, which should be gradually increased. As in the last assignment, the student should then give himself the jabber stimulation and attempt to repeat as closely as possible. The syllables may also be recorded phonographically for stimulation.

3. Student distorts certain speech sounds and then attempts to repeat these distortions exactly. The teacher should illustrate using the "dark *l*" sound or the lateral lisp.

4. It is often wise to begin these assignments with the direction of the speech defective's attention to the duration of his sounds, since this feature is more easily recognized and judged. Thus the student is instructed to repeat after the teacher the nonsense word *laaaaaaalo*, seeking to keep the relative and total durations of the repetition as close as possible to those of the stimulation. Other similar nonsense words, including those which prolong the continuant consonants, are given. Phonograph records in which the duration can be identified are useful in providing a checkup. The student should then give himself similar stimulation, and repeat it after an appropriate interval, while the teacher checks.

5. Assignments similar to the above but using inflections as the stimulus material are helpful in training the individual to listen to his speech.

6. The student is told to pronounce certain continuant consonants or vowels (both in words and by themselves) five times, prolonging the consonant or vowel slightly each time. The same type of assignment may be used for inflected vowels and consonants. The teacher checks. Written material may be used for this, such as *sso, ssso, sssso, ssssso*.

7. The student, using a stage whisper, prolongs, inflects, or distorts certain vowels or continuants. He then repeats vocally, as closely as possible.

8. The student should be given frequent self-listening periods, in which he makes a sound and listens closely to it. Not more than two or three words should constitute a period, and the student must be extremely alert. Later in the treatment it is wise to have the student use these periods for judgments of correct sound production.

When poor muscular co-ordination is an important factor in producing the articulatory errors, we devote part of our therapy to improving the speed and precision of the articulatory musculature.

Tongue exercises. Many speech defectives, especially younger ones, or those with some abnormality of the tongue, who have had mouth injuries or paralysis, need these exercises. Their tongues do not move with the speed and precision demanded by good speech. They can assume only the simplest tongue positions. Therefore, they raise the front or middle of the tongue instead of the back, and protrude it rather than lift it. It is difficult for them to curl the tip or groove the tongue. Tongue exercises are useful and necessary for these cases.

The exercises that follow are given in a form suitable for adults where we may be direct in our therapy. For children, it will be necessary to cast the same activities in the form of games. The principles governing the use of tongue exercises are as follows:

1. Learn to recognize the movement as part of some familiar biological movement such as chewing, swallowing, coughing, or others to be mentioned later. Practice these basic activities.
2. The finer movements should be taught first in conjunction with larger movements, then alone.
3. The movement should be used with increasing speed, strength, and accuracy.
4. The movement should be combined with other movements (breathing, phonation, and so on) used in speech.
5. The emphasis in this training should be on the activities (lifting, thrusting, drawing, tip-curling, and grooving) and the contacts (upper gum ridge, lower teeth, interdental, palatal) and the positions actually used in speech, rather than random and generalized tongue movements.
6. Not only the tonguetip, but the blade, middle, and back of tongue should be exercised.
7. In any drill period, use a few from each of the lists of exercises under each major activity heading rather than complete one section at a time. Practice the activity exercises *A, B, C, D,* until these are fairly well mastered before using contact exercises *E.* Use position exercises *F* last.
8. Avoid fatigue and hurry. Identify movement by imitation or mirror observation rather than by oral description. Identify contacts by stroking or pressure. Identify new positions in terms of their variation from other well-known positions.
9. After movement is well learned, combine it with production of other speech sounds.
10. Compare, contrast, and combine the various movements.

A. *Lifting*

1. Chew in an exaggerated fashion with mouth openings and hand movements for thirty seconds.

2. In a manner similar to the chewing exercise, alternately do the following two sets of opposite movements:

a. Beginning with open mouth, lower your head and as you do so shut your jaws and lift your tonguetip in unison. (Be sure that tongue lifts itself and is not merely lifted by jaw.)

b. As you raise your head, open your jaws and let your tongue flop back to the bottom of your mouth. Do this to a simple rhythm tapped out by teacher, very slowly at first, then increasing speed. Finally combine with pretended chewing.

3. Repeat exercise (2) but omit large head movements. Hold head still and merely move lower jaw in unison with the lifting or lowering tongue. Use rhythms and increase speed.

4. Repeat exercise (2) but hold head still and mouth open (do not move lower jaw) and merely lift tongue. Use rhythms and increase speed.

5. Repeat exercises (2), (3), and (4) one after another. Then repeat again and again, using rhythms and increasing speed.

6. Repeat exercise (5) but breathe out first silently then in an audible stream as in a stage sigh. Then repeat vocalizing the vowels *ah, ee, a, o,* and *oo.*

7. Protrude lips and at a sudden signal lift tongue. Then alternate protrusion of lips and lifting of tongue, using rhythms and speed.

8. Practice sudden shifts from prolonged consonants *m, n, v, th,* to the upward movements of the tongue. Follow procedure of exercise (7).

9. Get a small piece of sponge rubber and sterilize it by boiling. Put into the front of the mouth and repeat exercise (5), forcing rubber to roof of mouth and compressing it with the tonguetip. Use this device to strengthen tongue.

10. With spoon or tongue depressor hold tip of tongue down. Mouth is held open. Use rhythms and increasing speed in lifting tongue against the pressure.

11. *Repeat those of the above exercises which can be modified to employ the back of the tongue. Do the same for the blade or middle of tongue.*

B. *Thrusting and withdrawing*

1. Using imitation and mirror observation, practice licking lips and cleaning teeth and cheeks with the tongue. Use tonguetip as a suction cup, pressing it firmly against back of teeth then quickly pulling it away. This results in a sound often spelled as "tsk" and used as a mild reproach.

2. Practice using imitation and mirror observation (1) tongue-sucking, (2) several varieties of tongue-clucking or -clicking (with mouth open), (3) Bronx-cheering (tongue between lips and forced into rapid vibration by expelled air blast, (4) tongue-wobbling (rounded lips and phonation of vowel *o* as tongue rapidly and alternately protrudes and withdraws), (5) cheek-pumping (alternately puffing out and pulling in cheeks, which results in small back-and-forth tongue movements).

3. Round lips and hold sterilized blunt pencil or heavy probe in hole so that the tonguetip, pressing and yielding against it, can make it move

in and out like a plunger.   Begin with half-inch oscillations then increase
to in-and-out movements of at least an inch each way.   Use slow rhythms
and gradually increase speed.   Give frequent rests.   Repeat, exerting
enough pressure on plunger so that tongue will become stronger.

4. Use rhythms and increasing speed in performing the activities of
exercise (2).

5. Protrude tongue as far forward (*not* up or down) as possible.   Use
rhythms and increasing speed.   Allow head and jaw movements at first
but end with head and jaw fixed.   Then get set and protrude tongue to its
farthest extent the moment a sudden signal is given.   Work for an almost
automatic reaction.

6. (*a*) Blow out a stream of air and then protrude tongue to its farthest
limit without stopping the blowing.   (*b*) Repeat but phonate the vowel *ah*
as you protrude tongue.   Repeat this exercise until it becomes very smooth.

7. Shut teeth and suck air through them as you inhale.   Then as you
blow through the teeth thrust your tongue lightly against them.   Make
sure that some part of the tonguetip is in contact with the teeth as the air
is exhaled.

C. *Curling*

1. Practice licking stick candy or spoon or other object held at right
angles to and in contact with the upper teeth.   Lick a thin scattered sprin-
kling of sugar from a plate.

2. Facing a mirror, hold a sterilized probe or match horizontally about
half an inch from the mouth.   Reach out with tongue and, by curling the
end of it, pull it back to the teeth.   The strength of this action may be
increased by holding match more firmly.

3. With mouth wide open (and allowing jaws to close with the tongue
action), thrust tongue out and then curl the tip to touch exact center of the
upper edge of the upper lip.   Use rhythms and increasing speed.

4. Repeat exercise (3), but with jaws barely open enough to let tongue
through; and do not permit any jaw or head movement.

5. Open mouth and curl tonguetip as in preceding exercises but do not
protrude tongue.   Keep it entirely within mouth.

6. Repeat exercises (3) and (5) but curl tongue during forced exhalation.

7. Repeat exercise (5) but use a sudden signal to set off an instantane-
ous tongue-curling.   Work for quick reaction to the signal.

D. *Grooving*

While many people with perfectly normal speech do not have the ability to form a narrow tubelike groove in the tongue which they can maintain
even when the tongue is protruded, some form of shallow grooving is essential to the production of the *s*, *zh*, *sh* and *z*, *j*, and *ch* sounds.

1. Round the lips as in producing the vowel $\overline{oo}$, and as you do so protrude tongue barely between teeth, then cough easily several times.   Observe self in mirror and you will see that the tongue is grooved as you

cough.   Practice this until you can hold the groove even after the cough is completed.   "Listen" to the muscular sensations coming from the tongue when it is in this position.   Shutting your eyes will help you to focus your attention.   Finally, produce the groove by merely getting set to cough.

2. Repeat exercise (1) but insert sterilized probe or pencil in mouth so as to help the rounding or grooving of the tongue.   Withdraw probe but maintain groove.

3. With mouth open wide and tongue relaxed, place bowl of spoon on front third of tongue.   Ask child first to squeeze the sides of the spoon without lifting, then to squeeze and lift.   After this is successful, pretend that you are using an imaginary spoon and repeat.   Repeat this but with teeth together.

4. Practice whistling between the teeth.

5. Practice forcing tonguetip against upper teeth (when teeth and lips are closed).   Then suck air through narrow lip opening.   Then exhale through same opening.   Alternate exhalation and inhalation, increasing speed.

6. Once grooving has been clearly identified (without mirror) and can be produced at will, use rhythms and increasing speed in producing the movement.

7. Practice grooving tongue (do not insist on tubular groove; a shallow groove is adequate) while lowering jaw, while rounding and unrounding lips, while smiling.

8. Using different varieties of grooving, produce many different sibilant sounds, ranging from a high-pitched whistled *s* to a sloppy *sh* sound.

Delayed speech development.   We have mentioned the fact that interruptions in speech development seem to produce typical errors. Severe illnesses often occur during the first years of a child's life, and these may interrupt the practice of inflections, or the babbling period, or the naming period.   Occasionally, very clear case histories point to these interruptions as causal factors, and it is interesting to note that these cases progress much more rapidly if they are allowed to begin with the type of activity they have missed.   In many cases, it is impossible to get definite histories of the type of speech being used by the child at the time the illness or accident occurred.   Nevertheless, we have found that if illness occurred during the babbling period it is well to have the student practice some of this vocal play.   From this activity, many adults seem to get a peculiar pleasure, which is out of all proportion to its novelty, and without suggestion from the clinician they proceed to go through many of the same phases which the child experiences, using doubling first, then true disyllables, then inflections. Certain combinations are practiced much more than others, and frequently the sounds which they have never been able to say are used over and over, although they are so lost in the matrix of the babbling that a keen ear is needed to distinguish them. We often recommend that they combine swallowing, chewing, biting, and smiling movements with this vocal play. The student should do it alone, and with a clear understanding of its purpose, to avoid self-consciousness. He should keep out analysis and purposeful combinations, and should relax and let the babble go where it may. After the student has practiced babbling in this way for about ten five-minute periods, scattered throughout several days, the speech correctionist should try to get him to repeat certain combinations of the nonsense material as they occur in the babbling.

Ear Training

The vast importance of ear training. Many texts in speech correction agree that the first step in remedial treatment of articulatory cases should be ear training, and most speech correctionists employ it. The exact nature of this ear training is too often vague, unsystematic, and perfunctory, although it is probably the most important tool in the clinician's kit. If the preliminary ear training is done well, little difficulty is experienced, even with the most severe cases. The speech-correction teacher is prone to slight it because immediate results are not forthcoming, because it demands strong motivation, because it necessitates lesson preparation and clever techniques, and because she does not realize its nature or importance. Many parents and teachers feel that all they need to do to get rid of such a speech defect is to tell the child that he has said the word wrong and must try it again. Often they attempt to show him by increasing the loudness of the correct word as though he were hard of hearing, a proceeding which is obviously poor pedagogy. *It may be said with the utmost emphasis that no teacher should attempt to get a child to try to make a new speech sound without first giving him systematic ear training.*

The teacher of the articulatory case must appreciate the point of view of the speech defective with respect to the errors involved. To the uncorrected lisper, for example, the substitution of *th* for *s* in the word *soup* is entirely natural. He is often unaware that any substitution has occurred. The liquid's name just happens to be *thoup.* The auditory sensations for *s* and *th* are fairly similar even when produced by some other person. Unless one has learned to isolate them from the words in which they normally occur, or has associated them with some specific object such as a goose's hiss, or has produced them with different tongue movements, there will be very little discrimination in hearing them. Discrimination of sounds involves, as we shall see, recognition, identification, association with symbols, and differential bodily reactions. The lisper without correction or training has no power of discrimination because he has none of these attributes of discrimination. Frequently the lisper can be taught to tell the difference between the *s* and the *th* when produced by another person without being able to recognize his own substitution of those sounds. This is due to the fact that a speech sound is a complicated combination of hearing and feeling. Both are blended and integrated into a perceptual whole, into a configuration. Thus, to the lisper, the *s* and *th* sounds are not different enough to overrule the similarity of the habitual tongue movements which he has always made in identical fashion for each. If he attends to the auditory sensations alone, he can tell the difference, but, if he must also attend to the feel of the tongue, which is similarly placed for both sounds, the sounds will be perceived as being more alike than different.

If this is the case when the sounds are isolated, it is clear that, when the sounds are incorporated within the unitary sound sequences called words, there will be even less chance for discrimination between correct and incorrect sounds. As students of phonetics know, there are no such things as syllables in speech, although there may be in orthography. In most spoken speech, even the words are but parts of the sentence as a whole, and may not be considered as units. Therefore, within the word, any individual sound can have little perceptual importance. Most children learn words as wholes, and not as sound sequences. Each word is a complex configuration, having within it patterns of muscular movements, patterns of sequences of auditory sensations, and a unitary meaning. It is a unit and an organized whole.

Recognizing this unitary nature of the word and the subordinate nature of the sounds which compose it, we can easily understand why the articulatory case does not recognize his errors and why he frequently refuses to believe that the correct sound, when used in an old familiar word, is indeed correct. Indeed, the correct sound frequently appears to these cases not only as strange and unfamiliar but as definitely incorrect. Moreover, the fact that the lisper has so thoroughly incorporated the *th* sound in the configuration whose meaning is *soup* gives us the explanation for the curious relapse that occurs when a new sound is used in familiar words without previously being strengthened. Many lispers, for example, can learn to make a good *s* when it is isolated, but, if the teacher insists upon their using it in familiar words, they go right back to their old error, and frequently lose the ability to make it even in isolation. It therefore becomes necessary to build up the new sound in isolation and in simple configurations, to tear down the old configurations and isolate the error, to synthesize the new sound with various sound sequences and meanings, and thereby to produce the new and standard configurations—the correct words.

If the student has not been convinced by this time of the urgent need for ear training as a prerequisite to speech-sound production, he will probably have to learn the same truth through sad experience with persistent error, frequent relapse, and slow progress. When articulatory cases are seen daily, it is customary to spend at least a week or two in intensive ear training before the student ever attempts to produce the correct sound. Most teachers and speech defectives hurry this part of the work. They are impatient to see actual results, to get to the correction of the speech errors; and because of this attitude, they interfere with future progress. Adequate ear training is the best insurance for successful speech correction where articulatory and voice cases are concerned.

Types of ear training. Ear training should consist of definite exercises and activities fitted to the age, interests, and understanding of the speech defective. There are four main types of this ear training, and every one of the early speech periods should include exercises of each type. The four types, with their distinguishing characteristics, are as follows:

Isolation—training in listening to sound sequences, nonsense words, or connected speech in order to detect the presence of certain sounds; training in isolating any sound, correct or incorrect, from its context; training in breaking up unitary speech-sound configurations into sequences of fairly independent sounds.

Stimulation—training which bombards the speech defective with a barrage of the correct sound.

Identification—training in identifying the characteristics of the correct sound and in identifying the characteristics of the error. No comparison is involved. The student learns the distinguishing traits of each.

Discrimination—training in comparing the correct sound with the error, in hearing the differences between the two sounds, and in recognizing the contrasts involved.

In the following paragraphs, we outline some of the techniques through which the four goals mentioned above may be obtained. Those cited are, of course, but a few of the techniques that may be used. Any worth-while teacher can and will invent others. Moreover, it is seldom necessary to use all of them with any one case. The medicine must be fitted to the symptoms. However, each case should be given an intensive course of ear training to convince the child that he has a speech defect and enable him to isolate, recognize, identify, and discriminate between the correct sound and the error.

Isolation techniques. We have pointed out that, as long as a sound is lost within a word, it cannot be heard or felt with any clarity. The word configurations must be broken up so that the correct sound can be heard by itself. One adult declared that he had sincerely tried to hear the sound that his teachers said he used incorrectly, but, when they pronounced the words, the part in which he was interested was gone before he could perceive it. This adult could make the sound at will when he said it separately, but was unable to use it in familiar words. To the child speech defective, spoken words are lumps of sound. Indeed, he hears them as single sounds rather than as sound sequences. The older methods of teaching reading, in which children learned to sound out their new words, probably helped the articulatory cases much more than the new methods, which stress the acquisition of whole words. It is possible for an articulatory case to learn new word-wholes in which the correct sound is used, but it is much more economical, in terms of time spent in remedial work, to teach him to disrupt the incorrect word-wholes, to recognize the error, and then to integrate the correct sound into a sequence that is acceptable. He will then be much more likely to recognize his errors, and he will be able to master new words by himself.

A few illustrative exercises in isolating sounds from their contexts may be given. The individuals concerned were lingual lispers—hence the use of *s* as the sound illustrated. Any other sound may be used in the same exercises, and many other similar exercises may be easily invented.

Sample isolation techniques for children.

1. The teacher hides, in different places about the room, nine or ten pictures of various objects, one of which begins with the *s* sound. The moment the child finds this picture, he can run back to the teacher and ring a bell.

2. The teacher gives the child an old catalogue and a pair of scissors.

A box is shown the child, and he is told that when he gets five pictures whose names begin with the *s* sound and one picture whose name ends with that sound, he can open the box and have what is in it.   He does so and gets the jelly bean.

3. The child is covered with a bath towel and told to play Jack-in-the-box.   The teacher tells him that she has three funny word keys, only one of which will open the box.   The word key that fits has the *s* sound in it. The child is to jump and throw off the towel and say *boo* when the teacher uses the proper key.   The three keys are nonsense words or sound sequences such as "mo-bo-to-pay," "ka-pa-la-tha," and "ro-ssso-fa-ta."   The length of the nonsense word key and the location of the *s* sound within the word may be varied to fit the needs of the child.   Word keys may be simple monosyllables at first.

4. The teacher arranges five boxes on a table and tells the child that she is going to put a word in each box.   He is to watch and point to the box in which there is a word with an *s* sound in it.   The teacher may use word lists first and then progress to interesting sentences.

5. The teacher sounds out words and asks the child to locate the appropriate picture, putting all *s*-word pictures in a special envelope.

Sample isolation techniques for adults or older children.

1. Student reads silently, underlining all *s* sounds (not only *s* letters). He reads the passage and notes how many he missed in silent reading.

2. The teacher and student read from the same material (or recite sentences previously agreed upon), the teacher omitting all *s* sounds and the student speaking them, or, in the earlier stages, the student reading and omitting all *s* sounds and the teacher speaking them.   Thus:

    Student: Thi . . can . . ertainly run fa . . t.
    Teacher: ss   ss   ss.

3. The student should make a list of words in which the *s* symbol refers to some other sound (as in "measure" or "his"), and also a list of words in which other symbols are sounded as *s* ("ice," "extra").

4. The student should talk while having pencil and paper before him, writing the symbol *s* each time it occurs in the teacher's speech.   This can also be done for each time it occurs in his own speech.

5. Pause for a count of five after each occurrence of the correct or incorrect *s* sound in his speech.   Repeat, pausing prior to the sound.

6. Teacher stimulates student by omitting, prolonging, or repeating *s* each time it occurs.   Use reading material in which the *s* sounds have previously been underlined.

Stimulation techniques.   It is not sufficient to isolate and identify the correct sound during the preliminary period of ear training.   The student must be stimulated with the sound so thoroughly that it may almost be said to ring in his ears.   Every available agency should be used to provide this stimulation. Parents, friends, and classmates can help. Through various devices, the speech defective's attention to the sound must be focused and heightened. He must become aware of it not only in isolation but also as it occurs within spoken words. If there is any law governing speech acquisition, it is the law of adequate stimulation.

Obviously, many of the techniques used in isolating the correct sound may be modified to provide adequate stimulation. The adult should be required to listen carefully and discriminatingly to variations in intensity and rhythmic presentation of the stimulus. He can be required to write the symbol simultaneously with the teacher's utterance. He may signal his perception of the presence of the sound within a jumble of nonsense material. Phonograph recording may be used, and so also may such tongue twisters as "Sally sold silk and satin at the store on Saturday." The student, of course, does not pronounce these sentences. This is the period for ear training. He merely listens, or writes from dictation.

A correct attitude on the part of the speech defective is of the utmost importance to the success of this auditory stimulation. Koepp-Baker [1] gives this advice to his adult articulatory cases:

When your clinician produces the sound, over and over again, for you, it is highly important that you pay the strictest attention. This listening must not be a passive act, but a highly active one. You must be listening— not just sitting. It would be much the same kind of listening you would do if you were studying a piece of music being played by an orchestra or single performer, to determine the nuances, variations, and subtleties of execution. Should you grow tired, inattentive, or disinterested, tell the clinician at once, for auditory stimulation is of value only when you are fully participating in the process of listening.

As you listen, try to determine exactly in what way the sound which you are hearing differs from all other sounds of speech and in what way it is like them. Remember that your ability to detect the slight differences in sounds which give them their identity will develop slowly. At first you will hear nothing of any significance. *As you learn to listen discriminately,* you will discover much you have missed before.

Do not be misled by the fact that your clinician *seems* to be doing all the work during the auditory stimulation period. His part is relatively simple and makes no great demands of him. On the other hand, your task of actively listening far transcends his in importance. All that really happens occurs in you. What you do during these stimulation periods determines the extent of any improvement to occur in your speech habits.

---

[1] By permission of the author, from *A Handbook of Clinical Speech,* Ann Arbor, Edwards Brothers, 1936, Vol. 2, pages 346–347.

Psychologically, the most important thing which will ever happen during your speech training is happening as you listen. Don't be fooled. Listening is hard work—and of greatest importance.

The co-operation of adults may usually be enlisted by such direct reasonable appeals, but younger children must be motivated to listen by the interest inherent in the activity itself. It is always wise to call for some type of performance to indicate the efficiency of the student's reception of the stimulation.

Sample stimulation techniques for children.

1. Procure a calendar mailing tube or similar device. Hold one end to child's ear as he winds a string upon a spool. The moment the teacher stops making the sound, he must stop winding.

2. The teacher, parents, or classmates act as animals, machines, or objects which produce the sound. The child may be asked to tell a story in which these objects are mentioned, and, whenever he mentions them, the teacher makes the sound. Little dramas may be invented in which the child, for example, pretends to be an automobile with a flat tire in need of air, and the teacher is the station attendant who fills the tire with hissing air.

3. Certain objects are set aside as demanding the hearing of the correct sound before they can be touched. Such rituals appeal to children and compel attention.

4. A secret signal is arranged between the child and the parent or teacher. Whenever the child makes it, the parent or teacher must respond by a prolonged *s* sound.

5. A certain room in the home is set aside as a room which the child cannot enter until he knocks three times and hears the *s* sound.

6. Alliterative sentences using the correct sound in the initial position of most of the words are used as commands or requests. The child performs the activity.

7. Nursery rhymes, jingles, and even tongue twisters may be read to the child.

8. One minute of each hour is set aside as the *s* minute. Some associate of the child must pronounce the sound for a full minute. The child or teacher records the time in a little book.

Sample stimulation techniques for adults or older children.

1. The teacher prolongs or repeats the correct sound, using variations in rhythm or intensity. The student follows the type of stimulation by drawing a continuous line or separate lines on a sheet of paper, using dips to indicate decreases in intensity and crests to show increases. Rhythms may be indicated by spacing.

2. Phonograph records which carry variable durations of the correct

sound can be played.   The student is requested to time each of the durations until he makes a perfect score.

3. The teacher dictates to the student, prolonging all the *s* sounds.

4. The teacher holds a conversation with the student, interjecting the correct sound between all words.

5. Two students, one of whom is the lisper, sit side by side, with their eyes closed.   The teacher produces a prolonged *s* sound as she slowly walks away from them.   They indicate by raising their hands when they can no longer hear the sound.

Identification techniques.   As we have said, it is necessary to make the correct and incorrect sounds very vivid if the child is to learn to discriminate them in his own speech.   The techniques for isolating and recognizing the sounds do a great deal toward this end, but they need to be supplemented by other methods which give the sounds their identities or personalities.   This identification is largely a process of observation of the sound's characteristics, in terms of both audition and mechanics.   It is also a process of association.

Each correct sound and the error must come to have an individuality and an identity.   Many people fail to realize that before we can have discrimination we must have identification.   All good teachers of speech correction give personalities to the sounds with which they work.   They give them names, traits, and even faces.   From such identification comes recognition; from recognition comes discrimination; from discrimination comes success.

Sample identification techniques for children.

1. It is always well to begin the identification by giving names to the correct and incorrect sounds.   These names are frequently those of objects which make noises similar to that of the sound in question.   Thus *th* is called the windmill sound; *s*, the snake or goose sound; *ch*, the train sound; *r*, the growling-dog sound; *k*, the coughing sound; *f*, the spitting-cat sound. Many others are easily invented, for literalness is not nearly so important as repetition of the name.

2. Many teachers of speech correction find it advisable to give faces to certain sounds.   These may be drawn on cards and used for stimuli.   The faces can illustrate some of the more simple mechanics of making the sound. Thus *f* has a face with the upper teeth biting the lower lip; *s* is smiling; *th* is barely protruding a very red tongue; *l* seems to be looking for peanut butter, with his tongue exploring the roof of his mouth.   Mirror work also helps.

3. It is wise to associate the sound with a symbol, either in script or printing.   Children readily understand that the snake sound looks like a snake, and that it is entirely natural for the sound with the lip-biting face

to wear a sweater bearing the monogram *F*. Hiding cards with such symbols around the room and requesting the child to find them, during which time the teacher keeps repeating the sound, will prove useful. So also will be the technique which calls for the child to pick out the symbol, whose sound the teacher speaks, from a pile of cards.

4. Little stories, frequently repeated, about the sounds will often produce associations which will help identify them. No one can tell just what will best identify the sound for any one child, but once the child shows a clear and strong reaction of emotion or curiosity, that association should be remembered.

5. It is not well to get too many traits associated with any one sound. Not the number of traits, but their pertinence, interrelationship, and contrast to the traits of the error give them their value. It is important that the teacher work for close co-ordination of the associations with any one sound. The sound of *s* should bring to mind immediately the snake, the symbol, the smile, and the story of how the snake hissed when the filling-station man turned the air hose on him. It should also bring to mind that the little red tongue is never between the teeth as it is with the *th* sound.

Sample identification techniques for older children and adults.

1. Identification for the adult can also be enhanced by giving names to the correct and incorrect sounds. Thus, for one adult lateral lisper, the correct sound was always referred to as the "whistled hiss," while the incorrect one was called the "old sloppy shush." Derogatory adjectives which need not be truly descriptive are often used. The auditory characteristics of the sound also may give rise to the names used. Consequently, we speak of the "high-pitched" and "low-pitched" *s* sounds, the "whispered *f*," and the "sounded *v*." They may also be identified by names descriptive of the shape of the lips, the position of the tongue, or the use of the nasal opening. The teacher should always bestow some name on both correct and incorrect sounds. Other traits and characteristics of the sound are thereby given a nucleus about which to cluster.

2. Phonetic diagrams, palatograms, and models of the articulatory positions characteristic of the correct sound and the error may be used as identifying agents. The student should be examined in his production of the incorrect sound, and his performance should be described in detail. He should examine the teacher's mouth as the teacher produces the correct sound and the error. Observation in the mirror is also useful. A tongue depressor may be inserted within the mouth to probe and investigate tongue positions. A slender-handled throat mirror may be employed for those sounds in which access to the speech organs is difficult. From all these data, the student should finally attain an integrated picture of what the teacher does when she makes the correct and incorrect sounds. It is often wise to insist that the student write out a complete description of this picture. Even though phonetically accurate descriptions are not obtained, the procedure has identification value.

3. Since adults and older children have associated incorrect sounds with the printed or written symbols, it is often necessary to use nonsense symbols to represent the new sound. All of the characteristics of the correct sound should be associated with this rather than with the old symbol. The student must be taught that his task is to learn a new sound rather than to change an old one, that the new sound has characteristics that he must discover, and that, for the time being, he should use a new symbol to represent this new sound. Typical nonsense symbols for several of the speech sounds will be found in the section of this chapter concerning methods for strengthening new sounds.

Discrimination techniques. The final step in ear training is that of discrimination, and, if the preceding types of ear training have been carried out, it should not be difficult. Discrimination consists of comparing and contrasting the correct and incorrect sounds, both in isolation and in incorporation within regular speech. Selecting, matching, and signaling techniques are used. They are employed even when the student discriminates successfully, for the practice is valuable in itself.

These discrimination techniques frequently call for an ability which many untrained teachers do not possess—the ability to mimic or produce a reasonably accurate imitation of the student's error. While such substitutions as *f* for *v* or *t* for *k* make no great demands upon the teacher's histrionics, the imitation of a lateral lisp, dark *l* or guttural *r* often present great difficulties. Nevertheless, the teacher may be assured that a little practice will soon bring about an approximation so close to the student's error that it will serve well enough for the usual discrimination exercises. In a sense, all preceding steps are pointed at facilitating this auditory discrimination, for it is the essence of the necessary ear training of which we hear so much. Without the ability to differentiate correct sound from error, the student becomes discouraged, the treatment becomes blind drill, and the teacher wishes she had taken up library work.

Sample discrimination devices for children.

1. *Selection.* Show the child an object such as a cake of soap. After a short review of the identifying characteristics of the correct sound and error, the teacher pronounces a series of isolated sounds or nonsense syllables, such as *k, p, th, s, f, r, n, s, f, th,* and requests the child to hand her the object when he hears the sound that starts the word when it is made correctly, but to hide it when he hears the sound that starts it when it is made incorrectly.

2. *Selection.* The teacher and student begin the game with ten tooth-

picks each.   The teacher holds up a series of pictures, one at a time, pronouncing the name of each.   In naming one of the pictures she uses the child's error.   If the child recognizes it, he can demand the picture and one toothpick.   If he fails to recognize it, he loses a picture and toothpick.

3. *Matching*.   The teacher produces two sounds, declaring that they begin words which name objects in the room.   The student is required to find three objects for each sound.

4. *Matching*.   The child is blindfolded and sits with his hands outstretched on the table in front of him.   He is allowed to pull only one hand away at a time.   The teacher names one hand as possessing the correct and the other hand as possessing the incorrect sound.   She then pronounces the sound name of one of the hands, rapping it lightly with a pencil as she does so.   This helps to speed discrimination and the children enjoy it.

5. *Signaling*.   The teacher asks the child to ring a bell and to rap the teacher's hand whenever the teacher uses the wrong sound.   The teacher then tells a story, occasionally using the error.   After every signal the teacher repeats the word correctly.

6. *Signaling*.   The teacher reads a list of *s* words with her back turned to the child.   The moment the child signals, she must pronounce the next word using the incorrect sound.   If she fails, the child gets some small reward.

Sample discrimination devices for older children and adults.

1. *Selection*.   The teacher tells the student that she will pronounce a series of thirty isolated sounds, some of which are correct and some incorrect.   The student is given a sheet of paper on which the thirty numbers are printed and is asked to encircle those numbers in the series on which the teacher used the correct sound.   The teacher then pronounces the sounds and checks up on his discrimination.

2. *Selection*.   The teacher pronounces three nonsense words such as "pa-sa-no-see."   She tells the student that each word will contain two correct sounds, two incorrect sounds, or one correct and one incorrect sound. She teaches the student to recognize the three types, then dictates ten or twenty of them, which he is to write phonetically or in any way he wishes, classifying them according to type.

3. *Matching*.   Using the symbols taught the student in the identification exercises, the teacher dictates a list of words, occasionally using the error.   The student is asked to write down the symbol corresponding to the sound used.

4. *Matching*.   The teacher slowly reads a newspaper article, occasionally using the student's error.   The student is asked to name each correct and incorrect sound, using the names taught in the identification exercises. He must interrupt the teacher to do this naming.

5. *Signaling*.   The student is asked to raise his right hand the moment he hears the correct sound and to raise his left when he hears the error.

The teacher pronounces a series of nonsense syllables, slowly at first, but with a gradual increase of speed.

6. *Signaling.* The teacher reads tongue twisters, occasionally using the error. The student is asked to rap on the table the moment he hears the error. If his response does not occur until after the teacher has said the next two words, he has failed. The procedure is continued until he collects five successes.

Besides these selecting, matching, and signaling devices, it is advisable to use a little direct comparison of the right and wrong pronunciations of common words, whether one is working with children or adults. Some such sequence as this is used: The teacher imitates the child as he says the word. Then the child says it. The teacher points out the similarity. Then the teacher says it correctly and very clearly, pointing out the contrast. The contrasts and similarities are put in the identifying terms previously used.

Methods for Teaching a New Sound

After the speech defective has been given a well-planned and thorough course of ear training, during which he has made no attempt to produce the correct sound, he is ready for the next step. The goal of this next step is the ability to make the correct sound by itself and apart from its usual context in familiar words. Remedial work must be continued until he can make the sound whenever he wishes. He must be able to produce it consistently and at will. There are a great many methods whereby a new sound can be taught: the stimulation method, the phonetic placement method, the modification of other standard sounds or biological functions, the babbling method with identification of chance production of the sound, and the method which uses a few words or imitative sounds in which the usually defective sound is made correctly. Each of these will now be described in detail.

Stimulation method. This method, which is the simplest and easiest, depends upon the preliminary ear training for its value. It should be tried first, for a sound taught by this method is much more stable and permanent than a sound acquired by one of the other methods. In a sense, it may be said that this is the natural method of sound acquisition. The baby hears and discriminates sounds. He is stimulated intensively by them. He listens. Then he makes the attempt, and lo!—he has produced the correct sound. In a similar fashion, when the teacher feels that the student has been given adequate ear training, she goes through a brief review of some of the isolation, identification, stimulation, and discrimination techniques and concludes with a request similar to this:

TEACHER: Now, Johnny, I'm going to let you have your first chance to make the snake sound, *sss*. Remember not to make the windmill sound, *th-th*. This is the sound you are to make: *sss, sss, ssssss*. Now you try it.

If the ear training has been adequate, this simple routine, in which the wrong sound is pronounced, identified, and rejected, then followed by the correct sound given several times, will bring a perfect production of the correct sound on the first attempt. Occasionally it will be necessary to repeat this routine several times before it works, and the student should be encouraged to take his time and to listen carefully both to the stimulation and to his response. He should be told that he has made an error or that he has almost made it correctly. He should then be encouraged to attempt it in a slightly different way the next time. No pressure should be brought to bear upon him, and a review of discrimination, stimulation, and identification techniques should preface the new attempt. He should be asked to make it quietly and without force. The procedure may be slightly varied by asking the child to produce it in a whisper. After the sound has been produced, the teacher should signal the child to repeat or prolong it and to sense the "feel" of it. The attempt should be confined to the isolated sound itself or to a nonsense syllable beginning with it. This stimulation method will produce excellent results in all but a very few cases, and it should always be tried thoroughly before the other methods are used.

Phonetic placement method. The phonetic placement method of enabling a speech defective to produce a new sound is the old traditional method. For centuries, speech correctionists have used diagrams, applicators, and instruments to ensure appropriate tongue, jaw, and lip placement. Children have been asked to watch the teacher's tongue movements and to duplicate them. Observation of the teacher's mouth in a mirror has also been used. Many very ingenious devices have been invented to adapt these techniques for children, and often they produce almost miraculous results. Unfortunately, however, the mechanics of such phonetic placement demand so much attention that they cannot be performed quickly or unconsciously enough for the needs of casual speech. At best, they are vague and difficult to sense or recall. The positions tend to vary with the sounds that precede or follow them, and to teach all of these positions is an almost impossible task. Frequently dental abnormalities will make an exact reproduction of the standard position inadvisable. Many speech correctionists produce the sounds in nonstandard ways, if, indeed, there is a standard way of producing any given speech sound. Despite all of these disadvantages, the phonetic placement methods are indispensable tools in the speech correctionist's kit, and, when the stimulation method fails, they must be used. They are especially useful in working with individuals with hearing defects, and they certainly help to identify the sound.

Excellent diagrams and descriptions of the various speech sounds may be found in the texts by Koepp-Baker, Mosher, Borden and Busse, and West, Kennedy and Carr, to which references are given at the end of this chapter. The speech correctionist should have these texts available and should know the mechanics of articulation thoroughly enough to interpret the diagrams and assume the positions illustrated and described. The teacher should be able to recognize any sound from its description and diagram.

In using methods of phonetic placement, it is necessary that the speech defective be given a clear idea of the desired position prior to speech attempt. If an adult, he should study diagrams, the teacher's articulatory organs in position, when observed both directly and in a mirror, palatograms, models, and the written descriptions of the mechanics whereby the sound is produced. Every available device should be used to make the student understand clearly what positions of tongue, jaws, and lips are to be assumed. It is frequently advisable to have the student practice other sounds that he can make easily, using diagrams and printed descriptions to guide his placement. This will familiarize him with the technique of translating diagrams and descriptions into performance.

Various instruments and applicators are used to help the student attain the proper position. Tongue depressors are used to hold the tip and front of the tongue down, as in the attempt to produce a k or g, or they may be used to touch certain portions of the tongue and palate to indicate positions of mutual contact. Tooth props of various sizes will help the student to assume a proper dental opening. Thin applicators and wedges are used to groove the tongue. Curious wire contrivances are occasionally used to insure lateral contact of tongue and teeth.   Small tubes are used to direct the flow of air.   The texts by Borden and Busse and by Scripture provide examples of these instruments.   In our experience, they are more dramatic than useful. Enforcing a certain tongue position through some such device pro- duces such a mass of kinesthetic and tactual sensations that the ap-

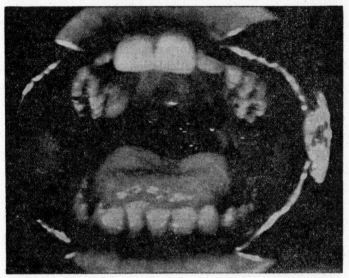

Courtesy of Dr. Kurt von Frowine

Fig. 6.   Photograph of the mouth of a child who had suffered a severe lye burn.   The tongue is being lifted as high as possible.   Despite the handi- cap, the child had learned compensatory movements sufficient to give him perfect speech.

propriate ones can seldom be attended to.   Usually, the moment the instrument is removed the old, incorrect tongue position is assumed, because, as Travis [2] puts it:

If a child used *p* for *f* from pressing the lips too tightly together, a thick stick or finger was stuck between the lips so that they could not close tightly.   As far as the child is concerned, he is still making *p* regardless of whether a stick or finger was stuck between the lips or not.   A sound cannot be broken up into its component parts, as into lip movements or tongue movements.   It is a unit, a whole, and can be learned only as such.

If these devices and instruments have any real value, it seems to be that of vivifying the movements of the tongue, and of providing a

---

[2] Travis, L. E., *Speech Pathology*, New York, D. Appleton-Century Co., 1931, page 193.

large number of varying tongue positions, from which the correct one
may finally emerge. Many individuals have difficulty in realizing
how great a repertoire of tongue movements they possess, and instruments frequently enable them to attempt new ones.

Tongue exercises. The same result may be attained through various articulation exercises. Although the value of tongue, lip, and jaw
exercises has been questioned and denied by many workers in the field
of speech correction, they can be said to be useful in teaching the student to manipulate his articulatory apparatus in many new and un-
accustomed ways. Too many articulation cases have only one or two
stereotyped tongue movements in their speech repertoire, although
they may have many more in their functions of swallowing, laughing,
chewing, or sneezing. They need to learn how adaptable the tongue
really is. Whenever possible, the articulatory exercises given should
proceed out of the movements used in the biological functions or in
babbling. The old, formal tongue exercises are of much less value.

When the correct sound has been produced (and frequently a lot
of trial and error must be resorted to before it appears), the speech
defective should hold it, increasing its intensity, repeating it, whispering it, exaggerating it, and varying it in as many ways as possible
without losing its identity. He should focus his attention on the
"feel" of the position in terms of tongue, palate, jaws, lips, and throat.
He should listen to the sound produced. Then he should be asked to
leave the position intact but to cease speech attempt, resuming it after
a long interval. Finally he should let the tongue assume a neutral
position on the floor of the mouth and then attempt to regain the desired position. Sounds produced by phonetic placement are very unstable and must be treated very carefully or they will be lost.
Strengthen them as soon as possible and keep out distractions. After
a successful attempt, one should insist that the student remain silent
for a time before taking part in conversation. This will permit
maturation to become effective.

Modification of other sounds. Another special method of teaching
a speech defective a new sound is that which involves the modification
of other sounds, either those of speech, those that imitate noises, or
those that imitate other functions, such as swallowing. These methods
are somewhat akin to those of phonetic placement, but they have the
advantage of using a known sound or movement as a point of departure
for the trial-and-error variation which produces the correct sound.
The modification method may take many forms, but in all of them the

sequence is about the same. The student is asked to make a certain sound and to hold it for a short period. He is then requested to move his tongue or his lips or jaws in a definite manner while continuing to produce his first sound. This variation in articulators will produce a change in the sound, a change which often rather closely approximates the sound that is desired. An illustration of this method may be given. A lateral lisper is told to make the *th* sound and to prolong it. Then, while continuing to make the sound, he is required to draw in the tonguetip slowly and to raise the whole tongue, slowly scrape its tip upward along the back of the upper teeth, and finally bring it to rest against the alveolar ridge. The *th* sound will change as the tongue rises, and a rather good approximation to the desired *s* will be produced. If this is combined with ear training and stimulation, it will be found to be very effective.

There are many of these modification methods, and each speech-correction teacher invents others. The student should go through the references given at the end of this chapter and collect examples appropriate to each of the commonly defective sounds for his notebook. The text by Nemoy and Davis is especially useful in this regard. Most of these techniques have been used by all speech correctionists for decades, and they are part of the standard equipment of any worker in the field.

We shall now provide some supplementary methods for getting the articulation case to produce the correct sound. The student should be warned not to use them indiscriminately. They have value only in their ability to get the child to make the sound in a new way, in varying his attack on the desired sound. The essential task remains the same: to give the articulatory case a clear auditory, kinesthetic, and tactual picture of the sound.

S *and* Z *Sounds*

1. Have the child protrude the tongue between the teeth so as to produce the sound *th* for the beginning of such words as *saw*, *glass*, and *rose*. Have him think of *th*. Then when he is thinking of producing the *th* for the *s*, force the tip of his tongue inward with a thin instrument such as a thick blunt toothpick. The result will be an *s*. The principle involved is that the child's thinking the *th* drives the air over the tip of the tongue. The value of directing the child's attention to the tip of his tongue when he is producing sibilant sounds is that he will eventually feel the current of air being emitted over it.

2. Have the child protrude the tongue as in the preceding exercise, and

form the sound of *th*; but as this is formed, have him slowly and gradually withdraw the tongue and, while still attempting to make the *th*, scrape the tonguetip along the back of the front teeth and upward. The result will again be an *s*, which he should be asked to match with the *s* produced by the instructor until an adjustment is made which gives an excellent lispless *s*.

3. Have the child begin by forming a *t* in a word like *tea*. Have him pronounce it with a strong aspiration (*tuh-hee*), with a strong puff of breath after the explosion of the *t*, before the vowel begins. Then, instead of this sudden explosion or puff, take away the tip of the tongue from the teeth-ridge slowly. This will give the sound *ts*. Hold onto this sound and you will have the *s-s-s-s*. The child must not think he is saying *ts* as in the word *oats* or he will use his usual pronunciation. Keep him rehearsing the steps of this procedure till they are fixed in his mind, before showing him that he is making a good *s*.

4. Have the child hiss, seeking to raise the pitch of the hiss until it approximates that held by the instructor. Often it is wise to tell the student to experiment with the tonguetip positions during the production of his hiss, not before. Sometimes, the instructor should change his hiss from the faulty one used by the student through several degrees until the correct *s* is made.

5. Have the child go through some brisk tongue exercises with special stress paid to the grooving of the tongue. The tongue should be grooved and protruded and the air should be blown through this groove. From this protruding position the tongue should be drawn back slowly while the blowing is continued, concentrating the attention meanwhile on the tip of the tongue. Sometimes use a thin stick or instrument to help the groove.

6. If the child can make a good *z* sound, take such a word as *zero* and ask him to listen carefully and to feel where his tongue is when he whispers it, prolonging the first sound. This is the sound which must become the child's model.

7. Put upper and lower teeth together. Ask child to stroke (with tongue) the back of his upper teeth as he blows a stream of air.

8. Put upper and lower teeth together and press lips tightly together. Keep teeth together but part lips to let a small hiss escape.

K *or* G *Sound*

1. Ask child to repeat the sequence *puh-tuh-kuh* in unison with the teacher. Teacher should give several samples first.

2. Ask child to imitate the teacher as she coughs up an imaginary wishbone in this fashion, *kuh-kuh*.

3. Ask child to anchor tongue against lower teeth and hold hand in front of his mouth so he can feel the puff of air as he imitates his teacher.

4. If the child can make the *ng* sound, ask him to do so and then give a little puff of air against his hand or a feather held in front of his mouth.

5. Ask the child to say *uhkuh* in a strong whisper.

6. Explore the child's vocabulary to see if he can say any word in which

the word ends with a good *k* sound.   Then ask him to repeat many times and repeat last sound, imitating teacher, thus: *sick-kuh-kuh.*

7. If child can say "guh" ask him to whisper it because the "(k_Λ) is a whispered (g_Λ)."

8. Press underneath child's chin and ask him to say *kuh* in a whisper as you release the pressure suddenly.

9. Tell the child of two Australian birds, one a big one who has a long tongue that moves up and down and who always says *tee-tee-tee* and the other who doesn't have any tongue at all that you can see move and who always says *ook-ook-ook.*   Ask the child to imitate both birds.

L *Sound*

1. Give strong stimulation through humming or singing the nonsense syllables *lay, lee, lie,* then ask child to hum or sing.

2. Give tongue-lifting and -lowering exercises, first in silence, then while blowing, then while whispering *ah,* then while saying *ah.*   Gradually lift tongue higher and higher until it finally makes the contact at the right place.

3. Form mouth for *ah.*   Keep whispering it softly as you place tongue in firm contact with upper gum ridge.   Then suddenly say the "ah" loudly as the tongue is released and a long *l* is subsequently made.

4. Practice this sequence very swiftly: *tah-dah-nah-lah.*

5. With a match or tongue depressor stroke the back of the upper gum ridge until child touches it with tongue.   Ask him to stroke the spot with his tongue.   Ask him to stroke it as he says *ee.*

6. Practice making the sound using a mirror and a wide-open mouth.

SH *Sound*

1. Tell the child to round his lips and flatten his cheeks and "sluch" the air out between his teeth.

2. Ask the child to make an *s* sound and pull back the base of tongue with a pencil stuck between the teeth.

3. Ask child to make a *th,* then to pull back the tongue, shutting the teeth and continuing to blow.

4. Ask child to whisper an *er* sound, holding it for some time during which he gradually brings his teeth together.

5. Ask child to round lips and raise tongue and shut teeth as he whispers a prolonged *ee.*

6. Put spoon in mouth, rim up.   Ask child to shut teeth over handle and to produce the *sh* sound.

7. If child can say "measure" have him whisper it and prolong the sound.

8. If child can make the *ch* sound, have him "let it leak out," prolonging it rather than releasing it suddenly.

9. During the production of an *s* sound, pull tongue one-half inch toward the back of the mouth.

F *and* V

Tell the child that today he is to have his first chance to make the new sound. Then say, "Now watch me. See how I bite my lower lip. Can you bite your lip in the same way? Now let's look at ourselves in this mirror. Don't bite hard, just lay the teeth on the lower lip. See how I do it? Now let's hold our mouths like that and suck in some air. All right. Now, don't move your mouth but blow some air out, like this, *f-f-f-* [give strong stimulation]. Now do it again and make this sound in a whisper *fuh, fffuh, fffuh*." Give child a little rest then some new trials. Then have him say *fuh* whenever you raise a finger. Spend some time talking about the new and old sounds, showing him how they differ. Tell him that the new sound may feel wrong but that it "sounds" right, and that he must *listen* rather than feel.

1. Ask child to hold lower lip against upper teeth, with a finger laid crosswise, then to blow.

2. Ask child to smile broadly as he tries the sound.

3. Have child bite far down beyond the upper lip (toward the chin) as he blows.

4. By holding a feather against the mouth, show child that *p* is a puff of air while *f* or *v* is a gradual stream of air.

R *Sound*

1. Ask child to say *l*. Then with the depressor gently push the tip of the tongue back until you can insert the depressor between the tip and teeth-ridge or until *r* sound results.

2. If this fails and the child can say *z*, ask him to make the sound and continue it while the jaw is dropped until the teeth are separated about one inch or until *r* results.

3. Have the child imitate you as you trill the tonguetip. Then use this trill to precede the vowel $\bar{ee}$.

4. Spread the sides of the child's mouth with your fingers; ask him to produce a prolonged *n* sound, then to curl the end of his tongue backward as he continues making the sound.

CH (tʃ) *Sound*

1. If child is able to make the *t* sound and the *sh* sound separately, these sounds can be combined to make a good *ch*. The *ch* sound is a combination of these two sounds. Have the child form his teeth and tongue as for the *t* sound, and then say the *sh* sound instead. You might also have him say *she* by first forming the *t*.

2. Tell the child to pretend to sneeze. Often a child who cannot follow instructions about tongue and lip formation will make a perfect *ch* sound this way. Playing train, and saying *ch-ch-ch* like an engine may work, too.

3. Have the child prolong *sh* as though to tell someone to be quiet. When you signal by clapping or raising a finger from the table, have him

quickly touch the gum of the roof of his mouth, and then go right on with *sh*. This will produce a prolonged *sh* with a *ch* in the middle.

The babbling method. This method for producing the desired speech sound is probably as close as any method to the one used by the child in learning to talk. Its greatest disadvantage is its lack of economy, for much time is needed to teach the student to throw off his inhibitions and to babble thoroughly at random. Most students resent this procedure and must be convinced of its utility before they will consent to give up their dignity and attempt it. It is usually wise to outline in advance the purpose and type of babbling desired. Both the teacher and the student should babble in unison. They should relax, get the babbling started, and then let it continue almost automatically, ranging where it will. For the first several periods, no attempt should be made to notice the sounds produced or to look for the sound desired. Random vocalization should be the goal for the time being.

After the student seems to be babbling adequately, the teacher should cease intermittently, and, finally, allow the student to babble alone. Then, when the teacher gives a prearranged signal, the student should repeat the sound being used at the time the signal occurred. He should repeat it over and over. In this type of babbling, the speech defective makes all the speech sounds, even those which he cannot make voluntarily or in words. The teacher's task is to get the student to select, out of the complex hodgepodge of vocalization, the sound which he has difficulty in making, to focus his attention upon it, and to make it voluntarily. The sounds attained by this method are very unstable and must be strengthened immediately.

Using words in which the usually defective sound is made correctly. As we have seen, one of the items in both the voice and articulation tests requires the examiner to record all words in which the usually defective sound is made correctly. Many teachers of speech correction fail to realize the value of these words in remedial work. They may be used to enable the student to make the correct sound at will and in isolation. They are also extremely valuable in getting the student to make clean-cut transitions between the isolated sound and the rest of the word. Finally, they serve as standards of correctness of sound performance. Speech defectives need some standard with which to compare their speech attempts at correct production of the usually defective sound. Although occasional cases are found who never make the sound correctly, the majority of speech defectives have a few words in which they do not make the error. The teacher should be alert enough to catch these when they do occur. Often these words are those which have the usually defective sound in an inconspicuous place—that is to say, the sound occurs in the medial or final position, or is incorporated within a blend; seldom is it found in an accented syllable. The teacher must train her ear to listen for it in the student's speech or it will escape her. At times it occurs in words in which an unusual spelling provides a different symbol for the sound. To illustrate: A child who was unable to make a good *f* in any of his words using that printed symbol, said the word *rough* with a perfect *f* sound. This was probably due to the strong stimulation given by the child's spelling teacher.

These words are worth the trouble needed to discover them, for they simplify the teacher's work tremendously, since it is possible to use that sound as a standard and guide and to work from it to other words in which error normally occurs. The experienced teacher greets these nuclei words as veritable nuggets. Similarly, even when the student is highly consistent in his errors, there comes a stage in his treatment when he is saying a few words correctly. These words may be used to serve the same ends as those mentioned in the preceding paragraph.

The procedure used in this method is roughly as follows: The teacher writes the word on one of several cards (or uses a picture representing it). Then she asks the student to go through the series one at a time, saying the word on each card ten times. Finally, the special word to be used is repeated a hundred times, accenting, and prolonging if possible, the sound which in other words is made incorrectly. Thus the lingual lisper who could say *lips* correctly repeated the word one hundred times, prolonging the *s*. He was then asked to hold it for a count of twenty, then thirty, then forty. Finally, he was required to hold it intermittently, thus; *lipssss.ssss..sss*. The purpose of such a gradual approach is that the sound must be emphasized in both its auditory and its motor characteristics to prevent its loss when the student becomes aware of it as his hard sound. For example, one baby talker made the initial *r* in *rabbit* perfectly until told that he did. Immediately the child changed to the *w* substitution and was unable to make the initial *r* again.

After the child has emphasized the sound a large number of times, has listened to it and felt it thoroughly, and can make it intermittently and in a repetitive form, he may be asked to think the word and to speak the sound. It is often wise to underline the sound to be spoken, asking the student to whisper all but the letter underlined. Other sounds and other words may be similarly underlined if a careful approach is necessary. Through these means, the child finally can make the sound in isolation and at will.

Strengthening the New Sound

One of the greatest causes for discouragement in treating an articulatory case may be traced to the parent's or teacher's ignorance of a very important fact. A new sound is weak and unstable. Its mechanics are easily forgotten or lost. Its dual phases of auditory and motor sensation patterns are easily confused. Many people believe that a complicated skill (such as that involved in a speech sound) once achieved is never lost, although any musician or tennis player will tell us that a new stroke or fingering sequence must be practiced and strengthened a great deal before it can be used in competition or composition. Many speech-correction teachers become discouraged and blame the speech defective for his frequent relapse into error or his sudden loss of the sound he had been taught to make. Many children who can make the correct sound at will never learn to incorporate it within familiar words. All of these unfortunate occurrences are due to the fact that a new sound must be strengthened before it can win the competition which the error provides in the speaking of common words. A lisper who has said "yeth" for "yes" several thousand times cannot be expected to say the latter as soon as he has learned to make the sss sound in isolation. Perhaps that sound has been performed only three or four times. Yet parents and teachers constantly ruin all of their preliminary work by saying some such sentence as this: "Fine, Johnny. That was fine! You said sss just as plainly as anyone. Now say 'sssoup.' " And Johnny, ninety-nine times out of one hundred, will say triumphantly, "thoup." Most speech correctionists have to train themselves to resist this urge to hurry. When the child has been taught to make the new sound, the utmost patience and restraint are needed. Careful strengthening of the sound will pay dividends in progress, and it is wise to practice the sound in nonsense material for some time even with those cases who can make a quick transition to familiar material. Otherwise, certain sound combinations will always present trouble. If there is one principle in speech correction more important than any other, it is this: strengthen every new sound before it is used in familiar words.

There are two main types of techniques used for strengthening a new sound: those using the sound by itself, in isolation, and those using the sound in nonsense material. Included under the first classification are prolongation, repetition, exaggeration, attending to kinesthesia, shortening initiation time, inclusion in babbling, and simultaneous talking-and-writing. Included in the second classification are the methods which use nonsense syllables, symbols, and names, and those which employ signal practice and other transitional techniques. Although no one case will ever require all of the techniques, we shall describe some of them under each heading. All cases should be given some strengthening technique of each type.

Techniques for strengthening the new sound in isolation. In general, it is advisable to use these techniques before those employing nonsense material. As we have said, after the new sound has been obtained, it should be repeated and prolonged immediately. During this repetition and prolongation, the student should be told to keep a poker face and to move as little as possible. A sudden shift of body position occasionally produces a change in the movements of articulation as well. As soon as the new sound tends to lose its clear characteristics, the teacher should insist upon some rest and should then review the procedure used to produce the sound. Rest should be silent in order to let maturation take place. Little intensity should be used, and when working with a pair of sounds, such as *s* and *z*, the unvoiced sound is preferable. Often sounds such as *l* and *r* should be whispered or sung.

After the speech defective is able to produce the sound readily and can repeat and prolong it consistently, the teacher can ask him to increase its intensity and exaggerate it. He should be asked to focus his attention on the "feel" of the tongue, lips, and palate. Shutting his eyes will help him to get a better awareness of the tactual and kinesthetic sensations thereby produced. Ask him to assume the position without speech attempt and, after a short period of "feeling," to try the sound. Many other supplementary devices will occur to the teacher.

After the student reaches the stage where he has little difficulty in producing the new sound, he should be encouraged to shorten the time needed to produce it. A sound which the student takes too long to produce will never become habitual. This speeding up of the time needed to initiate it may be accomplished by demanding fast repetitions, by alternating it with other isolated speech sounds, and by using signals. In this last activity, the student should keep his articulatory apparatus in a state of rest or in certain other positions, such as an open mouth, and then, at a certain sharp-sound signal, he should react by producing the new sound immediately.

One of the most effective methods for strengthening a new sound is to include it in babbling. The babbling should be initiated in the manner described in the preceding section, and the student should attempt to incorporate the new sound within the vocal flow as effortlessly as possible. It should not stand out and there should be no pausing before it. Doublings of the sound should be frequent. These babbling periods should be continued daily throughout the course of treatment.

The most important of all strengthening devices is the use of simultaneous talking-and-writing. In this procedure, the student writes the script symbol as he pronounces the sound. The sound should be timed so that it will neither precede nor follow the writing of the symbol, but will coincide exactly with the dominant stroke of the letter. Since this dominant stroke varies somewhat with different persons, some experimentation will be needed. At first, the teacher should supervise this talking-and-writing very carefully to ensure clear vocalization of the new sound and proper timing. Later, the student can be assigned to hand in several pages of this talking-and-writing every day. The continuant sounds should be pronounced by themselves (*sss, vvv, lll, mmm*), and the stops should use a lightly vocalized neutral vowel (*kuh, puh, duh*). Simultaneous talking-and-writing techniques not only provide an excellent vehicle for practice of the new sound, but also give a means of reinforcing it by enriching the motor aspect of the performance. They also improve the identification, and, as we shall see, make possible an effective transition to familiar words. For children who cannot write, the sound may be tied up with a movement such as a finger twitch or foot tap. In this case, as in writing, the timing is very important.

Strengthening the new sound through use of nonsense material. The second group of strengthening techniques includes those which use nonsense syllables, symbols, and names. It is obvious that such material provides a very effective means of practicing the new sound in all of its various combinations with other sounds. The student meets none of the competition which the error produces in speaking familiar

words.   He need not add to the speech attempt the burden of rejecting the error.   Fewer confusions arise.   New sound sequences are
strengthened, and new articulatory co-ordinations are learned.

The first type of nonsense material to be considered is the nonsense
syllable.   These syllables can be readily constructed by combining
the new sound with the fourteen most common vowels and diphthongs.
The first nonsense syllables to be practiced are those in which the
transitional movements from consonant to vowel involve the fewest
and simplest co-ordinations.   For example, *ko* involves less radical

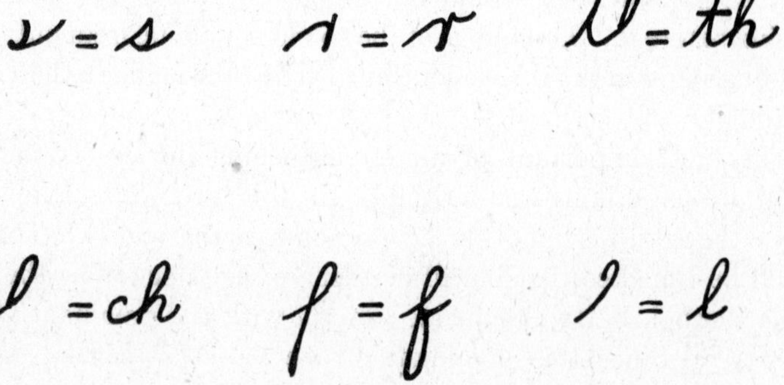

Fig. 7.   Typical nonsense symbols used in talking-and-writing exercises
for articulatory cases.

transitional movements than does *kee*.   The next nonsense syllables
should be those which use the new sound in the final position (*ok*),
and, finally, those in which the new sound is located in the medial
position (*oko*) should be practiced.   Double nonsense syllables may
also be used, but simple doublings are preferred (*kaka*).

These nonsense syllables should be practiced thoroughly before
familiar words are attempted.   The talking-and-writing technique
can be used to facilitate their production if any difficulty is experienced.   The student should speak the new sound as he writes the
symbol until he gets to the end of the line, then should add the vowel,
thus: *s s s s s s saaa*.   Signal practice, such as that described later
in this section, can also be used to form the nonsense syllable if it
is needed.   Generally, however, a simple request by the teacher to
repeat the nonsense syllable he pronounces will produce the desired
results.   This repetition from a model is the usual way in which the
syllables are used.   They may also be written by the teacher and read
by the student.   They may be used to precede each sentence of con-

versation or used as substitutes for such words as *the* or *and*. Lists of them may be used for practice, and all the various vowel combinations should be employed. The student should practice them finally at high speeds.

Although most young children have no difficulty in using the standard letter symbol for the sound in these nonsense syllables or talking-and-writing, many adults and some young children who have read and written the letter while pronouncing it incorrectly will have

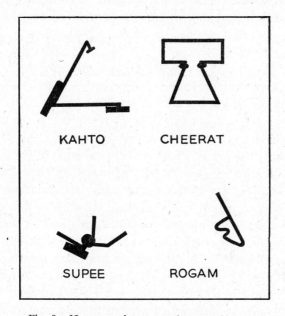

KAHTO   CHEERAT

SUPEE   ROGAM

Fig. 8. Nonsense pictures used to provide names which children with articulatory defects can learn to pronounce more easily than familiar words.

difficulty. The letter *s*, for example, means *th* to such a lisper, and he cannot use the usual syllables in talking-and-writing. For these cases, it is wise to use a nonsense symbol in place of the standard letter. In general, the symbols should be parts of the standard symbols, though the student should not realize this fact until later. These symbols should be used for identification techniques and for all strengthening techniques. After the student has finally begun to use them in regular words, he may be shown that the nonsense symbol is really a part of the true symbol for the sound.

It is also advisable to use nonsense names and meanings to provide new words in which the new sound can be incorporated. The fingers and toes may be given nonsense names. The doorknob may be christened. The teacher can make nonsense objects out of modeling clay, giving them names which include the new sound. Nonsense pictures may be drawn and named. Card games using these nonsense pictures seem to be peculiarly fascinating to almost all cases. Through talking-and-writing techniques, repetition from a model, reading, conversation, questioning, and speech games, these nonsense names can be used repeatedly. The various sound combinations are thereby practiced, and remarkable progress will soon occur. Examples of some of the nonsense pictures are given in Figure 8.

Making the Transition to Familiar Words

After the new sound has been strengthened sufficiently, the speech defective may attempt to use it in familiar words. If the preliminary work has been done carefully, there will be little difficulty, even though this is probably the most difficult and critical stage of the whole treatment. The teacher must always keep in mind that the speech defective has said these words in the wrong way thousands of times and that these words are units which include the error as a part of them. In retraining, we do not merely substitute one sound for another. We build new words, new configurations. The student must unlearn the old and learn the new. This process involves many techniques, among which the following may be cited: training in reconfiguring, signal practice, transitional techniques, and talking-and-writing.

Reconfiguration techniques. Frequently the reconfiguration techniques must be carried out rather gradually. Their purpose is to teach the individual that words are made up of sound sequences and that these sound sequences can be modified without losing the unity of the word. If, for convenience, we use a lingual lisper as our example, the reconfiguration techniques would follow somewhat the same sequence: (1) The student reads, narrates, and converses with the teacher, substituting the sound of b for that of f whenever the latter occurs in the initial position. He reads, for example, that "Sammy caught a bish with his hook and line." The purpose of using these nonerror sounds is to make a gradual approach. (2) The student substitutes his new sound for other sounds, but not for the error. Thus: "Sammy sssaught a fish with his hoos and line." (3) The student substitutes another sound for the s in the same material. Thus:

"Bammy caught a fish with his hook and line." (4) The student omits the *s* in all words beginning with it. Thus: "—ammy caught a fish with his hook and line." (5) The student "substitutes" his new sound for the *s*. Thus: "Ssssammy caught a fish with his hook and line." Many similar techniques are easily invented. It may seem to the young speech correctionist that such techniques are far too laborious and detailed. But, after he has met with persistent error in his articulatory cases, he will appreciate the fact that careful and thorough training will produce a thoroughgoing and permanent freedom from error. Sketchy and slipshod training will enable a speech defective to make the correct sound and perhaps to use it in a few words when he watches himself carefully, but this is far from the goal that should be set. Too many speech-correction teachers have blamed the student for failure when they should have blamed themselves.

Signal practice. There are several other methods of getting the student to use the new sound in familiar words, but one of the most effective may be called signal practice. In this, the student prolongs or repeats the new sound and then, at a given signal, instantly says the prearranged vowel or the rest of the word. The student should be given a preparatory set to pronounce the rest of the word by preliminary signal practice. During this practice he waits with his eyes closed until he hears the sound signal which sets off the response. Thus, during the student's prolongation of *sssssss*, the instructor suddenly raps on the table, and the syllable *oup* is automatically produced. With a preparatory set, the response is largely automatic and involuntary, and thus the new sound is integrated within the word as a whole. Often it is wise to require the student to say the word twice. Thus: *sssssss*(rap)*oupsoup*. Signal practice can also be used with repetition. Thus: *kuh-kuh-*(rap)*atkat*. After some training with this type of signal practice, the student may use other signals, such as those provided by the timing of a rhythm. Thus: *s-s, s-s-soup* or *s-s-soup, s-s-soup*. The student may also be required to repeat over and over some nonsense syllable which he can make well, suddenly saying the new word when the signal is given. Thus: *ssi-ssi-ssi-ssi* (rap) *ssip*. The nonsense syllable and the new word may also be used alternately. The isolated sound may be used in the above exercises in place of the nonsense syllable. Various other combinations may easily be invented.

Simultaneous talking-and-writing. The simultaneous talking-and-writing techniques previously described will be invaluable if used properly. The student should talk-and-write the symbol alone for one line, and then, on the next line, talk-and-write the first letter, the first syllable, and, finally, the whole word. Thus: *s s s s s s s s s s; s si sick s si sick*, and so on. Later he can alternate the symbol and the word, and finally he can write only the symbol as he says the word. Assignments can be given for home practice. Frequently such a gradual approach is not necessary, and the student need write only the symbol and say any *s* word.

At times, difficulty will be experienced in making the transitions into the words. The student will say *rwabbit* and be confident that he has pronounced the word correctly. The error must be brought to his attention by the teacher's imitation and by the student's voluntary production of the error. Signal practice will help a great deal to eliminate this error.

Another invaluable technique is provided by a signal used in a slightly different way. The student is asked to form his mouth for the vowel which begins the rest of the word; *i.e.*, for the vowel *a* in *rabbit*. He may whisper a prolongation of this vowel. Then, at a given signal, he is to say *rabbit* as swiftly as possible. This preformation of the vowel will often solve the problem. Similarly, the practice of pairs of words, the first ending in the vowel of the second, will be effective. Using pairs of words in which the first word ends with the new sound and the second begins with the same sound is occasionally useful, although the student should be cautioned to keep out all breaks of continuity.

Still another method of eliminating this error is to use some nonsense symbol to represent the part of the word which follows the new sound. Thus, one individual was asked to say *oup* every time he wrote a question mark (?), and, after ten minutes of this, he was told to read the following symbols, *t?*, *kr?*, and *s?*. The last symbol was pronounced *soup* rather than *sthoup*, and no further difficulty was experienced.

How to Get the Child to Use the New Sound Consistently

One of the most important steps in the treatment of both articulatory and voice disorders is getting the child to use the new sound consistently in his daily conversation. It is not enough merely to teach the child how to make the correct sound; he must follow a systematic program of effecting the transition into casual speech.

Such a program should include, first of all, definite speech periods at school and at home, during which the child uses speech primarily for correction purposes. These periods should be short, varied, and well motivated. Such a program should also include the use of speech assignments in outside situations; the use of checking devices and penalties; the use of negative practice; and the use of persons, words, and situations as nuclei of good speech. Each of these activities is outlined in the paragraphs which follow.

Some suggested activities for school and home speech periods are:

(1) Making and using scrapbooks or flash cards wherein the pictures represent words containing the sound on which the child is working. (2) Hiding word or picture cards about the room, and requiring the child to say the word correctly until he finds the proper card. (3) Reading passages in which words containing defective sound are underlined. (4) Teacher or parent uses error in his speech, asking child to correct him. (5) Child writes new word containing defective sound on calendar each day. (6) Use of jingles and sentences in which particular sound is emphasized.

Other speech games and activities can be readily devised by anyone truly interested in the child.

Speech assignments. Some typical speech assignments to illustrate methods for getting the child to work on his errors in outside situations are:

(1) Go downstairs and ask the janitor for a dust rag. Be sure to say *rag* with a good long *rrr*. (2) Say the word *rabbit* to three other children without letting them know that you are working on your speech. (3) Ask your father if you said any word wrongly after you tell him what you did in school today.

The teacher should always make these assignments very definite and appropriate to the child's ability and environment. He should always ask for a report the next day. Such assignments frequently are the solution to any lack of motivation the child may have.

Checking devices and penalties. Checking devices and penalties are of great value when properly used. Typical checking devices are:

(1) Having child carry card and crayon during geography recitation, making a mark or writing the word whenever he makes an error. (2) Having some other child check errors in a similar fashion. (3) Having child transfer marbles from one pocket to another, one for each error. Many other devices may be invented, and they will bring the error to consciousness very rapidly.

Similarly, penalties are of great service, when used properly. It should be realized, however, that painful and highly emotional penalties should not be used, for they merely make the bad habit more pronounced and cause the child to hate his speech work. Penalties used in speech correction should be vivid and good natured. Typical penalties used with a 10-year-old lisper were: put pencil behind ear; step in wastebasket; pound pan; look between legs; close one eye; say *whoopee*. Let the child set his own penalties before he makes the speech attempt.

Nucleus situations. Many parents and teachers make the mistake of correcting the child whenever he makes speech errors. It is unwise to set the speech standards too high. No one can watch himself all the time, and we all hate to be nagged. As a matter of fact, too much vigilance by the speech defective can produce such speech inhibitions that the speech work becomes thoroughly distasteful. Fluency disappears and the speech becomes very halting and unpleasant. Then, too, the very anxiety lest error occur, when carried to the extreme, seems to be able to increase the number of slips and mistakes themselves. Other errors sometimes appear.

Therefore, we recommend that the parents and teachers of the speech defective concentrate their reminding and correcting upon a few common words and upon certain nuclei speech situations. Use a certain chair as a good-speech chair. Whenever the child sits in it, he must watch himself. Have a certain person picked out who is to serve as the speech situation in which the child must use very careful speech. Use a certain speech situation, such as the dinner table, to serve as a nucleus of good speech, and, when errors occur in these nuclei situations, penalize them good naturedly but vividly. You will find that the speech vigilance and freedom from errors will spread rapidly to all other situations.

Finally, we recommend that, after a child has mastered a new sound and several words in which it occurs, he be required to say it occasionally in the wrong way. This is called negative practice, and it has no harmful effect. Indeed, it merely emphasizes the distinction between the correct and incorrect sounds.

Negative practice. By negative practice we mean the deliberate and voluntary use of the incorrect sound or speech error. It may seem somewhat odd to advise speech defectives to practice their errors, for we have always assumed that practice makes perfection, and certainly we do not want the student to become more perfect in the use of his errors. Nevertheless, modern experimental psychology has demonstrated that when one seeks to break a habit that is rather unconscious (such as fingernail-biting or the substitution of *sh* for *s*), much more rapid progress is made if the possessor of the habit will occasionally (and at appropriate times) use the error deliberately. The reasons for this method are: (1) The greatest strength of such a habit lies in the fact that the possessor is not aware of it every time it occurs. All habit reactions tend to become more or less unconscious, and certainly those involved in speech are of this type; consciousness of the reaction must come before it can be eliminated. (2) Voluntary practice of the reaction makes it very vivid, thus increasing vigilance and contributing to the awareness of the cues that signal the approach of the reaction. (3) The voluntary practice of the error acts as a penalty.

The use of negative practice is so varied that it would be impossible to describe all the applications which can be made of it. Variations must be made to fit each type of disorder and each individual case. There are, however, certain general principles which may be said to govern all disorders and cases. Make the individual aware of the reasons for his use of the incorrect sound, for unintelligent use of the error is worthless. Never ask the student to use the error until he can produce the correct sound whenever asked to do so. Negative practice is a technique for getting the correct sound into the student's speech; it is used to make the correct sound habitual.

Set up the exact reproduction of the incorrect sound as a goal. The use of mirror observation, teacher imitation, and phonograph recording is invaluable. This is a learning process and does not come all at once. The teacher should confine all negative practice to the speech lesson until the student is able to duplicate the error consistently and fairly accurately. One should begin the use of this technique by asking the student to duplicate the error immediately after it has occurred. That is to say, the student should stop immediately after lisping on the word *soup* and attempt voluntarily to duplicate his performance.

Work constantly to make the negative practice serve the purpose of comparing the right and wrong sounds. It is often well to provide lists of words for the students to work with, speaking each of them in this sequence: correctly, incorrectly, correctly, correctly. Work first on individual sounds, then on words, then on certain words in sentences containing two words which begin with the difficult sound, one of which is to be said correctly and the other incorrectly. Have the student read material in which certain words are underlined for negative practice.

Make speech assignments for the student's use in outside situations. Examples are:

(1) Collect (write down on cards) ten words on which you have used negative practice. (2) Write down on a card two words on which you have used negative practice during each hour of the morning. (3) Write the first sentences of five phone calls, underlining the words on which you are going to use negative practice. (4) Collect, during the day, twenty words which you have said wrongly and in which you have become aware of your error, have made a retrial and said them correctly, and then have made a second retrial using negative practice.

The preceding list of examples is merely indicatory of the type of assignments that may be used. It is vitally important that no assignment be made that does not call for an objective record of some kind. The teacher must ask for the card and discuss the fulfillment or non-fulfillment of the assignment. Assignment plus checkup will work wonders in the treatment of any speech defective. Vary the assignments to fit the case, and always make them purposeful, never a matter of routine or drill.

In concluding this section on articulatory disorders we wish to point out that in very few instances will it be necessary to spend more than five or ten minutes of individual work each day on any speech defective. Most of the work can be carried on in connection with the regular school activities, and so it should be, if the new habits are to be made permanent. Any teacher can see the possibilities for combining speech work with the language activities. In the names of the numbers themselves, arithmetic presents almost all of the speech sounds. Geography and science activities may be arranged so as to give the lisper recitations in which he is responsible for all new s words. Questions may be phrased so as to demand responses which involve the sound upon which error occurs. The teacher and student may have a secret signal for correction. The student should check all errors in a notebook. At times it is wise to post on the board a list of five words with which the student has trouble unless he watches himself. Occasionally, some other student may be asked to check on the speech defective's errors. Class recitations should be used not for teaching a new sound but for building up the strength of the new sound after the student can make it correctly.

Drill. Most texts on speech correction are heavily laden with lists of words, phrases, and sentences which contain the various speech sounds. Most of them imply or state that the speech defective must be drilled intensively on such material before he can hope to speak without error. Many of them advocate the use of tongue twisters and similar difficult sentences. Modern educational practice and theory are rapidly getting away from the older concept of drill as a valuable tool. If it provided any value at all, it was that of opportunity for stimulation and performance, both of which factors depend upon many other influences for their efficacy. Motivation, maturation, discrimination, and application to life situations are indispensable adjuncts of any therapy, and the old-fashioned drill lesson tended to kill their usefulness. In speech correction, very little of such dull routine is necessary. The teacher should constantly assume the role of a helper or an assistant, placing the entire responsibility upon the student. Even for little children it is wise to outline the major steps of treatment as soon as possible. The student must know what he is trying to do throughout the whole therapy. He should be cautioned against mechanical, unpointed repetition of sounds. He should always be dynamically learning or unlearning. Speech correction is an active, not a passive, process.

Nevertheless, since the errors occur in words, they must be eradicated in words, and for this purpose the word lists are very valuable. The speech-correction teacher should be familiar with the lists of Horn, and the words most commonly used should be practiced first and most frequently. The text by Schoolfield listed in the references at the end of this chapter is a most welcome addition to modern speech correction because the words most commonly used by children are classified according to sounds. These words should always be incorporated into games, errands, stories, or conversations. Practice of words in word lists will produce little transfer to real speech situations unless those words are taken out of their series and made part of the actual communicative function. Speech assignments such as those described in the preceding section need such word lists, and the good speech teacher can find many other uses for them; but they should never be used for meaningless, dull, repetitive drill. The meaningless sentences and tongue twisters can occasionally serve as challenges or speech games, but they should never take the place of intelligent speech correction.

ANECDOTAL ACCOUNT OF SPEECH THERAPY WITH LISPER

First Day

Today I had my first session with Sally. I told her how glad I was to be the one chosen to help her. We had an old magazine with us, and I asked her to find in it, and cut out with the scissors, pictures of (1) a can of *soup*, and (2) a bowl of *cereal*. Then I cut out pictures of (3) some *icicles*, (4) a *house*, and (5) a pretty little girl whom I told her we would call *Sally*. I told her these five words were the first ones we would learn to say in the right way, because she didn't say them like other children did. First, I pronounced each one of the five words and asked her to repeat it after me. She substituted the *th* for all the *s* sounds of these words. Then the second time I asked her to repeat the words after me. I repeated the word as *she* said it, prolonging the incorrect sound so she could hear which one it was. I explained to her that it was those sounds which made her speech sound a little different from the other children's (they had imitated her some at school). I asked her if she would help me so we could get the right sound into those words. She seemed eager to work so she wouldn't (as she said) always "talk like a baby." She asked if she could come again tomorrow.

Second Day

Sally was anxious to come in today. She told me she cut out 5 pictures at home just like the ones we found yesterday. I had a list of the 5 words we worked on yesterday printed in big colored letters. I said them slowly, asking her to repeat slowly, and then had her show me on the list which sound she made that was different from mine. We encircled those with a red crayon. Then I asked her to tell me what their house looked like. During her conversation I wrote down three more words she ended with the error sound, and I added those to her list. They were *fireplace*, *mess* (referring to her daddy's bookshelf), and *fence*. She repeated them slowly after me, and we encircled the incorrect sounds with the crayon. Then I told her I would hide the list, and she could try to find it. If she got close to it I would make the correct sound, and if she went away from it I would make the sound the way she makes it. She enjoyed the game immensely, and we hid the list three times. She showed no confusion when I said the correct and incorrect sounds to designate where the list was hidden. She suggested that she was good at that game because the "close" sound was a "Sally sound" because it always started her name. I praised her for the suggestion, and told her we would call it the *New Sally* sound, and would learn it in her name, as well as in lots of other words. I suggested she pin the pictures which she had cut out at home in her own room.

Third Day

I took the list of 8 words which we had collected the first two days, and asked Sally to shut her eyes. I told her I would say each word in both the right and wrong ways, and she was to shake her head (as for "no") when I used the incorrect sound in the word. She identified these very easily. Then I took a schoolbook, and read a page backward. I asked her to hold up both hands every time she heard a word with the sound we were working on. She missed only one of them. Then I had her make two columns on a paper—the right-hand one for the correct sound, and the left column for the incorrect. She was to make an *X* in the appropriate column as I read the words. I read the same page backward again, purposely using the error sound in 4 words. She checked all of those, but missed 2 words in which the sound was used correctly. These were in final positions. I made the "New Sally sound" 5 times before reading her a sentence from the story book, and asked her to hold up her hand whenever she heard the sound in a word. I read 4 sentences in this manner, and she designated all the "New Sally sounds" correctly. Next, I had her draw lines on the board as I produced a prolonged *s* sound. The longer I held the sound, the longer she was to draw the lines. Then I gave her a paragraph from a story in a child's magazine. I told her to take it home and ask her parents to read it to her slowly. She is to hold up her hand when she hears a word with the "New Sally sound," and they will encircle each word in which she makes an error. She will bring this clipping back tomorrow.

Fourth Day

I took the list of 8 error words, pronouncing them correctly and incorrectly at random, and asked Sally to pull her ear each time I said it in the wrong way. She did this easily. She brought back the clipping which her mother had read to her—there was only one error, on a medial *s* word. So I gave her a magazine and told her to cut out pictures in which our sound came in the middle of the word. She found pictures of *ice cream*, *candlestick*, and *bicycle*. Then I gave her a paper with the numbers 1–15 on it, and a red pencil. I combined the sound with different vowels (such as *sa*, *see*, etc.) and asked her to follow the numbers and put a red circle around the number of the syllable I said incorrectly. I purposely made errors on numbers 5, 10, and 15, and she checked them correctly. We decided that from now on we would use an "¿" (upside-down question mark) to show the "New Sally sound" when it was made in the wrong way. I showed her that if I said *song* incorrectly, she would write it *¿ong*. She was a little confused at first, but was enthusiastic over it when she understood, as she said "The wrong sound is no good, anyway." Then I read her a list of 15 simple words, and she printed them after I said them, using the ¿ symbol instead of the letter *s* when I said it incorrectly. She got the entire list correct, and asked hopefully if we could play that again tomorrow. Her discrimination is good, and she can judge between correct and incorrect sounds much more rapidly now.

Fifth Day

Using the first list of 5 error words, I read them several times, sometimes correctly, sometimes incorrectly. Sally printed the words as I read
them, using the symbol when I used the sound incorrectly. She got these
all right. Then I asked her to watch my lips and mouth as I made the
"New Sally sound" in isolation. I did it slowly, prolonging the sound as
I made it. Then I gave her a mirror and asked her to watch herself while
she made the sound. She noticed that her mouth didn't look like mine
and commented "I don't sound like you, either." I showed her that we
could see her tongue when she made the sound, but when I made the
Sally sound, you could only see my teeth. She began to imitate me so I
hurried on to our next activity. I told her a short story and asked her to
make an X whenever I used the *sssss* sound in a word where it didn't
belong. She detected all 8 errors in the story. Then I told her I was
going to say the sound by itself several times, and she was to write *s* when
it was right, and ʒ when it was wrong. I used the sound between 40 and 50
times, and introduced the error sound only 5 times. I felt that in this way
the error sound would be more distinct, and she would get maximum
stimulation with the correct sound. Her co-operation was excellent, and
she asked "When can I learn to make the New Sally sound right?" She
wanted to hug me when she said good-bye.

Sixth Day

Today I used the first 5 error words and added 5 other *s* words, including *ice cream, candlestick, bicycle, mister,* and *saucer.* I used each word
several times, in different order, asking Sally to clap her hands together
whenever I made the *sss* sound in the wrong way. She designated those
without an error. Then I told her that today she would have her first
chance to make the Sally sound. I took the picture of the soup and said
"Now you call this a can of *th*oup (sound it out slowly). Say it your
old way. Now listen to the way I say it—soup—*ssss-ssss-ssss-* soup.
That's the New Sally sound. You cannot see my tongue when I say it.
Now look in the mirror and see if you can say it that way, without showing
your tongue. *Ssss-ssss-ssss-* say it with me. Now you try it." Her first
attempt was a good *s*, so I asked her to try it again. The third time she
made the *th* again, so I repeated the above, showing her the difference
between *th*oup and *s*oup. Then I asked her to try it again. It was not
clear, but resembled an *s* more than a *th*. We finished by repeating the
syllable *suh* together 20 times. She tried to say her name as she was
leaving, but I asked her not to try to make the sound alone yet, as we
didn't want to put it in her name until it was a strong New Sally sound.
She seemed very happy.

Seventh Day

We tried the exercise we did yesterday with *soup* and then I experi-
mented with a few other ways of making an *s*, so there will be another

alternative if the auditory-stimulation method fails. I asked her to say *soup* in the old way *(thoup)* and then told her to say it again, holding on to the first sound—*th-th-th*. As she did this I took a tongue depressor and pushed the tonguetip behind her teeth. I cautioned her to keep on making the *th*, and we repeated this several times. After I pushed the tongue-tip back, I said the *s-s-s* sound with her. She got quite a clear *s* in this procedure. Then I showed her how to groove her tongue and blow the air through it. She did this easily, though sometimes it is necessary to use a long match or a small instrument to help her get the feeling of the groove. We practiced drawing the tongue back while it was grooved, blowing air through the groove all the time. After that I asked her to put her upper and lower teeth together and press her lips tightly together. Then she continued to hold her teeth together but parted her lips to let a small hiss escape. Finally, we slowly said the syllable *suh* together again about 20 times. Each time Sally approximated a good *s* sound she was very pleased. I told her to practice grooving her tongue and blowing air through the groove in front of a mirror at home. She enjoys having a home assignment to demonstrate to her mother.

Eighth Day

I read Sally the original list of 5 error words, using the correct *s* and prolonging it noticeably in each one. Then I asked her to groove her tongue and blow air through it as she drew it back behind her teeth. This seemed to be the most successful way to produce a good *s*. We did this several times. Then I told her I was going to count to 5, and after each number she was to make the Sally sound that many times. (After *one* she was to make it once, after *two*, twice, etc.) In this exercise, there were two *s* sounds made in the old *th* way. She had hurried too fast. I read a short story to her, and asked her to hold up her hand whenever she heard the *s* sound in a word and then to say the sound aloud for me. She missed only one of these words. She is so enthusiastic about her success at making some of these isolated sounds that I warned her again not to try to use the Sally sound in words yet, as it was not strong yet, and might get all mixed up with the wrong sound.

Ninth Day

I showed Sally again some of the ways we used to make the good Sally sound (grooved tongue, hiss, tongue depressor, etc.), and then asked her to make several after I made them. I did this because we must somehow get her out of her old tongue-thrusting habits. That tongue sometimes protrudes even when she hears me make an *s*. I told her I would count to 13, and after each number she was to make a good *ssss* sound. These came slowly but were very clear. I asked her several questions, such as "What are you going to do after school?" and she had to make three long *ssss* sounds before she gave me the answer to each question. I gave her a pencil and paper and asked her to make an *s* symbol each time she said a New Sally sound. If she said it incorrectly, she was to put down the (¿) symbol instead. I showed her how to do it, and she did half a page with only one error before our lesson was completed.

Tenth Day

After some tongue-grooving exercises I told Sally we were going to make the New Sally sound together, strongly. As we repeated the *s*, I gradually lowered my volume to hear how she was making the sound. Then I told her we would start together again, but I would quit in the middle of the exercise, and she was to keep on making *s* sounds until I clapped my hands. We did this 5 or 6 times, and her *s* was very clear. After that I told her to repeat the sound alone until I clapped my hands once, and then to start making it again when I clapped my hands twice. I varied the intervals, and she made only two poor sounds. She did several lines of talking and writing, then we tried the new sound with vowels. First I had her prolong an *ssss* until I added an *ah* or *uh*. Then I asked her to prolong the *ssss* until I tapped on the table with the pencil and then add an *uh* sound to it. We did this with *uh, ah,* and *oh,* and I shortened the time of the *s* prolongations. The exercise was quite effective and Sally said, "I'll bet I can make real words pretty soon." Her enthusiasm is a great help.

Eleventh Day

We practiced the Sally sound together about 10 times, then I let her continue saying it about 10 more times, as I gave her a signal to start by tapping my pencil on the table. After that we reviewed yesterday's exercises in which we added vowels to the *s* sound. She did this easily and accurately. Then I told her I would read a short story to her very slowly, and whenever I made the Sally sound incorrectly, she was to stop me by holding up her hand and saying the syllable *sah.* I read a three-page story and purposely made about 15 errors, all of which she detected and responded to with a good *sah.* I told her I wanted to ask her several questions, but before she could answer each one she was to first say *sah-say-soo.* I asked questions about her doll collection, which always brings enthusiastic responses, so there was some pressure on her, as she was so anxious to talk. In spite of that, only one *say* syllable had a bad *s* sound. Just before she left we tried her name—first separating the *s* from the *ally* with quite a long pause, then holding the *s* until I tapped for her to add *ally.* I gradually shortened the length of her *s*, until she finally said *Sally* twice with no noticeable break. She was a mighty happy child when she left, and I feel that giving her a successful experience with her name will add a lot of motivation for the next step.

Twelfth Day

Today I wrote Sally's original 5 error words in large letters on a piece of cardboard. We practiced sounding them out, sound by sound, and she imitated me after each one. Then we practiced the following sequence on each one. For example, on her name, we first said the sound alone three times—*s-s-s*. Then we added the *a* (*æ*) to it and said *sa-sa-sa* three times. Finally we said that whole word 3 times. First she did it with me, then alone. We used this on *Sally, soup, cereal, icicle*, and *house*. She had a failure when she first used the whole word *icicle*, but she insisted on retrial until it was correct. After this we tried some signal practice. I pointed to the word on the card which I wanted her to say, and she held the *s* sound until I tapped with a pencil and then finished the word. On *house* she prolonged the final sound until my signal. Then we used each word in several short phrases, which she repeated slowly after me, such as—"hot soup," "bowl of cereal," "big cold icicle," "new white house," "pretty girl Sally." She experienced no failures with these, and was almost jubilant because they sounded so well. She went out the door saying "pretty girl Sally," and I remarked how much prettier her name sounded now.

Thirteenth Day

We went through the same type of exercises that we used yesterday, first reviewing the original 5 words, and then adding 10 more common *s* words to the list. She had no failures with the sound or the words. Then I said a word at random from the list, and told her she was to repeat it after me and use another word with it.   For example, when I said *bicycle*, she responded with "Johnny's red *bicycle*," and when I said *house*, she said "pretty *house*." Then we reversed the order, Sally saying the original word and I using it in a combination. This was so successful that she begged to try it again. We concluded this period by using short sentences containing one or two *s* words. I read them first, and asked her to repeat after me. Typical sentences were—"I want a nice white house" and "Let me ride your bicycle." Her parting comment was "Now I'm talking the New Sally sound!"

Subsequent Therapy

In each of the days that followed we did some of the following exercises:
1. Signal practice—(where Sally held the *s* sound till I signalled her to release it and finish the word).
2. Negative practice—(in which Sally purposely used her old error *th* sound in some of the common *s* words which I listed).
3. Ear training—(some of the old exercises to continue her discrimination between the old incorrect sound and the "New Sally sound").
4. New words containing the *s* sound—(we usually used this about five times daily, although the new sound carried over into many of these without actual drill).
5. Telling or reading a short story—(I clapped my hands if she used an *s* sound incorrectly, and then we repeated the word, first by sounding it out, then as a whole).
6. Use of nucleus situations in which she paid close attention to the "New Sally sound." (It is too much to ask a child that he watch every *s*

sound. So we used telephone situations, experiences in which she took messages to other teachers, short recitations in certain classes, one meal at home each day, and conversations with one certain playmate. In these situations, when possible, another person also checked for any possible errors in *s* words. The schoolteacher often listed any words that were incorrect. Sally also brought reports from her mother noting any incorrect *s* sounds she used during conversation at lunch time.)

Finally she got to the point where she would voluntarily correct herself on any words which she had missed. After that she made all *s* sounds without conscious effort, and we discontinued the daily lessons, substituting a monthly conference which was devoted to spontaneous conversation.

References

1. Ainsworth, S., *Manual of Speech Therapy and Public School Procedures* (Mimeographed), Special Education Clinics, Indiana State Teachers College, 1944, pages 25–39.
One of the simplest yet most helpful books in the field. The treatment of articulation disorders is clearly and freshly presented. The methods for teaching the *s* sounds are representative of the usefulness of this book.

2. Abney, L. and Miniace, D., *This Way to Better Speech*, New York, World Book Co., 1940, page 92.
Each sound is presented simply and easily and words for practice are listed for each. Then sentences and jingles complete the lesson.

3. Baker, P., *Primer of Sounds*, Boston, Expression Co., 1943.
Contains a short discussion of baby talk and lisping. The material for teaching the blends, and some of the games, will be of value to public-school speech correctionists.

4. Barrows, S. and Hall, K., *Games and Jingles for Speech Development*, Boston, Expression Co., 1936.
Games and jingles to provide material for practicing sounds already taught.

5. Borden, R. and Busse, A., *Speech Correction*, New York, F. S. Crofts, 1929, Chapter 3.
A classification of separate vowel and consonant sounds, with diagrams of the speech-organ positions for each one, and a description of the method of correct production.

6. Berry, M. and Eisenson, J., *The Defective in Speech*, New York, F. S. Crofts, 1942.
An excellent discussion of general methods of treatment together with selections for practice.

7. Brigance, W. N. and Henderson, F., *A Drill Manual for Improving Speech*, Philadelphia, Lippincott, 1939.
Especially useful for its word lists and sentences. Combinations of the sound to be taught with conflicting preceding and following sounds make the book valuable during the latter stages of treatment.

8. Cable, W. A., "Dynamic Factors in the Moto-Kinesthetic Method of Speech Correction," *Quarterly Journal of Speech*, 1945, Vol. 31, pages 350–357.

This article describes the moto-kinesthetic method more vividly than any other we have seen.

9. Fairbanks, G., *Voice and Articulation Drill Book*, New York, Harper, 1940.
Especially useful for its lists of paired words for each sound, the one containing the correct sound and the other its most frequent substitution.

10. Garbett, W. L. and Campbell, G., "Speech Training for Children," *Educational Method*, 1935, Vol. 15, pages 150–153.
Describes the actual treatment of some articulatory cases.

11. Hahn, E. H., "Discussion of the Moto-Kinesthetic Method of Speech Correction," *Quarterly Journal of Speech*, 1939, Vol. 15, pages 417–423.
Describes the method and recommends it very highly.

12. Hawk, S. S., "Moto-Kinesthetic Training for Children," *Journal of Speech Disorders*, 1937, Vol. 2, pages 231–237.
The general principles underlying the method are explained and illustrated.

13. Heltman, H., "Devices for the Correction of Articulatory Defects of Speech," *Proceedings of the American Speech Correction Association*, 1933, Vol. 3, pages 1–7.
A group of phonetic-placement techniques and other devices for producing desired sounds.

14. Koepp-Baker, H., *Handbook of Clinical Speech*, Ann Arbor, Edwards Brothers, 1937, Vol. 2, pages 345–352.
An outline of the general principles involved in learning a new sound, including procedures in listening, experimentation, and practice.

15. Lloyd, M. P., *Our First Speech Book*, New York, Newson, 1942.
More drill material.

16. Manser, R., *Speech Correction on the Contract Plan* (revised edition), New York, Prentice-Hall, 1942.
Progressive assignments in the form of contracts enable the student to work in the direction of complete mastery of his defective sounds.

17. McCullough, G. A., *Work and Practice Book for Speech Improvement*, Boston, Expression Co., 1940.
Sentences and other material arranged according to phonetic units.

18. Nemoy, E. and Davis, S., *The Correction of Defective Consonant Sounds*, Boston, Expression Co., 1937, pages 26–27.
Exercises are given for enabling the student to hear good tone production and normal sounds.

19. Obermann, C. E., "Improving Pupil's Speech; A Practical Program of Correction," *Nation's Schools*, 1941, Vol. 28, pages 51–53.
Recommends the auditory-stimulation method as the best procedure. Criticizes phonetic placement methods.

20. Partridge, L. M., "Dyslalias of Southern Ohio," *Journal of Speech Disorders*, 1945, Vol. 10, pages 249–254.
Dialectal variations and mild sound substitutions in Ohio college students are classified as dyslalias.

21. Peppard, H., *The Correction of Speech Defects*, New York, Macmillan, 1925, Chapter 6, pages 96–97.
Chapter 6 gives general exercises for the correction of speech defects, with

special exercises for the speech organs. Pages 96–97, in considering the correction of baby talk, give rules for teaching new consonant sounds. The author recommends that no work be done on familiar words.

22. Porter, F., "Speech Correction in an Orphanage," *Journal of Speech Disorders*, 1945, Vol. 10, pages 241–249.
A series of brief case reports of articulatory treatment is presented.

23. Raubicheck, L., Davis, E., and Carll, L., *Voice and Speech Problems*, New York, Prentice-Hall, 1939.
The major articulatory disorders are discussed and some drill material is furnished.

24. Robbins, S. D., "Aids in Correcting Articulatory Defects," *Proceedings of the American Speech Correction Association*, 1934, Vol. 4, pages 22–31.
A new classification terminology is given for articulatory disorders, with some hints for treatment. Voiced and unvoiced errors are discussed.

25. Schoolfield, L., *Better Speech and Better Reading*, Boston, Expression Co., 1937.
A practice book with material chosen from Gates Word Lists and arranged phonetically.

26. Seth, G. and Guthrie, D., *Speech in Childhood*, London, Oxford University Press, 1935, pages 146–162.
Especially interesting for its discussion of special devices and techniques for teaching the various sounds.

27. Stinchfield, S. M. and Young, E. H., *Children with Delayed or Defective Speech*, Stanford University Press, 1938.
The moto-kinesthetic methods are described in detail and there are many case reports which will be of interest to students in giving them concrete examples of the types of articulatory problems met in speech correction and the methods used by the authors.

 28. Stoddard, C. B., *Sounds for Little Folks*, Boston, Expression Co., 1940.
Pictures, words, and sentences provide drill material for young articulatory cases.

29. Walsh, G., *Sing Your Way to Better Speech*, New York, E. P. Dutton, 1940.
The author advocates teaching sounds through singing and provides tunes and words arranged phonetically for articulation cases.

30. Ward, I. C., *Defects of Speech*, New York, E. P. Dutton, 1923, pages 1–4.
General principles to be used in teaching a student a new sound are given, with three specific qualifications stated for the teacher: 1. The exact knowledge of sound formation. 2. A trained ear. 3. The ability to make both the right and wrong sounds. A later reference (pages 59–71) gives methods for making the individual sounds.

31. Welsch, J. D. and Nixon, G., *My Own Speech Reader*, Champaign, Ill., Johnson-Randolph Co., 1942.
Speech drills for articulation cases; designed to be read aloud.

32. West, R., Kennedy, L., and Carr, A., *The Rehabilitation of Speech*, New York, Harper, 1937, Chapters 15, 16, 17, 18, and 28.
Chapters 15, 16, 17, and 18 describe the *s, z, r, l, sh, zh, ch,* and *j* sounds, giving the defective substitutes for each one, and suggested remedial exercises.   Chapter 28 gives general principles for training and suggested exercises for children who make sound substitutions.

33. Wood, A., *The Jingle Book for Speech Correction*, New York, E. P. Dutton, 1934.
Useful during the last stages of treatment for memorized selections heavily weighted with certain sounds.

34. Yoakam, D. G., "Speech Games for Children," *Quarterly Journal of Speech*, 1944, Vol. 30, pages 85–87.
A very valuable group of suggestions about using games in speech correction.   Cautions are given to subordinate the game to the acquisition of speech skill.   Some modifications of well-known parlor games are described.

IX

The Treatment of Voice Disorders

Voice disorders account for only approximately ten or fifteen per cent of the speech correctionist's cases, but they are frequently the most difficult of all problems. The reasons for this difficulty are, no doubt, the lack of research, the complexity of the problem, and the fact that such cases have usually been treated by elocution and singing teachers rather than by members of the medical or speech-correction professions. The literature is scanty and scattered. Except for certain occupations such as the ministry, teaching, and entertaining, the average voice defect is not a handicap, since communication is still possible, a factor which does not hold true in stuttering or articulatory difficulties.

As we have said, there are almost as many names for voice disorders as there are adjectives to describe the voice; but in general they may be classified as disorders of pitch, intensity, and voice quality. Frequently any one case will be defective in more than one of these aspects, but for clearness of presentation we shall consider them according to the above classification.

Since voice disorders are classified according to defective pitch, intensity, and voice quality, the speech tests provide a method of analyzing each of these characteristics of phonation. For these tests, the speech correctionist needs a well-trained ear and experience enough to differentiate abnormal performance from the wide normal range of phonatory deviations. Many of these tests are very subjective and unreliable if administered by an untrained individual, but in the absence of the expensive, though time-consuming, laboratory apparatus which can give accurate measures, they are very useful in diagnosis and direction of treatment.

Voice tests—pitch.

1. *Ability to discriminate pitch.* This may be tested by whistling pairs of notes at low, middle, and high pitches, and requesting the subject to tell

whether the first is higher or lower than the second. Use ten pairs of notes at each of the pitch levels, using a random order. The same test can be given by humming the notes. Do not let the subject watch you, and keep the tones exactly two semitones apart. Record the number of errors at each pitch level. Students should practice giving this test under supervision until they are able to give adequate stimuli.

2. *Ability to produce a given pitch.* This may be tested by humming the nasal *m* at a low, middle, and high pitch. After each stimulus, the subject is required to attempt to duplicate it with his humming. Use different notes at each pitch level and continue the hum for at least five seconds. Score as an error any performance which does not come within a semitone of the stimulus or its octave, but note any tendency to produce a harmonic such as a musical fifth.

3. *Ability to carry a tune in unison or alone.* Tunes chosen should be simple and familiar. Use the unison test first. Use the same tune for both.

4. *Ability to follow inflections.* In this test the student is provided with a pencil and paper and is shown the following graphs of inflection as they are phonated and drawn by the examiner on the vowel *a*: _____↑ ‾‾‾‾↓ ——→ ‾‾‾↓. He is then asked to follow with his pencil a new series given by the examiner, who phonates the inflections according to the following sequence of graphs: _____↑ ——→ ——→ ‾‾‾‾↓ ——→ ‾‾‾↓ _____↑. The examiner's inflections should not range above a full tone. Record number and type of error.

5. *Normality of inflections in speech.* Use phrases or sentences which ask questions, make statements, give commands, indicate surprise, and express disgust, and have the subject repeat them after the examiner. Some examples are: *What's that noise? I liked that movie. You get out of here! What a* BIG *fish! Oh, I'm sick of this lousy place.* Record marked differences from your own inflections.

6. *Relation between pitch and stress.* Using the sentences in the preceding paragraph, notice whether stress changes are used instead of pitch changes. Underline certain words in sentences and ask subject to emphasize them. Note whether any pitch changes occur. Ask subject to phonate some vowel several times, alternating stressed and relaxed production. Note whether stressed notes are higher in pitch.

7. *Determination of pitch range.* Hum a middle-pitched note as a model for the case to imitate. Then gradually hum down the scale until the case cannot phonate at any lower pitch. Do this several times and note the place at which the individual begins to strain and falter. Locate this note on a piano or pitch pipe. Then, beginning with the same original note, hum up the scale until the voice breaks into the falsetto. Instruct the subject not to use the falsetto if possible. Locate the highest note accomplished without straining or falsetto. The difference between highest and lowest notes may be called the pitch range. If the falsetto keeps breaking in, determine the highest note of its range.

The importance of pitch-range tests is that they help us determine whether the speech defective is using a habitual pitch that is too near the bottom or top of his pitch range. If this is the case, intensity and quality defects may result. Moreover, the optimal or natural pitch at which the subject is most effective is usually located at a point a few semitones above the lowest third of the regular pitch range. If the falsetto is included, the natural pitch is usually located at about the twenty-fifth percentile of the total pitch range.

8. *Determination of habitual pitch.* This is much more difficult for the untrained or inexperienced examiner to determine, since it involves the disregard of inflections and a process of mental averaging of the pitch changes which exist in propositional speech. Nevertheless, the trained ear can spot the average pitch of another individual's voice with amazing accuracy. The subject is asked to repeat over and over, ten times or more, the sentence: "Now is the time for all good men to come to the aid of the party." Disregarding the first and last words, the examiner hums softly up and down the scale until he finds his voice synchronizing with the pitch of the subject's voice. Continuing to hum this pitch, he goes to the piano and finds its notation, which he records. Through similar technique it is also possible to determine the extent of habitual pitch range used by the subject. The reference by Root is recommended if supplementary information is desired.

9. *Determination of natural pitch.* Ask the subject to close his eyes, to begin with a low pitch, and to hum slowly and continuously up the scale, attempting to keep the intensity constant. The observer will note a certain pitch at which the intensity swells. Hum this pitch until it can be identified on the piano and recorded. Repeat the process while humming a descending scale. Give three ascending and three descending trials, and consider the place at which these pitches seem to cluster as the natural pitch. A range of three or four semitones about this note may be considered as optimal for performance. The natural pitch level may also be determined from the pitch range as described in test seven of this section.

10. *Effect of special influences.* By controlling the testing situation in the appropriate manner, study the effect upon the subject's habitual pitch of the following variables: change in quality (have subject speak gutturally, nasally, and so on); changes in intensity (very loud and very quiet speech); relaxation; distraction; imitation of another's speech.

Intensity tests. Although a few intensity voice cases whose disorder is due to too loud a voice are referred to the speech correctionist, most of these are due to defective hearing. The majority of defective voice intensity cases are of pathological or neurotic origin, or are due to overstrain and overuse. A laryngoscopic examination is usually required, and when the disorder is complicated by excessive breathiness an oto-laryngologist should be consulted. In cases of aphonia, or total loss of voice, the services of this specialist, and occasionally those of a psychiatrist, are recommended. Examination of the exterior of the throat will indicate whether a grossly malformed or underdeveloped larynx may be responsible. Since these cases are usually consistent throughout their speech in their weak intensity, no speech-sound analysis is necessary, except an aural scrutiny of the patient's speech to determine whether the vowels are being normally prolonged or the consonants sufficiently stressed.

1. *Maximum duration.* The subject is required to take three deep breaths and then phonate a front, middle, and back vowel. Each is held as long as possible, and the time recorded. Normal individuals should be able to hold any of these vowels for at least 15 seconds without difficulty. The vowels *i*, *a*, and *u* may be used, and the series should be given twice if the subject fails the first time.

2. *Breath economy.* The subject should be given a passage to read. Note the first words of sentences to determine whether the subject exhales abnormally prior to speech attempt. Also note the number of inhalations per fifty words of jumbled material, or in reading backward. Over eight inhalations per fifty words is definitely abnormal. It is wise to make a breathing record if possible, noting attack-exhalation, phonation on residual air, shallow breathing, and dysintegrations between thorax and abdomen. These can also be detected by the trained observer without such apparatus. Note also whether clavicular breathing is used.

3. *Muscular tension.* Firm pressure by the experimenter's fingers on both sides of the thyroid cartilage will discover hyper- or hypotonicity of the laryngeal musculature.

4. *Effect of special influences.* By controlling the testing situation in the appropriate manner, the examiner can study the effect of the following conditions on the habitual intensity: strong clinical demand for more intensity; pitch change; change in voice quality and presence of masking noise; distraction; relaxation; strong physical effort made simultaneously with speech attempt; expression of rage or disgust. It is also wise to determine if the subject can discard speech inhibitions by asking him, for example, to call a dog from across the street in the manner illustrated by the examiner. Determine also whether, in certain speech situations, the person's voice is adequate in intensity.

Tests for voice quality. Disorders of voice quality, with the exceptions of nasality and denasality, have always been difficult to classify because of the multidimensional nature of timbre. Pitch and intensity are fairly linear functions. One hears high and low or loud and weak tones. But voice quality or timbre is based upon a large number of overtones whose contribution to the auditory sensation depends upon their number and the frequency and intensity of each. Hence, there is no clear-cut variant which we can perceive. The terms we use to designate voice quality are as numerous as adjectives. Most of them are confused and inaccurate. Few of them mean the same to one person as to another. Nevertheless, within limits, such a classification is of some value and is included in the examinations given below. A laryngoscopic examination is usually needed, and a phono-photographic recording may be recommended. The amount of tension in the laryngeal, pharyngeal, and velar musculature should be noted. The natural and habitual pitches should be recorded to determine if pitch is a factor. The following items should also be administered.

1. Check adjectives which best describe defective voice quality: hoarse, husky, strident, guttural, breathy, throaty, noisy, pectoral, nasal, denasal.

2. Make an auditory analysis to determine which vowels are most defective. All vowels are seldom equally bad, and usually only a few need remedial work. Begin by having the subject read until you can be certain to identify the peculiar timbre responsible for the voice disorder. Then have the subject prolong each of the isolated vowels for about five seconds. Check those that are obviously abnormal, making a recheck to determine which of the vowels are most defective. After completing this, go through the articulation test sentences and words which deal with the vowels, underlining all those most defective. Note also whether the defective quality exists all through the prolonged vowel or merely at its initiation, and whether or not it seems to be affected by the consonants which precede and follow it.

3. Make a similar analysis for nasality disorders. With these, one can use a cold mirror held horizontally and placed with the mirror side up beneath the nostrils, but above the mouth. If clouding occurs on the mirror, the vowel has been nasalized. The same test may be used by placing the fingers on each side of the bridge of the nose and determining nasality by the vibration. When using the words of the articulation test, be sure to substitute others for those containing the m, n, and ng sounds. Note whether nasality is produced on certain vowels when no nasal air is discharged.

4. Once the two or three most defective sounds have been discovered, make a phonetic placement analysis to determine position of lips, jaws, tongue, and velum. Insist upon other methods of producing the same vowel (with tongue and lips in different positions), and note variations in quality.

5. Study the effect of pitch change on voice quality. Use isolated vowels at many different pitch levels, and also use continuous speech.

6. Repeat the preceding test, using variations in intensity.

7. Study the effect of relaxation, both general and specific, on voice quality. Use the vocalized yawn for the worst vowels.

8. Determine the quality of whispered vowels. Is it better than that

of phonated ones? If so, try to make gradual transition from whisper through stage whisper to phonation, without letting peculiarity come in.

9. Study the effect of distraction and imitation of other voices.

Need for medical co-operation in diagnosis. Many voice disorders are medical problems, and the speech correctionist must always keep this in mind. Much harm can be done by administering vocal training to a case whose disorder is due to active pathology or organic abnormalities. Whenever the case exhibits a chronic hoarseness, huskiness, or breathiness, it is essential that a specialist make an examination before the speech correctionist does any remedial work. Whenever the voice disorder follows a severe injury or illness, the physician must be consulted. Whenever the voice disorder accompanies such symptoms as extreme lassitude, extreme tenseness or activity, spasticity, or conditions of ill health, no speech-correction work should be done without medical approval. Moreover, voice is one of the most sensitive indices of mental health, and, whenever the voice disorder seems to be merely a part of a pronounced psychoneurotic condition, the psychiatrist should be consulted. The speech correctionist is favorably situated to contact many cases which the medical profession would never see, and he should always seize the opportunity to get co-operation from it. Unfortunately, laryngoscopic examinations by a specialist are rather costly, but they should be made whenever possible. Voice disorders demand more medical co-operation than do any other disorders.

Of course, many voice cases are functional, and the physician will readily advise speech-correction procedures for them. Other cases demand retraining even after the pathology or abnormality has been taken care of through medical or surgical therapy. Habits grow up about voice, even as they do about articulation. Generally speaking, the speech-correction teacher will do most of her work with cases of *nasality (including cleft palate), denasality, throaty, guttural, or harsh voices, monotones or peculiar inflections, high-pitched or falsetto voices, and weak or aphonic voices.*

Methods for removing the causes of the voice disorders and for minimizing their effects. The physician will take care of the eradication of most of the remediable organic causes for voice disorders. The speech correctionist should know enough about these causes to appreciate what has been done or could be done so that he can refer the case to the proper specialist and can modify the treatment according to his recommendations. He should also know whether the condition is likely to return. Since most of this information is rather technical and is available in other texts, the student is advised to use the special references given at the end of the chapter. The speech-correction teacher can do much to aid in building good habits of body hygiene, thereby preventing the development of foci of infection. Most cases of denasality and hoarseness can be helped by the institution of a careful routine of cleanliness and care of nose, mouth, and throat.

Hearing loss. When the voice defect is associated with a hearing loss, the teacher should take advantage of every opportunity to become familiar with the operation and use of hearing aids. She should refer the student to a lip-reading teacher, who will not only aid in the perception of speech but also help to clarify the various vowel positions through phonetic placement. Attention to kinesthesia, and the tying up of intensity and pitch levels and fluctuations with bodily movements, can do a great deal to compensate for the hearing loss, especially if the loss is not one of long standing.

Delayed sexual development. Another cause of voice disorders is lack of physiological or psychological sexual development, which produces the shrill high pitch termed juvenile or eunuchoid voice. Gilkinson [1] points out that his research findings corroborate the generally accepted idea that people are inclined to judge masculinity in terms of the speaking voice. When other secondary sex characteristics are also lacking, the speech correctionist should refer the case to the physician, who may prescribe hormonal treatment or other measures. Schicker [2] reports successful lowering of pitch in three of five cases as a result of administering testicular extracts. On the other hand, Crews [3] demonstrates how such techniques as silence, suggestion, relaxed vocal sighing, and mental hygiene can solve the same problem when the causes are psychological.

Puberty. The teacher should be able to recognize the symptoms of change of voice in early adolescents, and she can do much to minimize the emotional accompaniment which usually occurs. Education of parents, teachers, and associates of such children is often necessary,

---

[1] Gilkinson, H., "The Relationship Between Psychological and Physical Measures of Masculinity," *Genetic Psychology Monographs*, 1937, Vol. 19, pages 105–154.

[2] Schicker, H., "Die Eunuchoide Stimme und Ihre Hormonale Behandlung," *Arch. Gest. Phon.*, 1938, Vol. 2, pages 161–175.

[3] Crews, L., "A Case of Juvenile Voice," *Proceedings of the American Speech Correction Association*, 1936, Vol. 6, pages 142–149.

since many "boy sopranos" become voice cases if their mistaken parents or teachers seek to perpetuate the former pitch levels.   Often the child can be taught to control the fluctuations by relaxation and the use of accessory movements such as head and body gesturing.   The elimination of undue excitement and the common speech conflicts is always important at this time.

The speech problem of the man who has persisted in retaining his boy's voice is a very serious one, since many social penalties are commonly placed upon such symptoms.   West (22) in an excellent article describes other effects of puberty on voice:

In many cases the young person continues to use the prepubescent voice after the larynx has maturated.   With the boy this means that he will talk in a falsetto.   It is often difficult indeed after he has employed this falsetto for many months to persuade him to use his normal low-pitched voice. The social problems presented in this change are difficult to meet.   In the girl the change is not so much in the structure of the larynx as in the linings of the pharyngeal resonators.   The quality of the voice normally changes with the change in the texture of these surfaces.   However, many young women, having accustomed their ears to that quality that the voice showed before puberty, strive to continue it.   The effort to produce this quality in spite of the change of resonator produces a tense and unpleasant vocal timbre.

Sluggish articulators.   Many voice cases without organic defect have palates, tongues, lips, and jaws which are rather sluggish in their speech activity, and many other cases adopt fixed habits of speech in which the above-mentioned structures make but minimal movements. Nasality and a "mushy, hot-potato-in-mouth" quality often result from such habits, and, therefore, the habits require modification.   The general outline of treatment for these cases is as follows: (1) phonograph recording of voice and other techniques to promote self-hearing; (2) comparison with other individuals in the habitual use of the same structures (this may be carried out through testing the comparative abilities to make a certain number of tongue-palatal contacts per second, or through observation of self and model in a mirror while speaking in unison); (3) the use of swallowing, chewing, coughing, and similar biological movement sequences to promote speed of the articulators; (4) babbling practice while relaxed; (5) specific exercises in sudden initiation, repetition, or rhythmic timing of velar occlusion, tongue-teeth contacts, jaw openings, and so on; (6) exaggerated articulation of the vowels, compensating for error; (7) normal speech assignments; (8) negative practice. Many exercises for accomplishing these goals will be found in the references or may easily be invented.

Strain. One of the most frequent causes of voice disorders is overuse and strain of the voice. While the best therapy for this condition is to take care of it before it occurs—that is, to use preventive rather than remedial methods—it presents a very serious handicap when it does occur. Parents of children who show an especially prevalent tendency toward becoming very hoarse or dysphonic after strenuous play should be informed of the probable consequences and urged to do what they can to prevent the screaming and shrieking which seems to be such a large part of American childhood. During the period of huskiness or hoarseness following overstrain, it is necessary to prescribe and enforce whispered speech, which should consist of relaxed whispering rather than the tense, strained, aspirate quality frequently heard. The child should be prevented from engaging in any further strained vocalization during the period of recovery. While some voices seem able to withstand any amount of abuse, the majority of them definitely cannot, and certain voices need positive protection.

Individuals whose occupations demand a great deal of public speaking often misuse their vocal apparatus in several ways, especially when there is great competition for speech or attention. They use too high a pitch or too nasal a quality. They draw up the thyroid to a position directly underneath the hyoid bone, thereby producing a rather high-pitched and strident tone. Some of them, especially the announcers, hawkers, and newsboys, acquire habits of maintaining a constant pitch with a minimum of inflections. Others get stereotyped inflections so marked that they call attention to themselves and interfere with communication. Occupational voices, such as the "schoolma'am's voice" and "clergyman's tone," frequently result. Most of these conditions are readily cleared up through information as to the causes and the other possible vocal methods available to these speakers. Where the causes result in an actual voice disorder, that disorder may be removed by the methods to be described in the next sections.

When poor pitch discrimination, the use of an unnatural pitch level, or the presence of bad breathing habits are the causes of the voice disorder, remedial measures are necessary. The habits must be broken, and new ones must be built up. These measures will be discussed in the sections under the treatment of pitch and intensity disorders.

Imitation. A very common cause of voice disorders is imitation. Most children ape the mannerisms of all individuals for whom they have respect, affection, or hero-worship. This imitation is a form of identifying oneself with the person imitated. Unfortunately, it often causes the child to acquire the disabilities of the model. The child usually progresses through a series of such identifications as he matures, and so the bad effects of any single identification are usually canceled. Education of the parents or associates of the child will prevent any pathological fixation resulting from encouragement of such imitation. The best method to use in eradicating the influence of imitation is to bring the mannerisms up to consciousness with consequent insight into the mechanism involved. The child should be required to imitate the model in a very conscious manner, listening to the pitch, intensity, and quality thereby produced. Burlesquing and exaggerating the traits imitated often eradicate them. Good-natured and humorous penalties help a great deal. Other models should be imitated, especially in situations in which the student is somewhat insecure. Even when these habits are of long standing, such techniques are very useful.

Hypertension. Another common cause of voice disorders is the presence of excess tension in the vocal apparatus. The laryngeal valve is one of the first structures of the body to reflect any general tenseness. This is clearly demonstrated in the emotional states of fear, excitement, and rage. The popular expressions, "My heart was in my mouth" (globus hystericus), and "I was scared speechless," indicate the validity of this observation. Readiness for emergency action demands the holding of the breath with a resultant firm closure of the vocal cords, and tenseness is merely a synonym for such readiness. Moreover, excess tension causes constriction of the soft surfaces of the resonating cavities and difficulty in performing the quick transitions needed in speech. All of these factors produce symptoms of defective pitch, intensity, and voice quality.

The usual cause of this hypertension is insecurity and maladjustment. Feelings of inadequacy in a social situation always provoke tenseness, and, when this sense of inadequacy permeates the majority of the individual's life situations, a general and almost permanent hypertension results. Only through mental-hygiene methods and readjustment can such a problem be solved. Voice training will always be useless until such a cause is eliminated. Occasionally, however, hypertension becomes such a habitual associate of certain specific speech situations, such as the telephone or public speaking, that it persists long after the original insecurity has disappeared. It often becomes localized in certain structures, such as the throat or the tongue. In these instances, relaxation exercises are helpful and necessary.

Methods for relaxation. Many exercises and systems of relaxation have been invented and are in widespread use. The student should familiarize himself with these methods as they are described in the references given at the end of the chapter. Those by Jacobson are especially recommended. In general, the sequence is usually as follows: (1) The student is required to assume a position which requires a minimum of muscular contraction in order to maintain his posture. This is frequently accompanied by strong suggestions by the teacher of quiescence, peacefulness, freedom, and limpness. Biological functions such as yawning or stretching are used as reinforcing devices. Sleep and hypnoidal states, however, should be guarded against, for what is desired is conscious relaxation. (2) After the student has attained a rather consistent state of general relaxation, the teacher, speaking and moving slowly, should move the student's arm up and down or from side to side, requiring the student to remain entirely passive and without resisting the movement. This will give the student some of the sensations of the type of kinesthesia desired. (3) After this has been done successfully, the same procedure should be repeated with the exception that the student resists the movement while maintaining a passive and fairly complete state of relaxation with the rest of his body. The resistance should not be complete but yielding, resulting finally in thorough relaxation of the structure moved. Differential tension produced through the resistance should be gradually changed to differential relaxation. These techniques should then be repeated in an easy sitting and standing posture. (4) After the student has learned to employ the techniques consistently with his arms or legs, he should attempt a similar tensing and relaxing of the lips, jaw, tongue, palate, throat, and larynx, always seeking to identify, perpetuate, and produce the sensations which mean relaxation. Frequently, these sensations seem to be of a negative variety to the subject—that is, they appear when he seems to be "letting go" or "becoming limp." They consist of "not doing" something, of "not making some contraction." (5) Speech activity should be attempted first in a very effortless whisper, taking place on the regular expiration of silent breathing, without permitting any alteration in the regularity of the preceding inspiration. It should proceed through gradual stages, often employing a quiet yawning to produce the effortless vocalization desired. It should always be accompanied by the "feel" of relaxation in the structures of the laryngeal and articulatory musculature. (6) Beginning first with reading, repetitive, or memorized material when alone with the teacher, the student progresses to simple propositional speech, such as that involved in retelling stories or incidents. Then other people are included within the speech situation, and, finally, question-and-answer techniques are used. (7) The student is required to go, with the teacher as an observer, into speech situations which will produce mild emotional states. In these he attempts to speak while still maintaining both a general and localized relaxation. From this point, he should be required to keep a diary or daily check of situations in which he failed to carry out his new technique, and frequent checkups should be maintained.

Emotional maladjustment. Some authorities state that the most common of all causes of voice disorders is maladjustment. It is certainly true that a great many voice cases present personality problems and give a history of profound emotional conflicts. This is due, in part, to the influence of emotion upon intonation. The cries of animals and infants and the speech of primitive man demonstrate conclusively that one of the fundamental expressions of emotional states is that of phonation. Pitch level, inflection, quality, and intensity all show the influence of emotion. The long training required by actors in the perfection of their art, a training which frequently demands the artificial creation of an emotional state, shows this relationship. The phonatory aspect of speech always tends to reflect the attitude of the person speaking.

In view of these observations, it is not difficult to understand why emotional conflicts and maladjustment will produce voice defects. Aphonia, the complete loss of vocalized speech, is frequently hysterical. Too high a pitch level, nasality, and a harsh or strident voice quality are often due to the individual's desire to attack or dominate the group which makes him insecure. Individuals who tend to retreat or escape from unpleasant reality or social rejection often exhibit monotones or stereotyped inflections. Such symptoms are due to the desire to guard against the group's awareness of the emotion being experienced by their victim. And, as we said in the last section.

a sense of inadequacy to any situation results in hypertension, which itself can cause disorders in all the three aspects of speech. When such factors cause the peculiar voice, it is often necessary for the speech-correction teacher to help the individual solve his emotional conflicts.

Whenever possible, the speech correctionist should enlist the co-operation of the school psychologist, the parents, and the classroom teacher. Occasionally it will be necessary to refer the case to a psychiatrist or psychoeducational clinic. It must always be remembered that the solution of mental conflicts involves a great deal of responsibility for the teacher. Amateur experimentation with human lives is detestable. Nevertheless, parents and teachers are constantly being compelled to help the child solve his emotional problems, and the speech correctionist must often aid them. If he thoroughly realizes his limitations and adopts the attitude of an assistant rather than that of a Dr. Freud, he may be of inestimable value. Most persons beset with emotional conflicts need some assistance and guidance, even if it be no more than the presence of a human ear into which they can pour their troubles. If this ear belongs to a person with some background in mental hygiene and abnormal psychology, and some experience in self-improvement and adjustment, a well-planned remedial program will soon be devised and initiated. Suggestions for the treatment of maladjustment were given in Chapter IV.

The causes of voice disorders which have been mentioned are the most common ones which the speech correctionist will meet. Every effort should be made to discover and remove them and their influences. Voice disorders, more so than any other disorder, require the diagnosis and removal of etiological factors. Treatment of the symptoms is often necessary, but voice retraining is usually doomed to failure unless the reasons for the defect are eliminated.

The Treatment of Pitch Disorders

The treatment of these disorders concerns itself primarily with the teaching of new habitual pitch levels and the teaching of new inflection patterns. Since disorders of intensity and voice quality are often due in part to the use of unnatural pitch levels, the techniques discussed in this section are useful in the treatment of all voice disorders. Disorders of intensity frequently demand the teaching of a higher pitch level, especially when the speech defective is male; but the large share of remedial work consists of teaching lower habitual pitch levels.

The concept of a habitual pitch level must be clearly understood. Except in the case of monotones, it does not refer to a certain fixed pitch upon which all speech is phonated. It represents an average or median pitch about which the other pitches used in speech tend to cluster. For example, in the utterance of the sentence, "Alice was sitting on the back of the white swan," the fundamental pitch of each vowel in any of the words may differ somewhat from that of the others. Moreover, certain vowels are inflected—that is, they are phonated with a continuous pitch change which may either rise, fall, or do both. Of course, each inflection has an average pitch by which it may be measured, if the extent of the variation is also considered. If all the pitches and pitch variations are measured and their durations are taken into account in the speaking of the preceding illustration, we shall find that they cluster about a certain average pitch, which may be termed the "key" at which the speaker phonated that sentence. This may be determined experimentally through the use of the trained ear, as indicated in the chapter on speech tests and the reference by Gilkinson listed at the end of this chapter. It should be understood, of course, that different pitch levels will be used under different communicative conditions. Nevertheless, each voice can be said to have a habitual pitch and a habitual pitch range, in which most of the communication is phonated.

Methods for changing the habitual pitch level. The procedure for changing the habitual pitch should consist of the following techniques: (1) convincing the student of the inadequacy of his present habitual pitch; (2) ear-training techniques in the recognition and discrimination of pitch levels and variations; (3) methods enabling the student to use the desired pitch level and normal variations and inflections at that level; (4) techniques for making the new pitch level and range habitual. These will now be discussed in detail.

1. *Convincing the student of the inadequacy of his habitual pitch.* The most effective method of doing this is to provide an opportunity for the student to hear his own voice. Few of us are able to hear our own voices, for we are too concerned with the communication involved. It is difficult to consider discriminatingly anything that is very familiar. We are so "used" to the sound of our own voices that we cannot listen to them. The increased availability of voice-recording devices is of great value to the speech correctionist. Every voice

defective should have a phonograph record made of his speech. Other individuals with good voices should repeat the same speech material on the same record so as to allow comparison. If the recording is a faithful reproduction, the student will recognize the adequacy of the other voices and the inadequacy of his own in so vivid a manner as to provide a true psychological shock. Such a shock is frequently needed to provide the necessary motivation. The record can also serve as a basis for the measurement of progress. Besides the voice recording, the teacher can require each student to speak before a class, the members of which should be asked to rate the speakers as to pitch and general adequacy of voice. Other methods may be invented.

Improper pitch levels produce so many of the disorders of voice quality that they cannot be neglected. Many individuals have learned improper pitch levels owing to their personality problems, their imitation of poor models, their desire to identify themselves with other individuals, and many other reasons. It is usually necessary to recognize these influences and to cancel them before the student will really co-operate. A few cases may illustrate these points.

Bullowa described the etiology of certain voice disorders suddenly occurring in a high school as follows: "In order to acquire the low, lady-like voice which high school children believe suits their condition as opposed to the shrill shout of elementary school days, many students close their mouths, and inaudibility and nasality result." [4]

Ridpath, pleading for better co-operation between singing teachers and the laryngologist, says, "It is a fact that most vocal teachers try to make sopranos of all girls and tenors of all men, with resultant failures, whereas if they would consider the individual from the physiologic point of view they would not expect a student who is anatomically unsuited to produce high tonal effects to become a tenor, and vice versa." [5]

Felderman, in speaking of the folly of using an improper pitch level, declares that self-consciousness prompts the aping of elders by using coarse, throaty, guttural, or nasal voices, the use of which is continued even after the child passes through adolescence and does achieve a lower pitch. "Invariably the imitation fails." [6]

T.S., one of the author's cases, a schoolteacher, was dismissed after one month of teaching because the students could not hear her. It was found

[4] Bullowa, A. M., "The Need for Speech Work in High Schools," *Proceedings of the National Education Association*, 1912, Vol. 54, pages 870–874.

[5] Ridpath, R. F., "A Plea for a Better Understanding Between the Laryngologist and the Vocal Teacher," *Journal American Medical Association*, 1937, Vol. 109, pages 545–546.

[6] Felderman, L., *The Human Voice*, New York, Henry Holt and Co., 1931.

upon examination that her habitual pitch level was less than three semitones above the bottom of her range, whereas her optimal or natural pitch level was at least six semitones above her habitual level.   She possessed adequate intensity at the optimal level but declared she could not bear to speak in such a high voice.   Investigation showed that a series of experiences in which high voices had been penalized had caused her prejudice, which was truly unfounded since her optimal pitch was that of middle C.   The last of these experiences had been the scolding given by a critic teacher to another student.   Therapy consisted primarily of having her make phonograph recordings of the voices of twenty successful teachers and analyzing them with respect to habitual pitch.   Mental hygiene and insight into the role played by her early experiences in producing her old pitch level helped to convince her.   A course in practice teaching completed the re-education, and she experienced no further difficulty vocationally.

Perhaps the most important and frequent of all voice disorders due to improper pitch levels is the hoarse voice.   Williamson (75) has shown in a study of seventy-two cases of hoarse voice that:

The most common principal cause of hoarse voice was the throat tension resulting from the effort to speak at a level far below optimum pitch. When optimum pitch was established, the principal problem of correction was that of eliminating habits of tension.   Such "placing" the voice in an efficient pitch and removing throat tensions generally remedied the hoarseness.

Williamson feels that the throat tensions occurred as a result of trying to gain loudness while using such a low pitch level, and that they then became habitual.

2. *Ear-training techniques in the recognition and discrimination of pitch levels and variations.*   Before the teacher makes any attempt to get the student to lower or raise his voice, the student should be given a great deal of ear training.   This training should be concentrated upon the identification and comparison of pitch levels and the recognition of the types of inflections.   Many of these individuals have great difficulty in carrying tunes, in matching the pitch given by the teacher, in running a scale, and in recognizing or using inflections. When all of these abilities are defective, the prognosis is not favorable, though ear training will occasionally accomplish wonders.   Even when the student has no difficulty with these activities, he should be given a good deal of discrimination practice before he attempts performance.

The ear training should begin with the methods used in the voice tests.   Pairs of tones should be vocalized by the teacher as the student records or designates which of the two is lower in pitch.   If difficulty is experienced, very wide intervals should be used.   The Seashore musical tests for pitch may be played repeatedly, and the student should be urged to better his score of correct judgments.   Inflections, glides, and slides of all types may be used for stimulation.   Care should be taken to prevent the student from making his judgment in terms of quality or intensity.

Often the teacher needs to accompany her presentation of this stimulation with sample pairs of sounds phonated while she raises and lowers her hand to indicate the pitch level used.   The student should be required to follow pitch variations with similar movements, and after his judgments are consistently correct, he should make slight head movements to indicate higher or lower pitch levels.   It is often necessary to use much of this kinesthesia in order to reinforce and recall the stimulation.   After the student has been given some of this training with pairs of tones and inflections, simple melodies should be used, both in song and in speech.   These should be followed by the student's head or limb movements.   Empathic response to tonal variation should be encouraged.   The teacher should then speak whole sentences in a monotone, at various pitch levels, asking the student to judge the pitch levels used.   Finally, normal speech can be used for this presentation, first using higher, then lower, average pitches, and requiring judgment by the student.   This system may be supplemented by having the student and teacher judge the pitch characteristics of the various members of a class during recitation.   Through such methods, the student will soon acquire the necessary foundation for his later speech attempts.

The next phase of the ear training should consist of attempts to hear and match the pitch levels used by some other person.   Some musical instrument such as the piano should be used.   The student listens to the single prolonged note, the sentence said in monotone, and the conversational sentence in turn, and attempts to find the pitch on the musical instrument which corresponds with that used in stimulation.   He should be given a great deal of this matching practice.   Pairs of notes, monotone sentences, and conversational sentences should next be used, and the student attempts to match them on the musical instrument.   If the student possesses a very poor ear, the teacher should be content with his performance if he can indicate only the direction of pitch change given.

The final stage of ear training should consist of responding to stimulation by designated pitch variations. For example, the teacher hums a note and the student finds one on the musical instrument which is lower (or higher, depending on the level desired for the voice) than that given by the teacher. The teacher may give one sentence for a standard, then repeat it at various pitch levels, asking the student to designate the type he wishes. Occasionally during this practice, the teacher should give the wrong response in order to check up on alertness and discrimination.

We have found that the use of a hearing aid is very effective in this self-hearing. A good phonographic recording of one's own voice always seems strange despite its acoustic fidelity because one does not listen to the pitch or quality. The speaker is often difficult to convince that the recording is accurate, and so, much of the technique value is often lost. A hearing aid which amplifies one's own voice while in the act of speaking seems to prevent this objection. We have found it invaluable in both voice and articulation cases.

3. *Enabling the student to use the desired pitch level.* After the pitch level which the student should use as his habitual pitch has been determined through experimentation and voice tests, the speech correctionist should stimulate him with that pitch through every means at his disposal. The note may be sustained and a phonograph record made of it. The piano and other musical instruments should be used to make him conscious of it. The speech correctionist should speak in a monotone on the given pitch, or, if that is impossible, on its octave. The student should then attempt to speak certain prepared sentences in unison with the teacher. If necessary, he should hum several pitches until the right one has been found. It should then be reinforced by the playing of the record or the use of the piano and the teacher's voice. The student should repeat the same material over and over, maintaining the pitch. Often only a vowel can be used in this practice, but the student should progress to propositional speech as soon as possible. Attention to kinesthesia should be stressed. Accessory associative movements, such as those of head and arm, should be used after the student has been able to hit the pitch consistently. The speech used should have practically no element of communication.

As soon as the student has attained this pitch while speaking in unison with reinforcing stimulation, the latter should be gradually diminished until he is attaining the pitch alone. All strain should be avoided or eliminated. It is usually wise to stick to one sentence or one type of material until this can be phonated in the required manner. Then a short period of silence should be interjected, during which the student tries to maintain the pitch. After this, he tries to phonate again at the same pitch level. The silence periods are then lengthened and some distraction is introduced. After further reinforcement and repetition of the sentence on the new pitch, returning immediately to the former, the student should interject another sentence spoken at his old pitch. Such comparative activity should be stressed. The student must realize how much higher (or lower) his new pitch level is, and therefore the old pitch level may serve as a standard of reference. Often the difference in terms of the tonic scale may be used to indicate the amount of change. The teacher cannot hope to establish anything in the nature of the special talent of absolute pitch, but she can hope to establish a sense of the amount of deviation from the old pitch level. The exercises in maintaining a pitch are of great importance in providing the self-stimulation these voice cases need and in preventing the natural tendency to shift gradually back to the old pitch level.

For a time, the voice retraining should be confined to the teaching periods, and all of these should begin with ear training and end with monotone speech on the desired pitch. Then the student may begin to use other material than that with which he learned to use his new pitch level, and when speaking these new sentences he should be encouraged to use all the inflections normal to him. At first, he should alternate the key vowel or sentence and the new material, and the teacher should require the student to do much of the speech in unison with her, perhaps with the reinforcement of the phonograph record or piano. Gradually this reinforcement should be withdrawn, until the student is phonating easily and flexibly at his new pitch level. Frequent review of the methods for finding his new pitch level in terms of his old habitual pitch is necessary.

Although the above method for teaching a new pitch level is most effective, there are several others. One frequently employed uses the vocalized sigh or yawn to produce the desired pitch. These sighs and yawns must be accompanied by decreasing intensity and relaxation in order to be most effective. Another method employs exclamations of disgust or contempt in order to provide a lower pitch. Still another makes use of the grunts and noises symbolic of relief or feeding. Clearing the throat may also be used to provide a lower pitch. These methods are often effective with true monotones when the former stimulation or matching method fails. Many of the techniques included in the stimulation method are combined with the biological activity methods in order to provide the necessary stability of performance.

4. *Making the new pitch level and range habitual.* As in the treatment of the articulatory disorders, the new type of speech must be made habitual or the treatment has failed. The speech correctionist must realize how unnatural the new pitch level seems to the student and to his associates, who have become accustomed to the old pitch level. The student himself must gradually become accustomed to the new level or it will create such a psychological shock that he will not be able to stand it. One youth declared that he did not know himself when he used his new deep voice instead of the high-pitched piping tones he had always phonated, because it seemed to change his entire personality. It is usually wise to prescribe a great deal of oral reading at the new pitch level. This reading should consist of simple narration or the recital of the lines of some dramatic character with whom the student can identify himself. The student should read alone before a mirror. Later, other people may be asked to enter the mirror situation to listen. Finally, conversation can be used. It will be found that, as this therapy is carried out in a few restricted situations, the voice in other situations will gradually change to the new level.

After the student has become thoroughly accustomed to his new level, definite procedures can be used to make the student consistent in its use. These procedures, explained in Chapter VIII, are the same as those outlined in a similar connection for the articulatory cases. There should be definite speech periods at school and at home in which the student concentrates on the use of the new pitch. Speech assignments to get the student to use the new voice in outside situations should be formulated and carried out. Checking devices and penalties will serve to motivate the student and to make him conscious of his return to the old pitch levels. Negative practice in which the student uses the old pitch levels serves a similar purpose. A consistent program including these activities will soon make the new pitch level and range habitual.

The Treatment of Intensity Disorders

Types of intensity disorders. These disorders include too loud voices, too weak voices, and aphonia (the lack of phonated speech). Since the causes of too loud a voice are hearing loss, occupational influence (farmer's voice), personality problem (exhibitionism or over-aggressiveness), or imitation, little special therapy other than that sketched in the first section of this chapter is required.

Voices which are not loud enough for efficient communication are fairly common, but they seldom are referred to the speech correctionist. Imitation, overcompensation for hearing loss, and feelings of inadequacy leading to retreat reactions account for most of them. Many pathological reasons for such disorders are common, but they are frequently accompanied by breathiness, huskiness or hoarseness, or other symptoms sufficiently evident to necessitate the services of the physician, who should rightfully take care of them.

Improper breathing habits. There are, however, certain speech cases possessing voice defects of weak intensity which require other treatment than that sketched in the section concerned with removing the causes of voice disorders. These individuals, owing to the influence of several of the functional causes above mentioned, have built up inadequate breathing habits which markedly interfere with efficient speech. They lack what the speech teachers and singing teachers have termed "support for tone." When the latter is analyzed in more objective fashion, using actual breathing records, support for tone is found to consist, not of deep inhalation, but of controlled exhalation. Inhalation for good speech is seldom any deeper than for silence. The air supply is merely expended very efficiently. Poor speakers, and especially those of the weak voice intensities, often speak on residual air. They sometimes attempt to speak while inhaling. They interrupt their exhalation by quick gasps, even though sufficient air is retained for speech.

Although Wiksell (see references) found in recent experimentation that for normal subjects there was no relationship between type of breathing and voice intensity, it is obvious from Figure 10 that individuals possessing such abnormal breathing patterns should tend to be handicapped in phonation. Efficient phonation demands continuous and sufficient air pressure below the vocal folds. Clinicians have found that training in breath control is of great usefulness in such cases.

Breathing habits for speech are difficult to modify. Retraining necessitates a carefully planned program which must be based upon the breathing anomalies habitual in each case. The speech correctionist should first make a careful examination of the student's breathing under various conditions. Unemotional propositional speech, conversation, oral reading to self and to audience, and public speaking should be provided for such study. Whenever possible, an objective record should be made of the breathing. Vital capacity measure-

Fig. 9.   Apparatus used in recording breathing. *From left to right:* pneumograph, polygraph, experimenter's signal key.

ments may be made by the school nurse. Care should be taken to discount the breathing abnormalities produced by emotional states, since they are to be eradicated not through breath control but through emotional readjustment. This section is concerned with the stereotyped breathing habits that interfere with efficient phonation. If no apparatus is available for the objective recording of breathing, the speech-correction teacher who has been given training in comparing such recordings with her observation of the movements of the thorax and abdomen can rely upon observation alone.

In the past, much stress has been placed upon the necessity for teaching certain types of breathing habits. Thoracic breathing, abdominal breathing, diaphragmatic breathing, and many other more or less meaningless terms have been espoused by various elocution and speech teachers. Gray has shown that it is difficult to isolate specific types of breathing, that all of the so-called types are used by most individuals, and that, if speakers be classified according to their "type of breathing," there will be as many abdominal and thoracic breathers in a group of the worst speakers as in a group of the best speakers. Type of breathing, therefore, does not differentiate between the good and poor voices. One exception to this statement may be mentioned. Clavicular breathing, which involves the raising of the clavicles and the humping up of the shoulders into a strained position, tends to produce unsteadiness and jerky exhalation during speech. Wiksell's experimentation indicates that, in the cases in which breathing was predominantly thoracic, the subjects could hold a tone for a longer time and could get much better control of breathing than the cases in which abdominal breathing was most prominent. In speech correction, little attention is paid to type of breathing in terms of the musculature involved. We are interested only in providing sufficient breath and in teaching efficient habits of controlled exhalation. If the student attains these goals, he may breathe in any way he wishes.

The teaching of new breathing habits. The procedure to be followed in retraining the breathing used in speech is as follows: (1) The student must be made aware of what he is doing wrongly and convinced of the necessity for the formation of new breathing habits during speech attempt. (2) The old habits must be brought up to consciousness, disrupted, and penalized. (3) New habits of breathing must be taught and strengthened. (4) The student must learn to use the new habits consistently.

The best method of attaining the first goal is to have the student watch his breathing during phonation, comparing it with that of the teacher. Two pneumographs working onto the same polygraph will provide the necessary apparatus. Both student and teacher should speak the same sentences in unison. If this is impossible, the student and teacher should sit before a large mirror in a position that will provide a profile view of both chests. A turn of the head will enable both the teacher and student to watch the rise and fall of the thorax. Sentences should be spoken in unison, the student attempting to control his exhalation synchronously with the teacher's. A yardstick placed across the surfaces of both chests will aid in this observation. Reading material checked according to the amount read per exhalation is convenient. Through these methods, the student will soon come to realize how much more inefficient his breathing is than that of the teacher, and also wherein his breathing differs. A rubber tube attached to a mouthpiece which fits closely about the mouth may be easily contrived, and if this instrument is used during speech and the end of the tube is placed near a candle flame, the student can readily see the effect of any preliminary exhalation which precedes the attempted phonation.

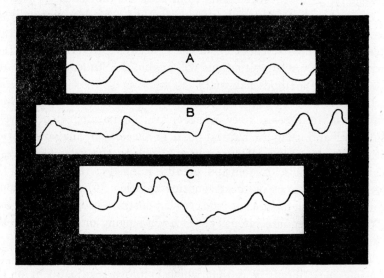

Fig. 10.   Three breathing records.   *Upper record:* normal silent breathing; *middle record:* breathing during normal speech; *lower record:* breathing during speech of a woman who talked on inhalation.   Inspiration is represented by the upward strokes, expiration by the downward.   Read from left to right.

The student should then use the same apparatus during conversation or recitation from memory, but with his eyes closed, seeking meanwhile to sense when his breathing has been faulty. The teacher can watch the apparatus and tell the student whether his judgments have been accurate. He should then seek to duplicate consciously the old habits, and the teacher may imitate them. Through these and many other techniques which may easily be devised, the student becomes aware of the bad breathing habits.

Using reading material previously prepared for breath groupings and using the apparatus and techniques just described, the student will soon adopt methods which are so much more efficient that they appear almost as soon as the old habits are removed. The speech correctionist does not need to teach the new habits, but merely needs to remove the old. The student needs only to imitate a good model and to understand and experience what is meant by smooth, controlled exhalation in order to perform adequately. The real difficulty is experienced in carrying these new habits into normal, everyday speech.

In order to accomplish the latter end, the student should spend some time each day in oral reading, choosing material which is conversational in form. Selections from some of the modern "patter" plays are excellent material. They should be read as normally as possible. Lines can be memorized and used for speech practice. Speech assignments, checking devices, negative practice, penalties, and the use of nucleus situations will enable the student to make the new breathing methods habitual.

Other methods for increasing voice intensity. Other devices which can be used to increase voice intensity are: (1) nasalizing the vowels; (2) finding and using the natural pitch, (3) accompanying vocalization with strong muscular effort, such as clenching the fists; (4) using a loud masking noise to demand greater intensity; (5) changing the openings and shapes of the resonating cavities; (6) using emotional expressions, such as cries of pain, to demonstrate to the student that he possesses adequate intensity; (7) using singing or chanting as the vehicle for louder speech.

Readjustment of resonating cavities. Among the methods for increasing vocal intensity is that which employs readjustment of the resonating cavities.

Talley [7] found that trained public speakers used three different ways of modifying the vowel when they wished to "project" their voices in the audience situation. There was a rise in pitch, an increase in intensity, and a shift of energy from the lower to the higher overtones of the vowel. Laase [8] performed an experiment which corroborates the latter finding. Tiffin and Steer [9] found that normal speakers produced stress and emphasis by prolonging the stressed

[7] Talley, C. H., "A Comparison of Conversational and Audience Types of Speech," *Archives of Speech*, 1937, Vol. 2, pages 28–40.

[8] Laase, L. T., "The Effect of Pitch and Intensity on the Quality of Vowels in Speech," *Archives of Speech*, 1937, Vol. 2, pages 41–60.

[9] Tiffin, J. and Steer, M. D., "An Experimental Analysis of Emphasis," *Speech Monograph*, 1937, Vol. 4, pages 69–74.

words, and by increasing their pitch, inflection range, and intensity. Russell [10] believes that the epiglottis and false vocal cords tend to act as filters to "muffle complex sounds as a whole and particularly the high pitched metallic partials." West [11] believes that a narrow open-ing between the wings of the epiglottis or between the pillars of the fauces will cause a decrease in the volume of tone produced. Negus [12] demonstrated the importance of resonation to intensity by removing a larynx from an animal and forcing air through its tensed cords. The tone was extremely weak and lacking in quality when compared to the sound normally produced.

These research studies and many others indicate that appropriate adjustment of the resonating cavities can increase the intensity of the voice. Unfortunately, we do not possess exact knowledge of what resonator sizes, shapes, types of tissue, or openings are needed to pro-duce increased intensity. So much individual variation occurs both anatomically and physiologically that no laws of efficient resonation have been formulated. Teachers of public speaking and singing all seem to agree that the resonators must be relaxed and that their orifices or apertures should be as open as possible. They use many vague terms to describe their techniques, which, if they are successful, prob-ably produce the desired results by helping to identify successful performance or by insuring adequate manipulation of the resonating structures. Some of these terms are: "bringing forward the tone," "mouth focus," "voice placement," and "rounded tones." Such terms as "nasal resonance" and "sinus resonance" are probably of the same type.

The speech correctionist seldom uses these vague terms, though, we must confess, he has few more specific techniques to offer. He demonstrates to the student how resonation can increase intensity with little additional expenditure of energy. He insists that the stu-dent use a variety of new resonator openings, shapes, and sizes. He requires the student to experiment with relaxation and tension in the various oral and pharyngeal musculatures, noting the effect upon in-tensity. The student is asked to increase the loudness of a certain tone as he backs away from the microphone of a recording device so

---

[10] Russell, G. O., *Speech and Voice*, New York, Macmillan, 1931, pages 175–176.
[11] West, R., Kennedy, L., and Carr, A., *The Rehabilitation of Speech*, New York, Harper, 1937, pages 98–100.
[12] Negus, V. E., *The Mechanism of the Larynx*, St. Louis, C. V. Mosby, 1930, Chap-ter 11.

that the record will show no decrease in intensity. He is to increase the intensity by varying the resonators rather than by expending more energy. Similar exercises employ an auditor walking away from the speaker rather than having the speaker withdraw from a phonograph recorder. Asking the student to close his eyes as he performs these exercises will help him to attend to the kinesthetic sensations. He should be asked to describe each successful experience. Thereafter the teacher should use the student's own terminology in identifying the more efficient type of resonation.

Effect on intensity of raising pitch level. Vocal intensity can also be increased by raising the habitual pitch used by the voice case. Scripture[13] quotes an experiment in which a vowel was sung at a constant level of loudness but at varied pitch levels. When the expenditure of air per pitch level was measured, it was found that the air expenditure decreased with rise in pitch. It is a common observation that children's voices "carry" much better than do adults'. While this may be due in part to the concentration of energy within a narrow group of overtones, the higher pitch level is also important. In general, most of the weak intensity cases are using habitual pitches far below their optimal or natural pitch levels. After the latter has been taught, adequate intensity is achieved. Occasionally the student is taught to make his speech more nasal, using humming exercises as the basic technique.

Influence of psychological factors. A lack of adequate intensity is often due to psychological factors. For example:

One individual with a history of prolonged laryngitis, but with a clean bill of health from the physician, claimed that she was afraid to talk loudly because of the pain she had experienced in the past. Something seemed to stop her whenever she decided to talk a little louder. She constantly fingered her throat. She declared that she was losing all her self-respect by worrying about her inability to speak as loudly as she could. Use of a masking noise during one of her conferences demonstrated to her that she could speak loudly without discomfort. Under strong clinical pressure, she did make the attempt, but the inhibition was automatic.

When a masking noise is used with one of these cases, it should be increased very gradually, and then, as the case adjusts the intensity

---

[13] Scripture, E. W., *The Elements of Experimental Phonetics*, New York, Scribner's, 1902, page 221.

level of speech to the new level, it should be shut off suddenly during his conversation. One of the author's cases was "cured" when he suddenly emerged from a noisy factory and found himself shouting. Vocalization accompanied by strong muscular effort often produces a stronger voice. Cries of pain or warning may often prove to the individual that his difficulty in speaking loudly is not insurmountable. Singing and chanting in unison with a large group will often accomplish the same purpose, especially if the group, at a secret signal from the clinician, suddenly stops. Mental hygiene and an insight into the nature of traumatic experiences usually precede this type of therapy.

Aphonia. Aphonia, or the complete loss of voice, is usually due to overstrain, organic defects, or emotional causes. If the cause is overstrain, rest and silence, or, at the best, whispered speech, should be prescribed. Occasionally the case is required to use a different pitch level when his voice begins to return. If the disorder is due to pathology, medical and surgical care is necessary. If it is due to emotional conflicts, psychiatric treatment (or the type of treatment discussed under readjustment methods) should be administered. In any case, if voice retraining is used, it is merely an accessory tool.

Suggestion is frequently used with hysterical aphonias. Physicians often use a faradic current or ammonia inhalation or massage as the culminating procedures in a period of treatment marked by complete cessation of speech attempt and strong cumulative suggestion. In many instances, coughing is used to demonstrate to the patient that voice exists. Persons who have once had such aphonia are likely to have it again unless the cause is removed. In some instances, when the cause cannot be discovered, a relapse is prevented by having the individual perform some simple vocal ritual each day, such as prolonging each of the vowels for ten seconds.

Some quotations from an article by Sokolowski and Junkerman (53) will illustrate some of the methods for treating hysterical aphonia:

First, we administered breathing exercises in connection with a systematic speech and voice retraining . . . (using a humming breathing; speech attempt while "pressing together the hands of a nurse standing behind him";) . . . By means of this phonetic re-education we succeeded in restoring the voice to about 60 per cent of our aphonics, a rather meager result considering the relatively tiresome treatment which sometimes lasted several weeks.

Induced by the publications of Muck and his extraordinary results we then tried his method—the introduction of a pellet or small ball into the larynx between the vocal cords, in order to bring about a sensation of being suffocated which superinduced a cry of fright. We have to confess that our own results with Muck's ball were not very encouraging.

As soon as the anamnesis pointed to a psychogenic aphonia and the laryngoscopic mirror confirmed this assumption a short remark such as, "You will be all right quite soon," or, "You will be getting your voice back quite soon," was made. After that the patient was not permitted, so to speak, to "collect his wits." All manipulations such as setting the head in proper position and pulling out the tongue were carried out as quickly as possible, and accompanied by short, crisp and somewhat commanding words. Then followed the deep introduction of the mirror and the attempt to obtain a vocal retching reaction. After this was accomplished, it was brought into the consciousness of the patient with short, crisp remarks, such as "Here we are," "Now your voice is back," or "Do you hear your voice?" After that it required but relatively little effort (the mirror, of course, remaining continually in the throat) to elicit from the patient the unpleasant gag-reminding but nevertheless audible "ah."

Eisenson (3) mentions a case of hoarse voice in a child who became hoarse during spanking and remained that way until he was cured by a magic incantation and sudden statement in unison with his clinician.

Indistinct utterance. Indistinct speech is so frequently confused with intensity voice disorders that it will be discussed in this section. Many individuals possessing this type of speech phonate with sufficient intensity to be heard, but their intelligibility is affected by improper rate, indefinite articulation, and unprecise resonance. These individuals are frequently asked by their auditors to speak more loudly. When this is done, the intelligibility is often decreased still further, owing to the masking of the high-frequency consonant sounds by the lower tones of the vowels. Fletcher[14] concludes from his experiments that consonants are generally harder to recognize correctly than vowels, and that *th*, *f*, *v*, and *z* are the most difficult to perceive at weak intensities. He also demonstrates that a small improvement in articulation produces a great improvement in intelligibility: "If the articulation shows an improvement of from 5 to 10 per cent, the intelligibility will show an improvement of from 20 to 38 per cent."

These indistinct speakers are therefore taught to emphasize their consonants. The four continuants mentioned above as being responsible for most of the distortion are prolonged. The student is further taught to produce them with a more energetic airflow and a

---

[14] Fletcher, H., *Speech and Hearing*, New York, D. Van Nostrand, 1929, pages 266–289.

tenser lip or tongue. Since other research studies indicate that the stop consonants p, b, t, d, k, and g are among the least powerful of all speech sounds, these are also singled out for special attention. Sudden, precise, and energetic closures and openings are taught. At first it is wise to use prescored material in which only one or two of these sounds are underlined. Speech assignments and nuclei situations will carry the new attack into normal speech. Improving such general considerations as the student's posture, neatness, and self-respect often facilitates this more specific therapy.

The Treatment of Disorders of Voice Quality

These disorders are the most common of all voice defects. They include excess nasality, denasality, throatiness, harshness, and all the other descriptive terms which may be used to denote peculiarities of timbre. Only when these peculiarities are sufficiently noticeable to interfere with communication and call attention to themselves can they be considered voice disorders. An infinite range of voice quality variations is found in so-called normal speakers. Excess nasality is probably the most common of these disorders. Cleft-palate speech involves both a phonatory and an articulatory disorder, and the phonatory abnormality is that of hypernasality. The treatment of this disorder employs the techniques sketched both for hypernasality and for articulation, but, because it also requires specialized methods, it is not specifically described in this section.

Sequence of treatment. Although special devices are used for certain of these disorders, the treatment for most of them involves the same general sequence. This sequence is as follows: (1) Make an analysis of the voice to determine which vowels or continuant consonants are most abnormal in their voice quality. (2) The student must learn to recognize the unpleasant voice quality whenever it occurs in his speech. (3) Through the use of certain techniques, the student must learn to produce the correct quality on isolated vowels. (4) This new voice quality must be strengthened. (5) The student should learn to use the new quality consistently. In the following paragraphs, we shall use the disorder of hypernasality to illustrate the type of treatment to be administered.

Recognition of defective quality. In order that the student may learn to recognize the unpleasant voice quality whenever it occurs in his speech, the vowels that are least defective should be used. The teacher should imitate these vowels as the student produces them, and then repeat them, using excess nasality. The student will readily recognize the difference. He should be required to produce these vowels first normally and then with excess nasality, carefully noting the difference. Lightly placed thumb and forefinger on each side of the septum, or the use of the cold mirror placed under the nostrils, will provide an accessory check of the presence of the hypernasality. The student should then listen to the teacher's production of his worst vowel, with and without nasality. If difficulty is experienced in recognizing this, the student can correlate his auditory judgments with the visual and tactual sensations received from the use of the mirror and finger-septum contact. Requiring him to close and open his eyes during alternate productions of the vowel as the teacher uses the mirror under her nostrils will soon provide adequate discrimination.

After some of this training has been successfully completed, the teacher should read a passage in which certain vowels are underlined and are purposely nasalized. The student should listen carefully, checking on a copy of the passage all vowels in which he hears the unpleasant quality. Many of the games and exercises used in the ear training of articulatory cases can be modified to teach the student better discrimination and identification of the good and bad voice qualities. Although at first the teacher will need to exaggerate the hypernasality, she should endeavor to decrease it gradually until the student is skilled in detecting even a slight amount of it. After this has been done, the student should read and reread a certain paragraph, making judgments after each word as to whether or not excess nasality occurred. These judgments may be checked by the teacher, and the percentage of correct judgments ascertained. This procedure will serve as a motivating device. The student may also be required to repeat series of words or isolated vowels, using the mirror under his nostrils and making his judgment of normal or nasal voice quality before opening his eyes to observe the clouding or nonclouding of the mirror. Much home practice of this sort can be used.

Producing good voice quality. In most of the disorders of voice quality, it is advisable to work with the worst vowel first when the student attempts to produce clear and adequate phonation. Thus, in the nasality case, the vowel on which the student shows the worst hypernasality is singled out for his first trials. An exception to this policy is found in the cleft-palate and other organic disabilities, wherein one must often use the easier sounds first. Very little intensity should be used in the first attempts, and every type of available reinforcement should be employed. The hypernasality case should use warming-up exercises, such as yawning, puffing out the cheeks, blowing balloons, and other methods, to insure firm closure of the nasopharynx by the velum. Many of these exercises are given in the references. Care should be taken to prevent the student from constricting the nares during these performances. The student should use the mirror under the nostrils and the finger-septum contact to notice the first signs of nasal phonation. Often, a larger mouth opening or a slightly different tongue placement will help to keep the old habits from returning. As in the articulatory disorders, the actual attempt should be preceded by a review of the ear-training exercises. The teacher should use discrimination stimulation, giving the incorrectly nasalized vowel and then the normally phonated vowel, several times before requesting the student to make his first attempt. If this preliminary work has been carried out thoroughly, little difficulty will be experienced, and vowels relatively free from excess nasality will be phonated.

Strengthening new voice quality. After this vowel has been produced correctly, the student should attempt to maintain and prolong it, paying a great deal of attention to the "feel" and the sound of it. The student must be cautioned to keep out all hypertension. Without changing facial, mouth, or body positions, he should then cease phonation, take a deep breath, and attempt to produce it again. Series of alternate phonations and silences should be produced on each exhalation. Whenever the vowel becomes too nasal, the student should be given a rest and the entire procedure of preliminary exercises repeated. Through careful work of this kind, the student will soon learn to produce the vowel correctly whenever he wishes. It is frequently necessary to insist upon sudden initiation of the vowel, using signal practice, in order to insure nasality-free vocalization at the very first instant of phonation. Often the student will fall into this error, making the old adjustments first, then changing to the new as the vowel is continued. This is fatal to the swift production needed in speech.

Although the worst vowel is the one first chosen for remedial work because of its contribution to better speech and because its successful production will influence the production of other defective vowels, we use the easiest consonant and vowel combinations in strengthening the new adjustments. The vowel should be practiced alone until it

can be produced satisfactorily and consistently without the preliminary preparation. It is then wise to practice nonsense syllables
in which the consonant follows the vowel (*ob, op*), then those in which
the vowel follows the consonant (*bo, po*), and finally those in which
consonants both precede and follow the vowel (*bop, pob*). The first
consonants used in these combinations should be the plosives *p, b, t,
d, k,* and *g*, then the sibilants *s, z,* and *sh*, then the continuants *f, v, l,*
and *r*, and finally the nasals *m, n,* and *ng*. Such a sequence will be
found to be most effective. Familiar words can be used as well as
nonsense syllables without encountering much difficulty.

Making the new quality habitual. After the student has successfully mastered the majority of the above exercises, he can be required
to read from copy carefully prepared to indicate his difficult sounds.
Symbols and underlining can serve to teach him to reject the old
mechanics prior to speech attempt and to prepare for adequate phonation. They may also be used to indicate the words on which the
student should use negative practice. In voice disorders of all kinds,
it is necessary to use a great deal of this negative practice, for the consciousness of faulty phonation will soon be lost unless frequently reinforced. As soon as the student has fairly good control of an isolated
vowel, a nonsense syllable, or a familiar word, he should phonate it incorrectly to heighten the contrast. A brief illustration of such copy
is as follows:

O/n this joyful occasio/n Alice was sitting o/n
the back of the sa/me white swa/n.

Key to symbols: / Be sure to separate vowel from consonant!
                           * A difficult sound for you. Be careful!
                           # Use negative practice on this sound.
                           — Prolong this vowel.

During the early stages of treatment, it is wise to use the same
reading or memorized material over and over again until the student
has attained a rather good awareness of the sounds which are likely
to require more care. Often it is wise to prolong the vowel presenting difficulty and, for a time, to separate the vowel from the more
difficult consonants such as the *m* or *n*. Assimilation nasality, or the
carrying over of the nasality legitimately used in producing or preparing for the *m, n,* and *ng* sounds, often demands the use of signal

practice to insure clean-cut transitions. After the student has mastered the prepared reading material he may progress to unscored reading, then to careful conversation with the speech correctionist, and finally to speech in outside situations. Speech assignments, checking devices, negative practice, penalties, and nucleus situations will make it possible for the student to attain complete mastery of his vocalization.

Other voice-quality disorders and methods of therapy. Hoarseness, huskiness, throatiness, and all the other odd types of voice quality are frequently due to hypertension, emotional conflicts, overstrain, and organic defects; the treatment for these conditions has already been discussed. The student should become familiar with the references dealing with these aspects of the disorders.

When these other disorders of voice quality are due to functional causes such as imitation or improper habits of voice production, the same sequence of ear training should be used, although the accessory devices used for nasality cannot be employed. Phonograph recordings will enable the student to study the voice quality in a manner that can be obtained by no other method. These recordings may be used continuously during treatment, and the teacher may record her own voice quality to provide comparison with the student's. Whenever the student is required to listen to his own voice, the voice recorder should be used, as it saves a great deal of time. However, through intensive and well-planned training, the same results may be obtained without this apparatus.

When the voice is pectoral, guttural, or throaty, it is often necessary to show the student that it is possible to articulate the vowels in other than his habitual manner. The opening of the mouth may be widened, and increased in vertical dimension, or made with lips protruded. The tongue placement may be varied greatly during the maintenance of one vowel. The student should be required to vary these positions and the tenseness of the walls of the mouth and throat. These exercises will demonstrate that differences in quality can be produced, and often much better timbre will result. It is frequently necessary to teach a new manner of vowel articulation in order to get the desired quality. When denasality is due to habits formed during adenoidal and catarrhal childhood, voice retraining is necessary. The student should be required to snort the vowels and to work for nasalization of all speech. Humming exercises and the use of the mirror and finger-septum contact will usually produce the desired result.

Different pitch levels will also produce better quality.   The procedures for strengthening and habituating the new quality are similar to those used for hypernasality.

Falsetto voice.   The falsetto voice, which is partly a disorder of pitch and partly one of voice quality, is still not thoroughly understood in terms of its manner of production.   Negus[15] declares that only the very edges of the cords vibrate and that they move upward and downward rather than outward and inward.   When the higher falsetto notes are being produced, only a portion of the cords vibrate.   In the male voice, the lowest notes cannot be produced in a falsetto, and the highest notes are more easily phonated in this manner.   The falsetto is easily produced when phonating on inhalation, and it is seldom present in such biological activities as sighing or coughing.   Although little air pressure is needed to produce this type of voice, constriction of the laryngeal musculature usually occurs.   In treating this voice disorder, lowering the habitual pitch level, relaxation, and the vocalized sigh are the techniques commonly employed.   The student is required to diminish the intensity of his ordinary speech and to follow each "break" into the old falsetto quality by sighing and by using some stereotyped phrase or sentence such as "That is to say" or "What I mean to say is. . . ."   These sentences are practiced sufficiently so that they provide an easy vehicle for returning to the new voice quality and pitch level.

Throatiness.   The throaty quality of voice, when due to functional causes, is one of the most difficult to change.   It is occasionally the result of lowering the habitual pitch level, especially when a falsetto was previously used.   When the constrictor muscles of the pharynx are hyperactive, the choked, throaty voice is frequently found. Many of the individuals with such voice quality depress their chins against their necks when the throatiness is most apparent.   Tension of the extrinsic laryngeal and pharyngeal musculature is usually present.   The speech defective seems to be speaking as he prepares to swallow.   The treatment of throatiness usually consists of the following techniques: (1) raising the habitual pitch level three or four semitones; (2) insisting upon a very erect posture and eliminating the tendency to depress the chin through penalties, checking devices, and negative practice; (3) using chanting and singing exercises to reduce

---

[15] Negus, V. E., *The Mechanism of Phonation, Acta otolaryngology*, Stockholm, 1935, Vol. 22, pages 393–419.

the excess tension and silent semiovert rehearsals of sentences prior to utterance; (4) preceding utterance by flipping the tongue up and down in the mouth cavity so as to prevent the incipient swallowing movements from occurring, thereby breaking up the old pattern of vocalization; (5) using vocalized sighing to produce some vowel free from throatiness and thereafter using this vowel to "key" all vocalization in nucleus situations. This vowel can be phonated between sentences and between phrases in the same manner used by many normal speakers when they are at a loss for words.

Guttural voices. Some individuals are encountered whose voices probably merit the adjective *guttural* rather than *throaty.* The terminology is no doubt somewhat dependent upon sex differences or pitch, since a voice which would be termed *throaty* in a woman is called *guttural* when it occurs in a male. A distinction is sometimes made in terms of the mechanics of phonation, guttural voices being due to partial vibration of the false vocal cords in addition to the normal activity of the true cords. Constriction of the pharynx seems to occur in both types of voice, and the treatment is the same for both.

Harsh voices. Harsh, piercing, or rasping voices seem to be accompanied by this false vocal-cord vibration. Voelker [16] describes one form of the disorder as characterized by "a rattling, rumbling, cracking or ticker-like substitute for phonation." These extra vibrations range from six to thirty per second. Normal speakers often show this voice quality when grunting or in moments of indecision. It may be easily produced when vocalizing on inhalation. Voelker recommends breath training, speech with yawning, and vocalized sighing. The student must learn to hear these vibrations in his own speech before any therapy will be successful. Russell [17] describes the strident, piercing voice as primarily due to raising the larynx up under the hyoid. He describes the subsequent tension as follows:

As the voice begins to get strident and blatant, one sees the red-surfaced muscles which lie above the vocal cords begin to form a tense channel and press upon the vocal cords themselves. This pressure is brought about primarily by the ventricular bands. . . . Consequently, but a very small strip of the glottal lip is left free to vibrate. The resultant is that the edge

---

[16] Voelker, C. H., "Phoniatry in Dysphemia Ventricularis," *Annals of Otology, Rhinology and Laryngology,* 1935, Vol. 44, page 471.

[17] Russell, G. O., "Physiological Causes of Guttural and Piercing Deaf Voices," *Oralism and Auralism,* July, 1929.

is pushed up and these edges are forced to close together in cymbal-like fashion.

Treatment for this disorder is similar to that for guttural and throaty voices except that, in addition, the student is taught to recognize the raising of the larynx. This can be done by observation in a mirror and by feeling the notch between the thyroid and the hyoid with the forefinger.

Imitation as a clinical device. All functional voice disorders respond to direct imitation as a form of therapy. The model set for the speech defective should contrast as much as possible with the former voice defect. Thus, nasality cases are required to imitate denasality, weak voices simulate models who have excess loudness, and so on. Other characteristics of the persons used as models should also be imitated. A throaty voice defective may be asked to imitate some person who has a thin, twangy voice, not only in his speech, but also in his manner of walking, posture, gesturing, and nervous movements. It is also useful to employ a phonograph recording of some opposite type of voice, playing it over and over and requiring the student to say the same sentences in unison with the record. Other recordings may be used in which the model repeats each sentence twice, with a pause after each one to permit the student to repeat the same words, thereby enhancing the likelihood of more perfect imitation.

It must always be remembered that voice disorders become such intimate parts of the personalities of their possessors that they are not eradicated easily. The student must be allowed to become accustomed to the new voice, and this process should be a gradual one. He should not be asked to use the new type of voice in all situations, after he has first acquired its mastery. Nucleus situations should be designated and gradually extended so they will ultimately include all of his speech experiences. He should voluntarily practice his new type of voice in public speaking and in other emotionally loaded situations.

Hoarse voice. The adjective *hoarse*, like most of those used for voice disorders, is somewhat vague. It is frequently but not always accompanied by huskiness or breathiness. Frequently produced by laryngitis, it often persists long after the infection or inflammation has disappeared. Many boys develop a hoarse voice just before puberty in their effort to imitate the voice quality of an adult male and it disappears with the laryngeal change. It also is often found in athletes as a result of their strenuous efforts which entail excessive closure of the glottis. Any great muscular effort requires a firm and rigid thorax and this requires a closure not only of the true but often of the false vocal cords. A hoarse voice can also be produced by phonation with the false vocal cords. It is usually low in pitch. Moser (66) has even used this voice in order to lower the habitual pitch. The false-vocal-cord or ventricular voice is not only hoarse but harsh. Voelker (71) describes it very well:

> The voice is apt to sound rough and crackling. The more chronic the use of this vicarious sound source, the more unpleasant the sound. . . . Ventricular voice is apt to be weak, and it is this weakness which causes the patient to seek attention of the physician or the speech clinic. The complaint of phonasthenia (weak voice) seems strange, since ventricular phonation is related to the explosive physiological functions in which the sound, if it is produced at all, as in coughing, sneezing, thoracic fixation or grunting, has considerable volume and carrying power. In fact, an actor was once trained in it to save his vocal cord voice through the long rehearsals and extended performances. That roar was completely adequate to fill the auditorium and even had the lion's ventriloquial effect in that it seemed to come from everywhere. Patients coming to clinics for ventricular hoarseness or phonasthenia regularly complain of clearing mucus from the throat and of hacking and coughing.

With respect to the last observation it is interesting that Allen and Peterson (58) found that the habitual use of a falsetto voice produced an inflammation of the vocal cords rather than the inflammation producing the vocal defect. Voelker (72) has the following to say about the causes of ventricular phonation:

> One patient complained of dropping his voice at the end of sentences, and it was found that he did not lower his vocal cord pitch but actually stopped using his vocal cords at the end of the sentence and substituted for them a ventricular vibration. An actor, with an excellent stage voice, complained of hoarseness only in conversation. It was found that in intimate and quiet conversation he used a ventricular voice to "save for his art" his stage voice. A youth was criticized by his parents for having a high and squeaky voice and acquired ventricular phonia in order to lower his voice to a normal pitch. Thus, instead of lowering his voice to a normal pitch, of perhaps 150 cycles, he lowered it to one of between 48 and 57 cycles. A similar case was found in which a man 31 years old, who had a deaf wife, became self-conscious about his yelling and outside his home developed phonation with the ventricular bands to subdue his voice. A college student raised the pitch of his voice to read aloud or to recite but used a ventricular tone in conversation. Sometimes it is found in careless conversation only. A 5-year-old boy was kidded by his playmates for

having a high voice, and he lowered it by acquiring a ventricular voice. An 18-year-old youth, with a eunuchoid quality, substituted ventricular phonation for his weak and strident vocal cord voice and thought his new hoarse voice gave the impression of masculine virility.

Illustrative Case Report

The case was a young man, aged 25 years, who had suffered infantile paralysis at thirteen, and as a result could only walk through the use of crutches. He seemed remarkably well adjusted to his physical handicap but was extremely concerned and maladjusted about his speech defect, a high-pitched falsetto voice. His history prior to the illness had little significance for prognosis or treatment. Thereafter he had developed withdrawal reactions ranging from fantasy to isolating himself on the farm of one of his father's tenants. He refused to attend high school after his Junior year. This reaction was the direct result of a remark he had overheard which cast aspersion on his masculinity. He came to the clinic reluctantly and without hope.

Examination disclosed normal secondary sex characteristics, vocal cords of normal length and texture, superior intelligence and hearing, musical talent, and marked introversion. Analysis of the voice demonstrated the following: excellent pitch discrimination and placement within his range; normal inflection and singing ability; a pitch range of nine semitones from D above middle C to $G\sharp$ with a habitual pitch of F. All of his tones, both sung or spoken, possessed the falsetto quality. He could yodel occasionally at higher pitches than those given. In speaking he habitually drew the larynx upward and backward as in swallowing. This reflex did occur frequently both prior to speech attempt and within his sentences. The omohyoid muscle was excessively contracted and resulted in a peculiar shoulder posture. He usually spoke with the chin lowered. All of the extrinsic throat muscles were highly tensed. No breathing abnormalities showed up in the polygraphic record.

Phonographic recording of the voice and the use of a hearing aid which amplified his own voice were used to help him formulate the problem to be solved and information was given him concerning the etiology and therapy for falsetto voice. Then he was asked to lie down on a cot with his head hanging backward over the edge. In this position he was asked to whisper a prolonged *ee* (*i*) vowel, sustaining it as long as possible. We then asked him to produce the same sound in the same way but "to sigh it softly but aloud." The pitch produced was G below middle C, and he was so surprised that he sat up, so tense that we terminated the conference, instructing him not to do any practice by himself. The next day the same procedure was performed, this time after preliminary relaxation and cautions to remain that way. We were able to produce all the vowels and voiced continuant sounds both in isolation and in nonsense syllables.

The next day we used short phrases and sentences first uttered in a monotone at a pitch level of A below middle C, then with inflections. No failure was experienced but at the end of the practice period he expressed doubts concerning his ability to speak "in a man's voice" with his head held normally. In our next session we raised the head slowly until it was level with the cot, without losing the lower pitch level. We suggested that he try the same technique by himself at home when lying on his bed. When he returned the next day he was speaking normally at a pitch level of *A* below middle *C*, and he reported that he had "slipped" into the falsetto only three times, during excitement. He complained, however, that he felt strange and uncomfortable "as though there was a stranger using my mouth." We then gave him a play to read with parts for a small child and a father. He used the old falsetto for the child's role and the new deep voice for the father's. Within a week he had become accustomed to the new voice and a year later was entirely recovered.

References

General References.

1. Bartholomew, W. T., "The Paradox of Voice Teaching," *Journal of the Acoustical Society of America*, 1940, Vol. 11, pages 446–450.
The author criticizes some of the directions given by voice and speech teachers about relaxing the throat, placing the voice, and "getting the voice out of the throat."

2. Curry, R., *The Mechanism of the Human Voice*, New York, Longmans Green, 1940.
Perhaps the best reference on the function of phonation to date. The anatomy, physiology, and physics of the voice are treated thoroughly and scientifically. The chapter "Disorders of the Voice" is a very excellent one.

3. Berry, M. and Eisenson, J., *The Defective in Speech*, New York, F. S. Crofts, 1942, pages 148–176.
A general discussion of the nature, causes, and treatment of voice disorders. Exercises are given for each of the main voice defects.

4. Fairbanks, G., *Practical Voice Practice*, New York, Harper, 1944. Exercise material for voice retraining is provided. There is an excellent section on changing the pitch and another on rate control and phrasing.

5. Fairbanks, G., "Recent Experimental Investigations of Vocal Pitch in Speech," *Journal of the Acoustical Society of America*, 1940, Vol. 11, pages 457–466.
A summary of unpublished investigations in voice. Natural pitch of superior male speakers is *C* below middle *C*; for superior female speakers, *G*♯ below middle *C*. Other similar data.

6. Fletcher, H., *Speech and Hearing*, New York, D. Van Nostrand, 1929.
A scientific consideration of the speech mechanism and speech waves, music and noise, the hearing mechanism and methods of testing its acuity, and the perception of speech and music. Many figures of sound frequencies are included.

7. Fröschels, E. and Jellinek, A., *Practice of Voice and Speech Therapy*, Boston, Expression Co., 1941, pages 248 *ff*.

A description and theoretical justification of the chewing method for producing relaxed voices.

8. Glauber, I. P., "Speech Characteristics of Psychoneurotic Patients," *Journal of Speech Disorders*, 1944, Vol. 9, pages 18–30.
Case presentations of psychoneurotic patients demonstrate that the voice of such patients is often affected.

9. Harrington, R., "A Study of the Mechanism of Velopharyngeal Closure," *Journal of Speech Disorders*, 1944, Vol. 9, pages 325–345.
A technical but excellent description of how the soft palate is controlled.

10. Heltman, H., "Re-education Techniques in Speech Correction," *Proceedings of the American Speech Correction Association*, 1936, Vol. 6, pages 130–141.
Suggested re-education for voice disorders on the basis of the thesis that all speech is the modification of more primitive laryngeal and articulatory utterances.

11. Holmes, F. L. D., *A Handbook of Voice and Diction*, New York, F. S. Crofts, 1940.
Exercises in relaxation, in getting the optimal pitch, in flexibility of pitch and intensity, and in voice quality retraining are given.

12. Huber, M. W. and Kopp, A. E., *The Practice of Speech Correction in the Medical Clinic*, Boston, Expression Co., 1942.
Treats the more rare varieties of abnormal voice such as: vicarious voice; hoarseness; adenoidal speech; and dysphonias of functional origin.

13. Judson, L. and Weaver, A. T., *Voice Science*, New York, F. S. Crofts, 1941.
The anatomy, physiology, and physics of voice are described in detail. The examination technique for observing the larynx is clearly presented.

14. Manser, R., "Voice Problems of University Students," *Proceedings of the American Speech Correction Association*, 1938, Vol. 8, pages 90–102.
Especially valuable for the medical reports accompanying the diagnoses.

15. Moore, W. E., "Personality Traits and Voice Quality Deficiencies," *Journal of Speech Disorders*, 1939, Vol. 4, pages 33–36.
The results of personality tests administered to voice-quality cases are analyzed in terms of their causal significance. Anxiety leads to tension, and tension to vocal defect.

16. Negus, V. E., *The Mechanism of Phonation*, St. Louis, C. V. Mosby, 1930.
A scientific discussion of the physiological processes of the larynx, some of its evolution, the role of the vocal cords and the sphinteric, thyro-arytenoid, crico-arytenoid, and crico-thyroid muscles, the function of the arytenoid cartilages, the determination of pitch, and the influence of various resonators. Illustrative figures are included.

17. Pronovost, W., "Research Contributions to Voice Improvement," *Journal of Speech Disorders*, 1942, Vol. 7, pages 313–318.
The results of recent investigations in voice are summarized and their implications for vocal therapy are presented. There are good suggestions for breathiness, increasing the pitch range, and improving the quality.

18. Scripture, E. W., *The Elements of Experimental Phonetics*, New York, Scribner's, 1902.
This old classic is still the source of many novel ideas regarding voice. The section on overtone production is especially worth reading.

19. Stanley, D. and Maxfield, J. P., *The Voice, Its Production and Reproduction*, New York, Pitman, 1933.
A general treatise on the voice and its abnormalities. The sections on nasality and on harsh strident voices are very well done.

20. Stetson, R. H. and Hudgins, C. V., "Functions of the Breathing Movements in the Mechanism of Speech," *Archives Neerlandaises de Phonetique Experimentale*, 1930, Vol. 5, pages 1–30.
Description of normal speech breathing with emphasis on gradual relaxation of the thoracic muscles and the diaphragm and greater abdominal contraction during exhalation.

21. Van Dusen, C. R., *Training the Voice for Speech*, New York, McGraw-Hill, 1943.
A general text on the subject of defective voice and voice retraining. Exercises and exercise material (mainly poetry) are provided.

22. West, R., "The Function of the Speech Pathologists in Studying Cases of Dysphonia," *Journal of Speech Disorders*, 1938, Vol. 3, pages 81–84.
Brief discussion of the duties of a speech correctionist in diagnosing and treating functional speech disorders.

23. Wyatt, G., "Voice Disorders and Personality Conflicts," *Mental Hygiene*, 1941, Vol. 25, pages 237–250.
The emotional causes of voice disorders are discussed.

Pathological Vocal Defects

24. Ash, J. E., "The Laryngeal (Vocal Cord) Node," *Transactions of the American Academy of Ophthalmology and Otolaryngology*, May–June, 1944, pages 323–332.
Excessive use or abuse of the voice was reported in every one of 138 cases of nodes on the vocal cords.

25. Guthrie, D., "Pathology of Speech and Voice," *Edinborough Medical Journal*, 1940, Vol. 47, pages 391–405.
Besides cleft palates, other disorders of voice such as organic aphonia are discussed from a medical point of view.

26. Jackson, C. and Jackson, C. L., *The Larynx and Its Diseases*, Philadelphia, Saunders, 1937.
The best reference work on the diseases of the larynx that can produce vocal disorders.

27. Levbarg, J. L., "Vocal Therapy Versus Surgery for the Eradication of Singers' and Speakers' Nodules," *The Eye, Ear, Nose and Throat Monthly*, 1939, Vol. 18, pages 81–91.
Surgery should not be used until rest and vocal training have been tried.

28. Koepp-Baker, H., "A Rare Case of Aphonia Organica," *Archives of Speech*, 1936, Vol. 1, pages 231–247.
A description of the methods of treatment and re-education in a case of laryngeal web, with accompanying pictures.

29. Oldrey, B. N., "The Speech of Children with Enlarged Adenoids and Tonsils," London, *Speech, The Journal of the British Society of Speech Therapists*, 1936, Vol. 1, pages 28–33.
First remove the obstructions by surgery, then use relaxation, plus speech training.   Recommends several exercises.

30. Russell, G. O., "Etiology of Follicular Pharyngitis, Catarrhal Laryngitis, So-Called Clergyman's Throat, and Singer's Nodes," *Journal of Speech Disorders*, December 1936, pages 113–122.
The causes and treatment of nodes on the vocal cords are described.

31. Strother, C. R., "The Vocal Consequences of Various Surgical Procedures for Relief of Bilateral Recurrent Nerve Paralysis of the Larynx," *Journal of Speech Disorders*, 1940, Vol. 5, pages 121–127.
Do not do any speech training with bilateral paralysis of vocal cords or patient may die.   Describes a new operation which restores abduction of cords and then permits speech therapy.

32. West, R., Kennedy, L., and Carr, A., *The Rehabilitation of Speech*, New York, Harper, 1937, Chapters 7 and 25.
Chapter 7 considers the dysphonias (vocal disturbances) caused by pharyngeal and laryngeal deformities, and suggests voice training for the irregular glottis, for the insufficient laryngeal band adduction, for stenoses of the vocal outlet, and for the laryngectomized patient.

Disorders of Pitch

33. Barrows, S. T. and Pierce, A. E., *The Voice: How To Use It*, Boston, Expression Co., 1933, pages 145–155.
A classification of the defects of pitch, with remedial exercises for each type.

34. Crews, L., "A Case of Juvenile Voice," *Proceedings of the American Speech Correction Association*, 1936, Vol. 6, pages 142–149.
The description of the treatment of a youth with a child's voice.

35. Fairbanks, G., *Practical Voice Practice*, New York, F. S. Crofts, 1944.
Methods for determining the natural pitch of the voice are described and exercises and drill material for changing the pitch are given.

36. Gilkinson, H., "A Study of the Relationship Between Psychological and Physical Measures of Masculinity," *Genetic Psychology Monographs*, 1937, Vol. 19, pages 105–154.
This study gives methods for determining the habitual pitch levels, with an account of the reliability of the measures.

37. Guthrie, D., "Discussion of Functional Disorders of Voice," *Proceedings of the Royal Society of Medicine*, 1939, Vol. 32, pages 447–454.
A good discussion of pitch changes during puberty, and cautions concerning the use of the voice during this period.

38. Jerome, E. K., "Change of Voice in Male Adolescents," *Quarterly Journal of Speech*, 1937, Vol. 23, pages 648–653.
A controlled study of the relation of change of voice to chronological age, mental age, and skeletal age.

39. Lassers, L., "Some Possible Factors in the Development of the High-

pitched Voice in the Adult Male," *Speech Abstracts*, 1943, Vol. 3, pages 49–53.
Heredity or imitation seems to be an important cause of high voices in adult males. Puberty was delayed somewhat. Few signs of maladjustment. Delayed sexual development not a major cause of most of these disorders.

40. Ridpath, R., "The Falsetto Voice," *Laryngoscope*, 1928, Vol. 38, pages 469–471.
A résumé of the knowledge on the subject of the falsetto voice. Author cites the two theories concerning the cause of falsetto voices which are presented throughout the literature on the subject.

41. Root, A. R., "The Pitch Factor in Speech; A Survey," *Quarterly Journal of Speech*, 1930, Vol. 16, pages 320–335.
A survey of the historical concepts of pitch and pitch changes, with a summary of recent experimental investigations in the field. A long bibliography is included.

42. Seth, G. and Guthrie, D., *Speech in Childhood*, London, Oxford University Press, 1935, pages 200–203.
A short description of change of voice in both boys and girls, and an explanation of common voice disorders at puberty.

Intensity Disorders

43. Babcock, M., "Speech Therapy for Certain Vocal Disorders," *Journal of Laryngology and Otolaryngology*, 1942, Vol. 57, pages 101–112.
Treatment for aphonia and weak voices is included in this article.

44. Barnes, J., "Vital Capacity and Oral Reading," *Quarterly Journal of Speech*, 1926, Vol. 12, pages 176–182.
No relationship between vital capacity and poor speech. Control of breath more important than not enough breath.

45. Bullowa, A. M., "Need of Speech Work in High School," *Proceedings N.E.A.*, Volume 54, 1916, pages 870–874.
In order to get a low-pitched voice, these children close their mouths and have muffled, inaudible speech.

46. Felderman, L., *The Human Voice*, New York, Henry Holt, 1931.
Several cases are described of weak or aphonic voices together with their causes.

47. Fletcher, H., *Speech and Hearing*, New York, D. Van Nostrand, 1929, pages 266–289.
This section of the book lists the audibility characteristics of the various speech sounds.

48. Gray, G. W. and Wise, C. M., *The Bases of Speech*, New York, Harper, 1934, pages 125–126.
A short description concluding that extreme clavicular breathing will produce inadequate vocal intensity.

49. Greene, J. S., "Psychiatric Therapy for Dysphonias; Aphonia; Psychophonasthenia; Falsetto," *Archives of Otolaryngology*, 1938, Vol. 28, pages 213–221.

A description of the emotional causes of weak voices together with the psychiatric treatment for them.   Group therapy is outlined.

50. Laase, L. T., "The Effect of Pitch and Intensity on the Quality of the Vowels," *Archives of Speech*, 1937, Vol. 2, pages 28–40.
Improper pitch levels can alter the quality of the voice and reduce the intensity.

51. Marsh, F. D., "Functional Aphonia (Some Observations on Its Clinical Aspects)," *Lancet*, 1932, Vol. 2, pages 289–290.
A summary of sixteen cases of functional aphonia seen by the author. He shows that a determining cause for the disorder is often present, and should be treated by direct dealing with the septic focus.

52. Mithoefer, W., "Simple Treatment for Defects of Singing and Speaking Voice," *Archives of Otolaryngology*, 1941, Vol. 31, pages 16–22.
The author recommends the use of a faradic current of electricity as part of the treatment for aphonia and dysphonia.

53. Sokolowsky, R. R. and Junkermann, E. B., "War Aphonia," *Journal of Speech Disorders*, 1944, Vol. 9, pages 193–208.
The nature and treatment of aphonia.   The various methods for shocking the patient into vocalization are described.

54. Talley, C. H., "A Comparison of Conversational and Audience Types of Speech," *Archives of Speech*, 1937, Vol. 2, pages 28–40.
Methods for "projecting" the voice are analyzed.

55. Tiffin, J. and Steer, M. D., "An Experimental Analysis of Emphasis," *Speech Monographs*, 1937, Vol. 4, pages 69–74.
Pitch changes as well as intensity variations are used to emphasize certain words.

56. Watkins, D. E., *An Introduction to the Art of Speech*, New York, W. W. Norton, 1934, pages 97–123.
This chapter deals with the intensity of vocal sounds, and considers resonance, loudness, the amount and degree of force, with illustrative material for both stress and force.

57. Wiksell, W. A., "An Experimental Analysis of Respiration in Relation to the Intensity of Vocal Tones in Speech," *State University of Louisiana Studies*, 1936, Vol. 27, pages 37–51; 99–164.
An analysis of the relation between vocal tone and types of breathing, vocal capacity, and chest expansion.

Voice Quality Disorders

58. Allen, B. and Peterson, G. E., "Laryngeal Inflammation in a Case of Falsetto," *Journal of Speech Disorders*, 1942, Vol. 7, 174–175.
An outline of the analysis of a case of falsetto voice.

59. Drake, O. J., "Toward an Improved Voice Quality," *Quarterly Journal of Speech*, 1937, Vol. 23, pages 620–626.
A summary and brief description of the most important steps necessary to train better voice quality: hearing, breathing, frontal placement, valve timing, adjusted muscular tonus, and conscious attention during learning.

60. Holmes, L., "The Qualities of Voice," *Quarterly Journal of Speech*, 1932, Vol. 28, pages 249–260.
A discussion of the relation of infra-glottal resonance to "qualities of voice," with a description of several voice qualities.

61. Hultzen, L. S., "Apparatus for Demonstrating Nasality," *Journal of Speech Disorders*, 1942, Vol. 7, pages 5–7.
Describes a contact microphone to fit on the nose and thereby to help self-hearing and ear training.

62. Jacobson, E., *Progressive Relaxation*, Chicago, University of Chicago Press, 1938.
A practical clinical discussion of the method of progressive relaxation in which the person is trained to reduce or completely eliminate muscular tension. A long bibliography is given.

63. Kantner, C. L., "Four Devices in the Treatment of Rhinolalia Aperta," *Journal of Speech Disorders*, June, 1937, pages 73–76.
A description of four devices used in treatment of cases in which nasality is caused by an abnormal escape of air through the nasal cavity: balloon blowing, manometric flame, apparatus testing firmness of velar and pharyngeal closure, and wet spirometer apparatus.

64. Kelly, J. P., "Studies in Nasality," *Archives of Speech*, 1934, Vol. 1, pages 26–43.
A report of research carried out on a group of superior speakers and a group of hypernasal speakers to discover the duration of nasal air discharge during the performance of the various vowels.

65. Moser, H. M., "Diagnostic and Clinical Procedures in Rhinolalia," *Journal of Speech Disorders*, 1942, Vol. 7, pages 1–4.
Describes twelve methods, mechanical and otherwise, which will aid a case in lifting his soft palate, or in strengthening it.

66. Moser, H. M., "Symposium on Unique Cases of Speech Disorders; Presentation of a Case," 1942, Vol. 7, pages 173–174.
The author describes the use of ventricular phonation as a device to lower the habitual pitch of the voice.

67. Poe, D. L., "Further Studies of Rhinolalia Aperta," *Archives of Pediatrics*, 1933, Vol. 50, pages 147–157.
A further report on a previous study on nasal speech in children resulting from tonsilectomy. The author believed the underlying cause to be the pain incident to the operation. He suggests the use of electric current, stretching, massaging, and speaking exercises as the correct therapy in the elimination of excess nasality.

68. Raubicheck, L., Davis, E. H., and Carll, A. L., *Voice and Speech Problems*, New York, Prentice-Hall, 1931, pages 326–330.
A consideration of nasality and denasalization, with a list of exercises for the treatment of nasality.

69. Slattengren, H., "Nasal Speech," *Quarterly Journal of Speech*, 1934, Vol. 21, pages 542–546.
Drills for helping a child learn to resonate the *m*, *n*, and *ng* sounds.

70. Van Dusen, C. R., "A Laboratory Study of the Metallic Voice," *Journal of Speech Disorders*, 1941, Vol. 6, pages 137–140.
A description of the auditory characteristics of the harsh "metallic" voice. The fundamental and lower overtones are more prominent in the metallic voice.

71. Voelker, C. H., "Frequency of Hoarseness Due to Phonation with the Thyro-arytenoid Lips," *Archives Otolaryngology*, 1942, Vol. 36, pages 71–76.
Vocalization with the false vocal cords frequently produces hoarse voices.

72. Voelker, C. H., "Phoniatry in Dysphonia Ventricularis," *Annals of Otology, Rhinology, and Laryngology*, 1935, Vol. 44, pages 471–472.
Describes the unpleasant voice quality as "a rattling, tumbling, cracking or ticker-like substitution for phonation." Outlines the treatment.

73. West, R., "Recent Studies in Speech Pathology," *Proceedings of the American Speech Correction Association*, 1936, Vol. 6, pages 44–49.
An important discussion of nasality, considering especially the functions of the velum and the nares, and the nature of cul de sac resonance.

74. Williamson, A. B., "Diagnosis and Treatment of Eighty-four Cases of Nasality," *Quarterly Journal of Speech*, 1944, Vol. 30, pages 471–479.
An excellent summary of the nature of nasality and denasality. The author recommends general voice training and declares that soft-palate exercises are not as essential as had been thought.

75. Williamson, A. B., "Diagnosis and Treatment of Seventy-Two Cases of Hoarse Voice," *Quarterly Journal of Speech*, 1945, Vol. 31, pages 189–202.
Hoarseness, which has often been thought to be of pathological origin, is here shown to be frequently functional. The most frequent cause was the attempt to speak at too low a pitch level. Treatment is outlined.

X

Stuttering: Its Nature and Causes

Stuttering, perhaps the most dramatic of all the speech disorders, is also the most difficult to describe or treat.   Despite years of research the disorder presents many unknowns, and the current arguments and confusions which puzzle the beginning student of speech correction merely reflect our professional ignorance.   In reading this text and the other texts to which we refer, the student is cautioned to examine the statements of fact with a critical eye and to check them against his personal observation and pertinent research.

So far as stuttering is concerned, speech correction is at present in the era of "authorities" just as medicine was before Pasteur's discovery of bacterial agents in disease.   Some of those early medical authorities were able and wise physicians.   They had made some very keen and valid observations concerning diseases.   In some instances they discovered the cure for the disease long before they knew its nature.   For example, the witch doctors of native tribes on the Malay Peninsula diagnosed diabetes by putting specimens of urine near ant hills, and, when the ants were attracted, prescribed certain food taboos which helped their patients cut down on sugar intake.   The results were excellent, but the theories which they used to justify their diagnosis and prescription were, to say the least, confused and inaccurate. Stutterers have been helped by many different methods of treatment based on many conflicting theories.   In this text we shall endeavor to present the nature and treatment of stuttering in the light of our present knowledge.   There is much that we do not know about stuttering, yet we know enough to help the majority of our cases.

In Chapter II we defined stuttering as the disorder characterized by blockings, prolongations, or repetitions of words, syllables, sounds, or mouth postures, all of which (together with the contortions or devices used to avoid, postpone, disguise, start, or release the speech abnormality) produce interruptions and breaks in the rhythmic flow of speech. This is admittedly more of a description than a definition, and it indicates the complexity of the disorder. In its mildest form, its possessor is often entirely unaware of the interruptions. In very severe stutterers, the interruptions are accompanied by contortions so grotesque that they almost resemble spastic and epileptic seizures. In adult stutterers, an almost infinite variety of stuttering symptoms may be found, although in young children, when the disorder first tends to manifest itself, the symptoms are largely confined to the above-mentioned repetitions and prolongations. These seem to be the only symptoms common to all stutterers.

Stuttering is no respecter of persons. It afflicts king and beggar, savant and ignoramus, Hebrew and Hottentot, virtuous and sinful, and all other categories you might choose. Moses himself is said to have stuttered, and we know that King Charles I, Charles Lamb, and Charles Darwin (to select but three of the millions of people who have experienced this disorder) were likewise afflicted. There are approximately 1,400,000 stutterers in the United States alone, and one of every one hundred children is destined to suffer from this abnormality.

It is obvious that so universal and dramatic a disorder should provoke many attempts to cure it or alleviate its distress, and the history of these attempts comprises a large share of the history of speech correction. Witchcraft, the surgeon's knife, appliances for the tongue, drugs, hypnotism, psychoanalysis, arm swinging, and a host of other devices and methods have been employed, and a few "cures" seem to be obtained by any method, no matter how grotesque. Naturally, the charlatans and quacks have flourished in so fertile a field, victimizing many thousands of stutterers every year. The medical profession, however, has largely ignored stutterers, and only in the last few years have the scientists concerned themselves with their urgent problem. Much of the research that has been carried out has been sterile, resulting in a large number of antagonistic theories whose proposers have spent more time in defending their theories than in testing to discover more pertinent facts about the abnormality.

Theories concerning the nature and cause of stuttering. Although more research has been carried out on stuttering than on any other speech disorder, speech correctionists have failed to agree on any one explanation of its nature and its cause. The reasons for this lack of agreement have been the complexity of the disorder and the difficulty experienced by experimenters in controlling all of the many physiological and psychological factors which affect its frequency, form, and duration.   As the history of medicine clearly demonstrates, whenever a disorder or disease is produced or affected by many different factors, many conflicting theories arise, many authorities wrangle, and many kinds of medicine or treatment are used.

Most of the theories of stuttering are based upon observation rather than research.   Many of them confuse the nature of the stuttering block with its causation, although both phases of the disorder should be investigated independently.   The advanced student must be cautioned to scrutinize the research cited in evidence of any theory and to judge its adequacy in terms of all the phenomenology of stuttering. Every theory explains certain of the characteristics of some stuttering, but the author knows of none which is sufficiently comprehensive or substantiated to cover all the facts.   When considering each theory, the student should ask himself four questions: (1) What is the cause mentioned by the authority who espouses this theory?   (2) What is said to be the nature of the actual symptoms shown by the stutterer, the repetitions, prolongations, forcings, head-movements, fears, and so on?   (3) How does he explain the variation in stuttering symptoms from individual to individual, or the change in the symptoms of the same stutterer as he grows older?   (4) What research findings does he offer in support of these statements and what evidence seems to contradict them?

Almost every theory, including that espoused by the author of this text, seems to rest on a very insecure foundation when subjected to such a critical scrutiny.   Nevertheless, it seems wiser to select some explanation which seems to fit most of the characteristics of stuttering and to carry out research rather than to shrug our shoulders and wait for posterity to do the formulating and experimenting for us.   Meanwhile, stutterers are in great need of help and it is certain that we do know enough to do a great deal for them.

Since it is difficult to condense the statement of any theory without distorting it, the student is referred to the references at the end of this chapter.   Bender and Kleinfeld [1] enumerate and describe fifteen different major theories, but these probably can be reduced to six by combining those that are variants of the educational theory.   These six are the educational, psychoanalytical, neurological, neurotic, im-

[1] Bender, James F. and Kleinfeld, Victor M., *Principles and Practices of Speech Correction*, New York, Pitman, 1938, pages 241–266.

agery, and inhibitory theories. The educational theory holds that stuttering is a bad habit originating in the natural hesitations of children's speech and perpetuated by penalty and fear. Stoddard,[2] McDowell,[3] and Russell[4] are its exponents. The psychoanalytical theory holds that stuttering is the result of a fixation at the oral or anal stages of sexual development and that its symptoms are movements akin to those of nursing, micturition, or the expulsion of the flatus. Coriat[5] and Clark[6] are its chief exponents. The neurological theory is variously stated, but its major tenets are that the paired musculature used in speech does not receive properly timed nervous impulses from the various integrating centers of the central nervous system. This condition is thought to be brought about by interference of the thalamus, cerebellum, or nondominant hemisphere with the integrations of the dominant half of the cerebral cortex. The stutterers are said to possess less unilateral cerebral dominance than normal speakers, and hence are more susceptible to breakdown. The chief exponents of this theory are Orton,[7] Travis,[8] and Bryngelson.[9] The neurotic theory considers stuttering to be a symptom of a basic personality problem, of a maladjustment to the demands of normal life. The hesitations and anxieties are considered as symptoms of the stutterer's attitudes toward life itself. The chief exponents of this theory are Fletcher,[10] the Blantons,[11] and Brown.[12] The imagery theory claims that the stutterer lacks the visual or auditory imagery supposed by those who espouse this theory to be essential to normal

---

[2] Stoddard, Clara B., "The Correction of Stammering in Detroit," *A Symposium on Stuttering*, Madison, Wisconsin, College Typing Co., 1931, pages 92–99.

[3] McDowell, E., "Educational and Emotional Adjustments of Stuttering Children," *Teachers College Contributions to Education*, 1928, No. 314, pages 1–59.

[4] Russell, G. O., "Neuro-pedagogical Process of Treating Stammerers and Stutterers at Ohio State University," *A Symposium on Stuttering*, Madison, Wisconsin, College Typing Co., 1931, pages 188–192.

[5] Coriat, I. H., "Stammering. A Psychoanalytic Interpretation," *Nervous and Mental Disease Monographs*, 1928, No. 47, pages 1–68.

[6] Clark, P. L., "Study of the Psychogenesis of Confirmed Stammerers," *Journal of Nervous and Mental Diseases*, 1926, Vol. 63, page 238.

[7] Orton, S., *Reading, Writing, and Speech Problems in Children*, New York, W. W. Norton and Co., 1937.

[8] Travis, L. E., *Speech Pathology*, New York, D. Appleton-Century Co., 1931.

[9] Bryngelson, B., "Sidedness as an Etiological Factor in Stuttering," *Journal of Genetic Psychology*, 1935, Vol. 47, pages 204–217.

[10] Fletcher, J. M., *The Problem of Stuttering*, New York, Longmans, Green & Co., 1928.

[11] Blanton, S. and M. G., *For Stutterers*, New York, D. Appleton-Century Co., 1936.

[12] Brown, Frederick W., "Personality Integration as the Essential Factor in the Permanent Cure of Stuttering," *Mental Hygiene*, 1933, Vol. 17, pages 266–277.

speech. Swift [13] and Bluemel [14] are the chief exponents, although the latter has recently shifted his position. The inhibitory theory, now proposed chiefly by Bluemel,[15] claims that stuttering arises when the conditioned response of speech is inhibited by some traumatic experience, and the inhibition itself is conditioned to certain word cues or features of the speech situation. Criticisms of some of these theories are given in the articles and texts by Bluemel,[16] Brown,[17] Johnson,[18] West,[19] and Hahn.[20]

Johnson (84) has recently formulated a "semantogenic" theory of stuttering in which he identifies primary stuttering with the perfectly normal hesitations and repetitions of normal children. When these are wrongly labeled as stuttering, the child begins to react to the evaluations as though the symptoms were actually abnormal, and hence abnormal behavior is produced.

Is there any possibility of reconciling all of these theories into a single concept of stuttering? Thus far, several attempts have been made to do so (Hahn [11], and Ainsworth [1]), but the disparity of theories is so wide that none has been entirely successful. It is interesting to note that the attempts that have been tried have all involved the concept of multicausality. The *fallacy of the single cause* has been responsible for confusion in many fields of science, and we feel that it may be similarly responsible for some of the conflict in our own.

Predisposing causes. We feel that stuttering can result from any of three etiologies or combinations thereof. It can arise from (1) *a background of dysphemia*, from (2) *the speech hesitations of early speech learning*, or from (3) *neurotic emotional conflicts* which reflect themselves in hesitancy. We feel that the onset of every case of stuttering can be explained in terms of one or more of these factors. Scientists

---

[13] Swift, Walter B., "A Psychological Analysis of Stuttering," *Journal of Abnormal and Social Psychology*, 1915, Vol. 32, pages 3–13.

[14] Bluemel, C. S., *Mental Aspects of Stuttering*, Baltimore, Williams & Wilkins Co., 1930.

[15] Bluemel, C. S., *Stammering and Allied Disorders*, New York, Macmillan Co., 1935.

[16] *Ibid.*

[17] Brown, Frederick W., "Viewpoints on Stuttering," *American Journal of Orthopsychiatry*, 1932, Vol. 2, pages 230–241.

[18] Johnson, Wendell, "An Interpretation of Stuttering," *Quarterly Journal of Speech*, 1933, Vol. 19, pages 70–75.

[19] West, Robert, "The Phenomenology of Stuttering," *A Symposium on Stuttering*, Madison, Wisconsin, College Typing Co., 1931, pages 1–6.

[20] Hahn, E., "An Integration of Stuttering Therapies," *Journal of Speech Disorders*, 1937, Vol. 2, pages 87–94.

have been chasing the *one cause* of stuttering too long and with too little success. Is it not possible that speech hesitation (which is the common factor in all stuttering) can be produced by several factors? Some of our cases show vivid histories of neurosis. Others are indubitably clumsy in the rhythmic movement of the speech musculature. Still others are the victims of parental ignorance concerning the teaching of talking.

Dysphemia. By the term *dysphemia* we refer to an underlying neuromuscular condition which reflects itself peripherally in nervous impulses that are poorly timed in their arrival in the paired speech musculatures. Travis (51) has shown that during the stuttering block the action currents (which accompany nervous impulses from the brain) do not appear simultaneously. This may indicate a lack of cerebral dominance, according to his theory, or merely the disruption of co-ordination which results from emotional upheaval in the central nervous system. Most co-ordinations break down under great stress of fear or insecurity, and the co-ordinations of speech have always been known to reflect emotional blockings. The importance of the concept of dysphemia is that it explains the stutterer's speech interruptions in terms of a nervous system which breaks down *relatively easily* in its integration of the flow of nervous impulses to the paired peripheral muscles. In order to lift the jaw, for instance, nervous impulses must arrive simultaneously in the paired muscles of each side. In some stutterers these arrival times are disrupted; they are not synchronized. It is very difficult to lift a jaw or a wheelbarrow by one handle. The dysphemic individual is able to time his speech co-ordinations pretty well as long as the co-ordinating centers in the brain are not being bedeviled by emotional reactions and their back-flow of visceral sensations. He can talk pretty well when calm and unexcited. But his thresholds of resistance to emotional disturbance are low. His co-ordinations break down under relatively little stress. We have all known pianists and golfers who could play excellently by themselves but whose co-ordinations were pitifully inadequate to the demands of concert or tournament pressures. The dysphemic person is thought to be neurologically differentiated from other persons in what Gutzmann [21] speaks of as "a weakness of the central co-ordinating system."

It may well be true that the term *dysphemia* is merely a cloak for

[21] Gutzmann, H., quoted in the article by Fröschels (58).

our ignorance, yet there are many evidences that such a condition exists in certain individuals. Chief among these are research findings which indicate that (1) the tendency to stuttering seems to be inherited; (2) the stutterer is often more poorly co-ordinated in swift or rhythmic movements of the speech musculatures during silence; (3) the stutterer exhibits metabolic and biochemical differences; (4) the stutterer frequently shows confusion in handedness and other peripheral signs of central laterality; (5) the brain waves of stutterers differ from those of nonstutterers. These research findings are not entirely conclusive, since other investigations have challenged their accuracy; yet when we consider that among the groups of stutterers tested there must have been many whose stuttering was of neurotic or developmental origin, the positive findings seem to have increased significance.

Many phrases other than dysphemia have been used to indicate that stutterers are neurologically differentiated from nonstutterers. Some of these are: "neuropathic diasthesis," "lack of a sufficient margin of cerebral dominance," "constitutional in-co-ordination," and "nervous instability." Greene (34), for instance, says:

The stutterer is psychobiologically a variant. Whatever the exact nature of the underlying inferiority—and as yet we do not know—it appears to be an hereditary factor that predisposes the individual to emotional instability and disorganization in general, and to stuttering speech in particular.

Hahn (11), whose text summarizes the current views concerning the theories and therapies of stuttering, declares:

Most authorities view stuttering as the result of a malfunctioning nervous system, and contend that in the early or primary periods of onset the central nervous system has not reached a maturation point sufficient to withstand certain shocks, childhood diseases, ego competitiveness or malnutrition. These and other "trigger" causes affect the nervous system and speech, dependent so much on finely adjusted muscle groups under brain leadership, naturally is affected.

Developmental factors. Besides dysphemia and emotional conflicts as predisposing causes of stuttering, there are certain features in the developmental history of some stutterers which may serve as the soil out of which stuttering symptoms may sprout. Some of these developmental factors are *birth injuries, illnesses with high fevers,*

excessive thyroid medication, head injuries, and allergic disturbance.
Many cerebral-palsy cases stutter, and Milisen (42), Berry (21), and
others have found that more stutterers gave a history of these conditions than did a group of nonstutterers. Johnson's study (61) of a
smaller number of cases showed contrary results. We deem it reasonable that these factors could interfere with the maturation of the
speech skills. A severe illness between the ages of one and three
years could reasonably be expected to upset the mastery of syntax,
vocabulary, and phrasing. Co-ordinations of any sort are affected
by the above developmental factors, and speech should be no exception. They may serve only to let comprehension outrun motor
ability, but this could produce more hesitancy than would have occurred had the development been entirely normal.

Another type of developmental factor which could predispose the
child to stuttering is that inherent in the *poor methods used by parents
in the teaching of talking*. We have discussed this at some length in
our chapter on the development of speech. So many children begin
to stutter during the early months of speech learning that there must
be some relationship between their hesitancies and the type of
pedagogy used by the parents. Children frequently try to conform
to the fluency patterns of adults, to use compound-complex sentences,
when their speech skills only permit simple phrasing. Uncertainties
abound in every utterance. Words must be chosen; relationships must
be expressed; articulation must be mastered or the communication
will fail; inhalations must be timed to coincide with thinking; exhalation must be prolonged and yet conserved. When all these and a
hundred other skills must be simultaneously achieved, the presence of
parental interruption, correction, anticipation of desires, refusal or
penalty may create and perpetuate breaks in fluency. All children
meet some of these problems; a few children are overwhelmed by a
host of them and begin to show speech hesitancy to excess. They
may finally come to regard speech as though hesitation were a natural
part of it. Many young stutterers act as though their repetitions
were an integral part of their language. If a child learns hesitant,
broken-speech rhythms, he will continue to speak in the same pattern
until he finally realizes that it is not socially acceptable. We feel that
parental lack of knowledge about the teaching of talking is responsible
for the great difficulty many children have in mastering the fluency
aspects of speech as well as their articulation skills. The obstacles
which the parents unknowingly place in the path of speech learning

are no doubt responsible for much **primary** stuttering. **They** certainly help to lay the foundation for it.

Emotional conflicts. We are sure that some stutterers do not have dysphemia. Indeed we have examined certain children who had no stuttering in the family, whose brain waves were entirely normal, whose developmental history was without incident, whose diadochokinesis and rhythmokinesis were far superior to those of the normal speaker, and yet who stuttered severely. These individuals, however, were very hesitant in all forms of social adjustment. In each of these cases, we found a clear history of prolonged anxiety and insecurity.

Most normal speakers have been aware of hesitancy in their own speech during emotional excitement. All of us hesitate when in a condition of ambivalence. We hesitate to ask a favor that may be refused. We hesitate to make a statement that may be incorrect. We hesitate to confess a crime or misdemeanor. This hesitancy does not cease with the speech attempt. It often interrupts the fluency with repetitions, pauses, and blockings. These normal phenomena may help us to understand how a small child who lives in a continuous condition of uncertainty, anxiety, and insecurity might evidence so many breaks in fluency as to attract attention and interfere with communication.

An excerpt from a case history by Louttit [22] may illustrate this type of etiology:

The boy's mother furnished the key to his difficulty at the first interview. He had been badly affected, she said, by the death of his younger brother in July, four years ago. Since that day he had never spoken of his brother nor would he remain in the presence of others who were speaking of him. He began to stutter in the fall of the same year, the day he returned to school.

This boy was seen for a period of a half to three-quarters of an hour weekly for a period of twenty weeks, and was a member of the group of stutterers meeting once a week for conversation. Because of his high intelligence and the known existence of a serious emotional disturbance of which he was, in part, painfully conscious, his brother's death was made the point of direct attack, the conversation gradually leading up to it at the third interview. His memories of his brother, his relationships with him, and attitudes toward him, the circumstances leading up to his brother's death, and his own reactions to that event were carefully and systematically discussed.

In summary, it may be said that he had always been very jealous of his

---

[22] Louttit, C. M., *Clinical Psychology*, New York, Harper, 1936, pages 446–450, by permission of the publishers.

brother, had often knocked him about and hurt him, and had attempted, unsuccessfully, he believed, to get his parents to see that he was the smarter and better of the two. When the brother died, he was filled with remorse for having treated him so badly and, after a few weeks, the conviction developed that he had been responsible for his brother's death, that his parents knew it and would never forgive him, and that he could never hope to attain the position in their affections that his brother had held. He found some solace at first in lavishing the affection and care that he felt he should have shown toward his brother on the brother's pet dog. But he was soon deprived of even this outlet when the dog was killed by an automobile, and he felt that he had lost his last friend and confidant.

Stuttering began suddenly the day he entered seventh grade in a new school, where he was lonely, in strange surroundings, and with many new and unfamiliar faces around him. On his way to school, and after reaching the classroom, he kept thinking of his brother, grieving that he had been "put away" and that he could never again come to school with him or play with him as in former years. His mind was filled with such thoughts when the teacher called on him to tell his name and give other personal information to the class. As he arose to speak, he felt strange and frightened and could think only of his brother. He could not speak his own name, for only the name of the brother came to mind. He stammered and blushed and hung his head, and when the teacher remarked, "I guess he doesn't know his name," he sat down without speaking. From this time on his speech difficulty was present, varying from time to time from fear and embarrassment which prevented him from attempting to speak, to forgetting what he wanted to say or stuttering severely after he was on his feet. At home he stuttered badly and could not talk over the telephone at all.

Every speech correctionist has heard similar tales, and it seems impossible to escape the fact that some cases of stuttering are not only precipitated but actually produced by emotional conflict.

In summarizing our discussion of the predisposing causes of stuttering, we can say that the disorder may arise from a deep-seated dysphemia, from emotional conflicts in which the hesitant speech reflects an underlying anxiety, and from environmental factors which tend to interfere with the child's mastery of the fluency aspect of speech learning. Any one of these predisposing causes may serve as the foundation for stuttering, and in many cases they occur in combination. The child who suffers from all three malinfluences is almost sure to become hesitant.

Precipitating causes. Stuttering usually begins rather gradually and parent's testimony concerning the onset of the disorder is often unreliable, especially when the stuttering is of several years' duration. The testimony of adult stutterers concerning the precipitating causes must also be carefully scrutinized.   People seem eager to blame the cause of stuttering on some relatively dramatic incident such as an accident.   While these precipitating factors may actually exist, we must not accept them without checking.

One of our cases testified—as did his parents—that he first began to stutter after a severe fall from a moving automobile.   This incident occurred when he was in the third grade.   He had been unconscious for three days and when the coma left he stuttered badly whenever he spoke.   We interviewed the first- and second-grade teachers, however, and they independently testified that the boy had stuttered very frequently but with simple hesitations and repetitions during the years spent in their grades. One of them declared that the boy's stuttering occasionally became so severe in "one of his bad spells" that she had made a practice of not calling on him for recitation.   She added that he never seemed to be aware of his symptoms.

Despite these remarks, we do know from our examination of young children immediately after onset of stuttering that the disorder can occasionally occur very suddenly and dramatically.   In one of our cases it appeared immediately after a severe and sudden punishment during the verbal confession of guilt.   In another child, whom we had known prior to the incident, it resulted from a sudden fright when a dog attacked and bit her.   Another child of our acquaintance began to stutter during the delirium of a high fever and even after her recovery from the pneumonia her speech blockings were frequent and apparent.

Besides *shock*, *fright*, and *illness*, the stuttering may be precipitated by various symbolic or cumulative factors.   Especially when the predisposing causes are emotional, the stuttering will first occur in situations that symbolize the conflict.   Thus, one of our cases, whose mother had died when he was seven and who was then placed in a boarding school by his father, began to stutter, and stuttered only during his father's visits to |the school.   He next began to stutter when asking for mail, and by the end of the year he was having difficulty in almost every speech situation.   Another boy began to stutter while uttering grace in the Dutch language at the command of his step-father whom he hated.   Often when the stuttering begins suddenly we do our best to explore the features of the situation in which it occurs.   We sometimes get our first view of the essential emotiona conflict from exploring the onset of stuttering.

Again, the precipitating cause of stuttering may be some incident of little importance in itself but which has significance in its "last straw" or cumulative effect. Few children are so unstable as to show complete disruption of speech fluency under the normal pressures of communication. Yet we find stutterer after stutterer who exhibits his first volley of speech abnormality in some ordinary speaking situation. One of our cases, for example, first stuttered when calling to his mother through a closed door. This is not an unusual situation. It might often provoke some hesitancy, but in this instance the hesitations persisted and increased in frequency. Investigation showed that the child constantly had to struggle for the mother's attention, that she habitually ignored his efforts of communication, and that she frequently interrupted his efforts to converse with unmerited and unpleasant corrections. Again, the stuttering may first occur in the "speaking of pieces" or other forms of vocal exhibition. There is always a breaking point for all of us, and when a little child who is still in the process of mastering his speech skills is driven beyond his capacities, hesitancy will result.

Imitation has been said to be an important cause of stuttering, and parents seem especially eager to adopt it as an explanation if there is any other stutterer in the neighborhood. We have not found it to be nearly as frequent as might be expected. In the more than 2,000 cases we have examined, there were only two instances in which imitation might be said to be of importance in precipitating the symptoms. We have run down many reported cases of imitation, only to find no similarity in the symptoms of the stutterer and of the person he was said to have imitated.

There probably are a good many normal-speaking individuals who possess the predisposing conditions out of which stuttering ordinarily arises, and yet who, because of their uneventful and happy lives, never develop it. Were these persons subjected to some of the same precipitating factors we have mentioned, the hesitant speech would probably have made itself manifest. Then, too, there are some stutterers who could have remained fluent speakers, had they not been bombarded by more disrupting influences than their nervous systems could resist.

Maintaining causes. Stuttering, as we shall see when we describe its development, is peculiarly able to maintain itself once it gets started. This strange situation results from the hesitancy which hesitant speech can create in its possessor. Once the stutterer becomes aware that his symptoms produce unpleasant social penalties, he becomes anxious and uncertain about making speech attempts. Moreover, words and speaking situations become feared, and this fear can become so intense as to resemble utter panic. Thus, the emotional disturbance, generated by the perception of words and situations as omens of unpleasantness, can make the speaker more hesitant. He tries to avoid the unpleasantness and each avoidance increases the fear. Thus, a vicious spiral is established. The more he stutters, the more he fears stuttering, and then the more he avoids speaking. This in turn increases the fear, which can precipitate more stuttering. And so the stutterer struggles in his trap. In many adult cases, we are sure that the original dysphemia, neurosis, or developmental factors have long passed their effectiveness and are no longer existent. The precipitating causes can even have been forgotten. And yet, through the building of abnormal habits of approach or release from stuttering, the disorder can still maintain itself indefinitely. Some of the "miraculous" cures of stuttering are no doubt due to the fact that the causes of the speech defect have vanished and the vicious circle has been broken. Unfortunately, most of our cases do not present this picture.

The nature of the stuttering block. The nature of the stuttering block has never been determined, if indeed there is an actual blocking present. Nevertheless, there are several reasons for believing that the stutterer does at times experience a temporary inability to move certain speech musculatures. For an instant in the movement sequence that is necessary to produce a spoken word, certain muscles of the tongue, jaws, or other speech structures seem unable to contract. The fluency is thereby interrupted.

This temporary inability to move the speech muscles can be explained in many ways: as a manifestation of a latent dysphemia; as a conditioned inhibition; or as a moment of emotional blankness. It may be merely symptomatic of a chronic speech hesitancy which has been practiced so often that it has become habitual. It may be only the result of simultaneous and opposing desires to speak and to remain silent. But introspectively, the dominant feature of the stuttering experience is the feeling of being "blocked" in the forward flow of speech. As one stutterer said:

What happens is that I can't go on. I can't complete the word I want to say. I'm stuck. I either hang there struggling on a consonant or find my mouth repeating the same syllable over and over like a broken record.

Sometimes I'm talking great guns when bang! I'm hung up higher than a kite. Something seems to freeze my tongue or throat shut or else it turns it over to an automatic repeater.

The earliest symptoms of stuttering also demonstrate this interruption to the forward progress of speech. The child automatically repeats a sound or syllable (or monosyllabic word) over and over until finally it comes out whole, and then the fluency flow proceeds until the next

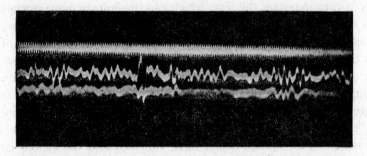

Fig. 11. Action current record showing unequal reception of nervous impulses in the paired masseter muscles during the stuttering act. *Upper line:* time in thousandths of a second; *middle line:* action currents in right masseter; *lower line:* action currents in left masseter.

interruption. The phrases "speech impediment," "tonic and clonic blocks," "spasms" all refer to this aspect of the moment of stuttering. Normal speech consists of a series of muscular movements, each of which must be timed to split-second exactness. If one of these movements is delayed, the whole sequence is broken up.[23]

Not only do observation and introspection point to this temporary blocking as the dominant feature of stuttering, but there is some experimental evidence as well. Travis (51) and Strother (48) have shown that during stuttering the volleys of nervous impulses which come from the brain to the muscles used in speech do not arrive simultaneously or in similar strength. The increase of alpha brain waves during the act of stuttering (32) also points to a similar interference, since the act of speaking usually decreases them in favor of the beta-wave activity. Theory alone cannot as yet explain why the volleys of nervous impulses do not arrive at the paired-speech muscles at the same time.

[23] Hill, H. E., "An Interbehavioral Analysis of Several Aspects of Stuttering," *Journal of General Psychology*, 1945, Vol. 32, pages 289–316.

Conscious and habitual reactions to the fear or experience of the neurological block. We have said that this inability to utilize speech structures is a temporary one. Indeed, most of the experimental evidence indicates that it is of extremely short duration, usually being but the fractional part of a second. And yet the symptoms manifested by the adult stutterer often last for minutes. This seeming confusion is removed when we consider the speech abnormality itself. Stuttering, as the term is commonly used, is nothing but a wastebasket term. It includes symptoms of all varieties, from repetitions and prolongations to tongue protrusions and jerkings of the feet. Many of these so-called symptoms, however, are nothing but reactions to the fear of stuttering.[24] They occur prior to speech attempt. They are often habitual in nature, with a history of having been first adopted as deliberate devices to avoid, disguise, or postpone the blocking.[25] Other reactions seem to be due to the effort made by the stutterer to release himself from block. The important point is that many of the so-called symptoms of stuttering are not true symptoms, but are habitual reactions to the fear or to the occurrence of block.[26] Thus, the true neuromuscular block in stuttering may be very short and yet may be incorporated within a speech abnormality of extremely long duration. Even if neuromuscular blocks form the nucleus of the disorder, it is obvious that treatment based upon the modification and elimination of fear and release reactions will be of great value in diminishing the handicap.

Automatic reactions to neuromuscular blocks: repetition and prolongations. Besides these conscious or habitual reactions to fear or experience of the speech block, there are other reactions which seem to be relatively involuntary and automatic.[27] The latter are the prolongations and repetitions that form so large a share of the stutterer's abnormality when it first begins. Many authorities have considered these to comprise the stuttering block itself. It is our contention that these automatic repetitions and prolongations are reactions to some interruption, and that they may be explained as the natural response

---

[24] Johnson, W. and Knott, J. R., "The Moment of Stuttering," *Journal of Genetic Psychology*, 1936, Vol. 48, pages 475–480.

[25] Wyllie, J., *Disorders of Speech*, Edinburgh, Oliver and Boyd, 1894, pages 18–19.

[26] Van Riper, C., "The Effect of Devices for Minimizing Stuttering on the Creation of Symptoms," *Journal of Social and Abnormal Psychology*, 1937, Vol. 32, pages 185–192.

[27] Fröschels, E., "Beitrage zur Symptomatologie des Stotterns," *Monatschrift f. Ohren-heilk.*, 1921, pages 1109–1110.

of any organism to the sudden interruption of a predetermined and habitual sequence of movements. In typing and piano-playing, for instance, the sudden sticking of a key will produce similar repetitions and prolongations of a preceding posture. Experimental evidence on this point may be found in the article by Bonnet.[28] H. Hill, in an unpublished Master's thesis, "Perseveration in Normal Speakers and Stutterers," from the University of Indiana, 1942, has provided further corroboration of the above statements.

In early stuttering, the sequence of the stuttering act may be described as follows. The child starts the series of simultaneous and successive movements which produce a given word. Suddenly the two halves of the tongue or some other speech structure fail to get their appropriate nervous impulses, and the structure cannot make its necessary movement. The sequence is thereby interrupted, and the preceding movements are repeated or prolonged. Thus the primary symptoms, repetitions and prolongations, are themselves not the actual block but automatic reactions to it.

The Development of Stuttering

The development of overt symptoms. Although the actual neurological block seems to be of short duration, the average adult stutterer presents a mass of severe contortion and long abnormality in his speech that has baffled both the stutterer and his teacher. If the fundamental blocking in stuttering is the same short interruption in the operation of the speech mechanism, the wide variety of observable symptoms must be explained before intelligent therapy can be initiated. We must know why one stutterer forces and protrudes his tongue, why another blinks his eyes and jerks his head, and why still another goes through strange bodily contortions when a stuttering block occurs.

A study of the stuttering phenomenon as it first appears in little children gives us the first key to the solution of this problem. When a child first begins to stutter, the only observable reactions are either rapid, easy repetitions or short, effortless prolongations. Bluemel has called these the "primary symptoms of stuttering." The child, not aware of their appearance, considers them a part of his way of com-

---

[28] Bonnet, C., *Etude Critique sur Parente Morbide du Bégaiement avec les Tics et les Crampes Fonctionelles*, Bordeaux, 1906, pages 52-54.

municating.   Stutterers in this first stage present a general similarity of symptoms, a similarity that is not found in adult stutterers.   Even those soldiers who develop stuttering as a result of their war experiences begin with the primary symptoms, though they develop the avoidance and struggle reactions much more quickly than does the small child.

Since these primary symptoms are similar to the hesitations shown by normal children when confused or excited, there is a tendency on the part of some authorities to refuse to use the term *stuttering* as a label for the repetitions and prolongations.   Johnson (60), for instance, feels that the parent's diagnosis of the normal hesitancies of speech as stuttering is the prime agent in creating the disorder.   He implies that without such an evaluation and labeling, no speech abnormality would occur.   This thesis we cannot entirely accept. There are some children who show so many breaks in fluency, so many hesitations, repetitions, and prolongations, that they are bound to be noticed, not only by others but by the child himself.   Frustration as a result of the interference to communication can by itself produce the anxiety and struggling.   We are sure that having parents penalize stuttering can produce the normal hesitations of a young child until they become a characteristic speech pattern.   But we are also sure that all stuttering does not have such a developmental history.   Children differ in fluency as they differ in every other aspect.   A child may be labeled a "primary stutterer" when his repetitions deviate so far from those of other children that they call attention to themselves and interfere with communication.   This difference is primarily in terms of frequency.   The stutterer has more repetitions and prolongations, and he has them under conditions of less emotional stress.   But the stutterer's repetitions may also differ qualitatively.   Davis's research (57), which has been quoted extensively in support of the thesis that primary stuttering is merely normal speech hesitation, found that all children showed repetitions.   But when her data are broken down into syllable, whole-word, and phrase categories, the repetitions of phrases and whole words account for 90 per cent of all those found in normal children.   As her own experiment also showed, the young stutterer's speech has a much greater proportion of syllable repetition, a finding which agrees with our own observation.   The young stutterer is not nearly so likely to say "Mother, may I have some, may I have, may I have some chocolate?" as he is to say "Muh-muh-mother, mmmmay I-I-I-I have some ch-ch-choc-ch-ch-chocolate?"   The researches of Voelker (115) and Egland [29] also indicate that while the stutterer has difficulty in uttering his words, the nonstuttering child shows most of his hesitancy in completing his thoughts.

Whether we label the symptoms as normal hesitancies or as primary stuttering, the disorder of stuttering has its beginnings in repetitions and prolongations. The child bubbles and bounces his way through his words. Periods of fluency alternate with periods of hesitant speech. Primary stuttering comes in waves. The child at first seems to be unconscious of any abnormality or interruption.

Sooner or later, however, this period of nonreacting acceptance is disturbed.[30] Parents, teachers, or playmates react emotionally or call attention to the speech blocks, and the child becomes aware of the fact that his manner of speaking is unacceptable to others. This penalizing of the automatic and unconscious reactions to the neuromuscular block is the usual way in which the child becomes conscious of his stuttering. He may also become aware of his stuttering in another manner. In the stress of hurried or important communication, he may first notice the slight blocks as obstacles to rapid and fluent speech. This thwarting is unpleasant to the child, and his first reaction of surprise and bewilderment is often followed by one of irritation. He realizes that there is something about his speech that others dislike and that interrupts his communication in some mysterious but objectionable manner. He is labeled as a stutterer and becomes vividly aware of his primary symptoms.

Behavior indicatory of this awareness soon appears. The once unnoticed repetitions and prolongations are followed by sudden pauses. The child begins to force or struggle with the speech attempt. The sound, word, phrase, or even the whole sentence is repeated. The rate, pitch, or intensity of succeeding words is altered. The speech attempt is given up, or the child leaves the speech situation. Compensatory behavior such as shouting, crying, laughing, spitting upon an auditor, hitting a playmate, or indulging in a temper tantrum may occur. Very soon primitive devices of release are attempted, and the child reacts to the feeling of a thwarting and unpleasant block by forcing. He increases the tension of the chest and mouth musculature, employing gross bodily movements at the same time and using

---

[29] Egland, G., "An Analysis of Repetitions and Prolongations in the Speech of Young Children," State University of Iowa, Unpublished Master's Thesis, 1938.

[30] Van Riper, C., "The Growth of the Stuttering Spasm," *Quarterly Journal of Speech*, 1937, Vol. 23, pages 70–73.

unnecessary force in articulation.   This frequently causes a rise in the pitch of the vowel.   When a repetition is felt, the child quickly interrupts it and pauses before he attempts the word again.

Development of fears and malattitudes.   As soon as the child recognizes the unpleasant aspect of his speech, he begins to fear stuttering.[31] *This is a natural development, since the basis of fear is the expectation of unpleasantness.*   This expectation may first be related to a general situation, or it may be specifically related to a certain word on which trouble previously occurred.   Study of the growth of this latter expectancy shows that the first "Jonah" (or feared) words or sounds to develop are either (1) those that by frequency of occurrence under communicative stress have had more association with past stuttering, or (2) those that have been severely and vividly penalized by other people when a block appeared on them.   The first situation fears develop in the same way.

Gradually these fears spread to other words and situations.[32]   As the fears increase, they become attached to certain sounds.   Words themselves become invested with various other cues which set off a specific expectancy of stuttering.   These cues have been mentioned previously in this chapter, and all of them can become vivid and terrifying signals of approaching word difficulty.   Words become things. Letters become either hard or easy.   In a similar manner, other cues develop which precipitate fear of stuttering in a general situation. These, too, have been cited in the first part of the chapter.   This generalized or situation expectancy often involves visualization of the abnormality of the situation and a subsequent rehearsal of the words to be used.   Such a rehearsal arouses specific word fears and intensifies the expectation of trouble.

When a stutterer has developed such decided fears of unpleasantness, both on specific words and in general situations, he immediately begins to devise tricks to prevent or reduce that unpleasantness.   Such devices have been observed in children only four years old, and nearly every adult stutterer exhibits them in either voluntary or automatic form.   These expectancy techniques at first offer temporary relief, but finally they become only a habitual reaction to the fear of block and thus a part of the handicap.

How reactions to fear or experience of stuttering become habitual symp-

---

[31] Fogerty, E., *Stammering*, New York, Dutton, 1930, pages 12–23.
[32] Boome, E. J., and Richardson, M. A., *The Nature and Treatment of Stammering*, New York, Dutton, 1932, pages 110–114.

toms. Expectancy devices are of four major types: those of avoidance, those that postpone the speech attempt, those that are used as "starters" to terminate the postponement and initiate the speech attempt, and, finally, those of antiexpectancy. A number of examples for each of these reactions are given in the section on examination procedures for stuttering at the end of this chapter. It is often difficult for the nonstutterer to realize that much of the abnormality he witnesses in examining a stutterer is due to the latter's efforts to avoid unpleasantness. The desire to avoid stuttering may lead to such jargon as "To what price has the price of tomatoes increased to today?" when the stutterer merely wished to say "How much are your tomatoes?" Dodging difficult words and speech situations becomes almost a matter of second nature to the stutterer. He prefers to seem ignorant rather than to expose his disability when called upon in school. He develops such a facility at using synonyms that he often sounds like an excerpt from a thesaurus. He will walk a mile to avoid using a telephone. And the tragedy of this avoidance is that it increases the fear and insecurity, makes the stutterer more hesitant, and doubles his burden.

Procrastination as a reaction to approaching unpleasantness is an ordinary human trait, and the stutterer has more than his share of the weakness. We have worked with stutterers whose entire overt abnormality consisted of the filibustering repetition of words and phrases preceding the dreaded word. They never had any difficulty on the word itself, but their efforts to postpone the speech attempt until they felt they could say the word produced an incredible amount of abnormality. One of them said, "My name is . . . my name is . . . my . . . my . . . my name is . . . my name . . . name . . . name . . . what I mean is, uh . . . uh . . . my name is Jack Olson." Others will merely pause in tense silence for what seems to them like hours before blurting out the word. Others disguise the postponement by pretending to think, by licking their lips, by saying "um" or "er." Postponement as a habitual approach to feared words creates an anxiety and a fundamental hesitancy which in themselves are precipitative of more stuttering.

Stutterers also use many tricks to start the speech attempt after postponement has grown painfully long. They time this moment of speech attempt with a sudden gesture, or eye-blink, or jaw-jerk, or other movement. They return to the beginning of the sentence and race through the words preceding the feared word in hope that their momentum will "ride them over their stoppages." They insert words, phrases, or sounds that they can say, so that the likelihood of blocking will be lessened.   One of our stutterers hissed before every feared word, "because I get started with the s sound which I can nearly always make."   Another used the phrase "Let me see" as a magic incantation.   He would utter things like this: "My name is LemeseePeter Slack."   Another, whose last name was Ranney, always passed as O'Ranney, since she used the "oh" as a habitual device to get started.   Starters are responsible for many of the bizarre symptoms of stuttering, since they become habituated and involuntary.   Thus, the taking of a deep breath prior to speech attempt may finally become a sequence of horrible gasping.

The antiexpectancy devices are used to prevent or minimize word fears from dominating the attention of the stutterer.   Thus, one of our cases laughed constantly, even when saying the alphabet or asking central for a phone number or buying a package of cigarettes.   He had found that, by assuming an attitude incompatible with fear, he was able to be more fluent.   Yet he was one of the most morose individuals we have ever met.   Other stutterers adopt a sing-song style, or a monotone, or a very soft, whispered speech so that all words are made so much alike that no one will be dreaded.   Needless to say, all these tricks fail to provide more than temporary relief, and all of them are vicious because they augment the fear in the long run.

In addition to these reactions to fear, we find the release reactions which occur after the stutterer has experienced the actual block.   In general, there are only two main types of release symptoms: (1) those with which the word is completed in some manner after the block occurs, and (2) those which involve a cessation of the speech attempt and a retrial.   Among the observable release devices of the first type are: to continue the word with increased force or tension on the speech muscles, to interrupt prolongation and finish the word, to continue with a changed voice pitch, to stop briefly and finish the word, and to continue with speech on inhalation.   In the second class we find these reactions: to stop at the feeling of block and try the entire word again, to stop and use some starting device on the retrial, to stop and use a distraction, to stop and assume a confident behavior, to stop and postpone the new attempt for a time, to stop and avoid the word, and to stop and wait until almost all breath is gone, subsequently saying the word on residual air.

A stutterer may use any number of these expectancy and release devices in an attempt to make his speech effort easier and less obvious. At first, many of these tricks do serve such a purpose. A slight *a* used as a starter may initiate a word seemingly impossible to utter; a word substituted for one that is feared may completely disguise any sign of stuttering abnormality; a slight force on release may bring the word to completion with little difficulty. But soon these techniques begin to lose their efficiency. The stutterer will have to use several *a*'s to initiate a word; spasms begin to occur on even the substituted words; and the force necessary to release a word increases to a degree where every bit of available breath is utilized in the activity. Not only must the tricks be exaggerated to produce any efficiency, but also they lose their voluntary characteristics. The stutterer cannot always use them when he wishes to do so, and he often finds them occurring whenever fear arises, even though he had no intention of using them.

In this way the characteristic spasm pattern of a stutterer develops.[33] *When devices are used so frequently in response to expectation of difficulty or the actual experience of block, they cease to be voluntary and become habitual reactions to that block.* Fear of a word brings an automatic reaction of the oft-practiced tricks previously used to reduce or counteract that fear; experience of a block brings an automatic manner of release. These reactions have become so closely integrated with the stuttering block that most people consider them the actual stuttering phenomenon. Indeed, they do comprise the greater part of the speech handicap and abnormality. But it is in this way that stutterers develop such widely varying symptoms. The devices most often used as reactions to fear of block or to the actual blocking ultimately endow the stutterer's speech with a characteristic spasm pattern.

Recently, research has turned to the investigation of the psychology of stuttering, especially in terms of the adult stutterer. Some of this has been mere armchair psychology similar to the article by Wilde,[34] who finds that the stutterer's situation is explained on the hypothesis that the mind, infected by the will, disturbs the soul-fantasy speech movements and becomes the master, whereas it should be the servant.

The better studies have shown the following important facts:

---

[33] Koepp-Baker, H., *Handbook of Clinical Speech*, Vol. 1, *Stuttering*, pages 103–104, Ann Arbor, Edwards Brothers, 1937.

[34] Wilde, F., "Stottern im Licht der Klageschen Philosophie," *Deutsche Sonderschule*, 1937, Vol. 4, pages 532–541.

(1) Most adult stutterers have marked fear of words and certain speech situations.   (2) These fears are set off by cues which are associated with general or specific memories of past speech unpleasantness and abnormality.   (3) The greater the penalty placed upon stuttering, the more frequent and severe are the blocks.   (4) The fear is increased by avoidance of speech attempt on feared words or in feared situations.   (5) Fear is frequently accompanied by rehearsal of the abnormality prior to speech attempt and by preparatory sets to stutter in certain specific ways.   (6) Stutterers can frequently predict the occurrence and duration of their blocks.   (7) Fear often manifests itself in the form of diametrically opposed urges to attempt and to retreat from the speaking of the word feared.   (8) The cues which set off the fear may be classified as the awareness of the following factors as tending to precipitate stuttering: certain sounds or classes of sounds (vowels or consonants, plosives or sibilants, and so on), the meaning of the word, the unfamiliarity of the word, the position of the sound in the word, the position of the word in the sentence, the relative difficulty of articulation, the inexact word, accented syllables, and confusions of all kinds.   The cues which set off situation fear are the perception of the following factors in the speech situation: similarities to situations in which speech unpleasantness has been experienced; the unexpectedness of the situation; expectation of interruption or help with the difficult word; pressing need for immediate or efficient communication; the probabilities of such social penalties as laughter, mockery, and impatience or rejection; and many others.

Stutterers' attitudes toward their disorder have been investigated, and, although many evidences of social and emotional maladjustment have been noted, most of them seem to be the results of stuttering rather than its causes.   These attitudes vary all the way from a casual acceptance of the disorder as a minor irritation to definitely psychopathic disturbances.   Although exceptions occur, the more severe the symptoms of the disorder, the more abnormal are the attitudes.   Stuttering is generally a social and economic liability and is penalized as such.   Severe stutterers tend to select occupations in which speaking is unimportant.

Examination procedures for stutterers.   It is vitally important that the initial examination of the stutterer be both systematically and carefully performed.   The case history should be thorough, and every source of important information should be exploited.   The case himself should be interviewed and explored at length.   All data bearing on dysphemic, emotional, or developmental etiology should be care-fully evaluated. The stutterer's basic attitudes of attack or with-drawal, both in terms of speech defect and other liabilities, must be determined.   The history of his secondary symptoms (see the special case history for stuttering in the Appendix) is often of great impor-tance to therapy, since the latest symptoms often yield most quickly to therapy.   The symptoms themselves, together with the character-istic communicative conditions under which they occur, must be identified.   The breathing abnormalities, if present, should be noted. The areas of great tension should be located, and since the struggle to speak often begins in one area, such as the lips, and spreads to other areas, the directions of this tension-irradiation should be observed. Since stutterers frequently block the vocal airway at the vocal cords, velum, hard palate, teeth, or lips by excessively hard contacts, the location of these hard contacts must be found.   The cues that set off fear of speech situations and "Jonah" words should be analyzed. Finally, the history of the stutterer's attempts to free himself from his impediment must be disclosed.   It is usually unwise to use methods of therapy which have previously failed.

If the above description of the stutterer's examination seems some-what vague, the following instructions, which were given to guide a beginning student in her first examination of a child who stuttered, may prove more specific

While the child is in the playroom, interview the mother. You need not investigate the predisposing or precipitating causes of his disorder at this time since you will have ample opportunity to do so in later interviews, but you should try to get (1) the *child's attitude* toward his problem; (2) the *parent's attitude* toward the disorder; (3) some indication of *how the child might respond* to your examination procedures; and (4) some of his *interests and experiences* about which he might be willing to talk.   Then ask the mother to go with you back to the playroom and tell her to let the child know she is right in the next room and will be through in a little while.   As the mother does so, be sure to talk with her in a friendly manner so as to establish a relationship.   If necessary, have her introduce you as the play-room teacher.

Let the child have the opportunity to size you up while you straighten up the room or do a few other things of the same sort.   Get acquainted with him in an unhurried manner by making some statements about the play materials available in the room.   Show him how some of the toys work.   Keep talking, but demand no answers.   As soon as you can, get out the materials for the (5) *Wellman Tracing Path Test* and, as you illus-trate, tell him to see how well he can draw between the lines.   Go directly from this to the (6) *Durost Asterisk Test*, and then to the (7) *Vertical Board Test of Laterality*. These tests seem to fascinate almost all children, and we doubt you will have much difficulty in this regard. Use the toy gun to determine (8) *eyedness* and throughout the examination observe his (9) *hand preference*. Watch him carefully for signs of negativism or fatigue, and temporarily shift to play activity whenever they occur. Then ask him if he would like to see you write with your stomach. Take him into the laboratory and hook yourself up to the polygraph and make a breathing record. Be sure to talk as you do so. Then make (10) a *breathing record* of him. If possible, go directly from this to the making of (11) *phonograph record*. Ask him to count to ten, but then ask him some questions such as: "Your mother tells me you have an older brother. What is his name?" Try to get a transcription of a few blockings and watch his reactions closely. Then play the phonograph record of the rhythms used to test diadochokinesis. After you demonstrate, ask him to keep time to the sounds by (12) *biting*, (13) *panting*, and (14) *tongue protrusion*. If this seems too difficult for him, use the metronome to give a rhythmic stimulus of a simpler sort. Watch for extra movements, flutterings, tonic contractions, and, of course, sheer inability.

Take him back to the playroom and let him choose his own activities for a time. By sharing one of them, initiate a conversation which should continue long enough to give you a pretty good idea concerning the presence of (15) *primary symptoms*, their number per word, their tempo, and whether or not they are accompanied by tension or awareness. Note any evidence of struggle or avoidance. If he does seem to be a primary stutterer without awareness, or struggle, or avoidance, introduce some pressure factors such as interruption, hurry, impatience, misunderstanding, strong demand for a certain specific answer, or disregard, etc. Note (16) which of these *disturbing influences* seem to produce the most symptoms. Get him to talk about his home, parents, brothers and sisters, friends, enemies, schoolmates and teachers, punishments, achievements. Note (17) any *certain topics of conversation* which produce the most symptoms. If you are still certain he is a primary stutterer, take him back to the waiting room and begin to take a careful case history.

If you are certain he is aware of his symptoms, and does struggle or avoid in his efforts to prevent or minimize his stuttering, engage him in enough further conversation to enable you to make a careful symptom analysis. This should include (18) *avoidance* devices or habits, (19) *postponement* tricks, (20) *starters*, and (21) *antiexpectancy* devices.

If the boy is so adept at avoiding or postponing that he shows few true blockings, ask him to say (quickly! and loudly!) such words as "BANANA-BANANA-BANANA" or his father's full name pronounced in similar fashion. Then try to analyze his stuttering to determine where the (22) major areas of *forcing* and *hard contacts* seem to be. Also note the (23) presence and location of *tremors* of the lips or tongue. Check to see whether (24) *false-vocal-cord phonation* occurs on the vowels during stuttering. Determine (25) the *manner of release* from blocking in terms of retrials, interruptor devices, or tension decreases. On what sounds did he place his mouth in position to utter the sound before actually making a speech attempt upon it? These we call (26) *preformation*.

Either through frank discussion of his problem, or through observation, try to determine what (27) *words or sounds* seemed most feared or stuttered upon. On which ones did he have the longest or most severe blockings? If possible, ask him what types of speaking seem most difficult or dreaded. To whom does he have most trouble speaking? Check home, school, play, or work activities to locate the (28) *feared situations*.

Observe (29) his *post-spasm reactions* and attitudes toward his speech difficulty. If possible, get him to tell you what unpleasant experiences he has had with stuttering. Find out from the boy, if you can, how his parents or teachers or playmates tease, punish, or otherwise react to his blocks. Finally, discuss with him what (30) *methods* have been used to help him overcome his stuttering and what he thought of them.

Record the results of your examination in terms of the 30 items numbered above. Then take a careful case history from the mother and summarize the information thereby procured under the following headings: (31) *predisposing causes;* (32) *precipitating causes;* (33) *maintaining causes;* (34) *manner of development*, including changes in symptomatology and growth of anxiety and frustrations; (35) the boy's major *assets* and *liabilities*, and his characteristic *reactions to penalty and approval;* (36) *environmental factors* which tend to perpetuate the disorder, with some estimate concerning their possibility of removal; (37) environmental factors indicating a good *prognosis;* and (38) *suggestions* concerning therapy.

In order to familiarize the student with some of the examinations mentioned in the above description of testing procedures we are describing some of them in greater detail.

Laterality tests.[35, 36, 37, 38] Much research has recently pointed out the effect on speech of a shift of handedness or of confused sidedness or laterality. Reliable histories of shift of handedness are difficult to procure because of the lapse of time, the effects of imitation, and the reluctance of parents to confess such a causal factor. Therefore, it is necessary to use laterality tests to determine whether or not confused laterality is a contributing or essential cause of the child's speech disorder. The speech disorders usually so affected are stuttering and delayed speech. Unfortunately, most of our measures of sidedness

---

[35] Durost, W. M., "The Development of a Battery of Objective Tests of Manual Laterality," *Genetic Psychology Monograph*, 1934, Vol. 16, pages 4–237.

[36] Hull, C. J., "A Reliable Hand Preference Questionnaire," *Journal of Experimental Education*, 1936, Vol. 4, No. 3, pages 287–290.

[37] Wellman, B. L., "The Development of Motor Coördinations in Young Children," *University of Iowa Studies in Child Welfare*, 1926, Vol. 3, pages 1–93.

[38] Whipple, G. M., *Manual of Mental and Physical Tests*, Baltimore, Warwick and York, Inc., 1924.

are either tests of speed, strength, and accuracy or expressions of hand preference, all of which are the features most susceptible to environmental influence and training. A few tests of so-called native-sidedness do exist, and, although crude, they are used in a battery together with the other measures to determine if laterality is a causal factor. Tests of speed, strength, and accuracy are most important diagnostically when they demonstrate ambidexterity or favor the usually nonpreferred hand. Many tests may be used for measuring these three factors, but the three most convenient and adequately standardized are the Wellman Tracing Path test for accuracy, the Durost Asterisk Test for speed, and the Smedley Dynamometer Test for strength. All of these tests must be administered in such a fashion as to reduce distortions due to training. Each of them is taken: first, with the nonpreferred hand; next, with the preferred hand; next, with the preferred hand; and last, with the nonpreferred hand. The scores should be averaged and expressed as fractions—the numerator representing the average accuracy of the right hand, the denominator, that of the left. Directions for administering the first two of these tests are given in their respective forms. Directions for the dynamometer test are simply to hold the dynamometer at full arm's length and apply the pressure. Scores should be recorded on a special test form similar to that given at the end of this chapter.

The most valid and reliable hand-preference questionnaire is the one standardized by C. J. Hull. It requests the student to indicate if the right, left, or either hand performs the activity when hammering, cutting with scissors, distributing cards, spinning a top, winding a watch, using a toothbrush, sharpening a pencil, writing, drawing pictures, throwing, and using a tennis racket. She expressed her results in terms of a handedness index computed according to the formula: $R + \frac{1}{2}E \div N = Index$.

Tests of so-called native-sidedness include: eyedness, convergence strength, thumbedness, footedness, and the vertical board or critical-angle board tests, the last mentioned being the most reliable and best standardized. Eyedness may be tested by providing the subject with a paper cone, the large end of which the subject is requested to place to his face as he looks through the cone to view the experimenter's eye. The cone prevents the use of both eyes at any one time, and the one used is termed the dominant eye. The experimenter should give at least ten trials as he moves about. Convergence strength is tested by requiring the subject to focus his eyes on the end of a lead pencil as the experimenter slowly brings the pencil in perpendicularly to the bridge of the subject's nose. The experimenter records which eye fails to "break" or swing outward. This eye is termed the dominant eye in convergence. At least ten trials should be recorded. Thumbedness is easily determined by requiring the subject to clasp his hands, interlocking the fingers in the usual fashion. The dominant thumb is that which is on top. Footedness may be determined by standing the subject with his back to the wall and asking him to kick

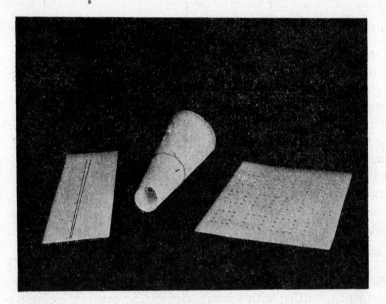

Fig. 12.   The cone used for testing eyedness, and the asterisk and tracing path tests of laterality.

the wall three times very quickly. The reliability of all of these measures is somewhat doubtful, but they are useful in indicating a general tendency in favor of one or the other side.

Vertical board test of laterality. This test consists essentially in simultaneous writing with both hands, one on each side of an upright vertical board. The patterns used are of three types. The first is the kinesthetic, consisting of a pattern learned while blindfolded by tracing with a bimanual stylus. The pattern itself is a deep spiral groove cut into a flat board or cardboard. The examiner places the point of the bimanual stylus in the center of the spiral and, during the first trial, helps guide it as the blindfolded subject traces it. Four trials without guidance are then required; the pattern is withdrawn, and the subject uses the stylus to draw the pattern on the table top. If the subject does not draw a good pattern, he is required to take more practice trials until he does. He is then asked to draw the same pattern reduced to one fourth its original size on the table top. If this is successful, he discards the stylus, takes a pencil in each hand, and, at command, draws the patterns, as swiftly as he can, simultaneously with both hands on opposite sides of the vertical board. Three such drawings are required, and other patterns may be used.[39, 40] A simple, two-handed stylus may be contrived by thrusting a pencil through the centers of two 4-by-1-inch strips of thick cardboard,

Fig. 13. A student being given the vertical board test of laterality. Bimanual stylus, visual pattern, and kinesthetic pattern are also shown.

separating them by about three inches, and using the projections of the upper strip as handholds and those of the lower as a means of steadying the forefingers. A large sheet of paper folded over the top of the vertical board will provide a permanent record of the performance; on each side, the hand with which the pattern was written correctly should be indicated. The second pattern is a visual pattern, held up above the examiner's head so as to prevent the subject from watching both his hands and the pattern at the same time. No blindfold is

[39] Van Riper, C., "A New Test of Laterality," *Journal of Experimental Psychology*, 1934, Vol. 17, pages 305–313.
[40] Van Riper, C., "The Quantitative Measurement of Laterality," *Journal of Experimental Psychology*, 1935, Vol. 18, pages 372–383.

used, and the subject is instructed to follow the pattern with his eyes
as he draws it with his hands on the vertical board.   The third, or
script pattern, consists of the drawing of a word spoken to the subject, who is again blindfolded.   Typical visual patterns are asymmetrical figures with the first stroke being made vertically.   Good
words for the script pattern are: *boy, catch, dog*.   The subject should
make clear patterns and should begin instantly at command, drawing
simultaneously with both hands *as fast as he can*.   The nondominant

Fig. 14.   Testing diadochokinesis.

hand will produce mirroring in all of these tests, while the dominant
hand will draw the pattern correctly.   In case of poor co-operation,
a new pattern should be used.   Keep the subject in ignorance of the
fact that the test is a handedness test.   If the subject mirrors with the
hand normally preferred, the results tend to indicate confused laterality.   Left-handed people mirror with the right hand; right-handed
people do the opposite; ambidextrous individuals either mirror with
both hands or do not mirror at all.

Diadochokinesis and rhythmokinesis.   These two polysyllabic verbal
monstrosities are terms used to refer to the stutterer's ability to move
rhythmically and rapidly the speech musculatures.   What we actually
measure is the stutterer's ability to protrude or lift the tongue, or move

his jaw, or pant with speed and accuracy.   Some stutterers, who can co-ordinate a hand or a leg with extreme facility, are very awkward in moving the paired speech muscles with precision or speed.   Their tongues are protruded not rhythmically but clumsily.   They show tremors, flutterings, and extra movements or even cessation of all movement.   Some stutterers when tested react to the above experiences by saying that they "blocked" or stuttered in these silent activities.   Certainly tonic and clonic reactions are very evident.   Not all stutterers show these malco-ordinations (49).   Our task in this testing is to discover whether the stutterer being examined is one of those who does.

A good deal of complicated apparatus has been used to test the stutterer's diadochokinesis, but we have found that a phonograph recording of a series of rhythmic sound stimuli is adequate to permit us to detect those stutterers who are grossly defective.   The record is made by having a trained musician tap out a series of musical notes, arranged in rhythmic patterns.   The first pattern consists of a fairly slow but regular series of notes evenly spaced: * * * * * * * * * * * * * * * * * * *.   The next four patterns are similar in form but are produced at increasing speeds.   Then more complex rhythms are introduced as stimulus patterns, and in successive trials they are produced at different speeds.   Some of the patterns we use may be represented visually in this way:

** *   ** * *   ** * *
* ***   * ***   * ***
* ** *   * ** *   * ** *

The instructions for administering this test are simple.   We say to the person we are examining:

In the record which I will play for you, you will hear some musical notes.   Your task is to click your teeth together (*or pant, or protrude the tongue*) in time to the music.   Listen to the music until you hear how it is arranged, and then start keeping time.   Try to do it as exactly as possible. Now watch me do it first and then we'll let you try.

Since some individuals find a little difficulty in understanding what is desired, it is always wise to use a practice session or two.   As indicated above, the stutterer should perform these patterns at different speeds, since different persons have different optimal motor tempos. With small children we employ only the simple, regular patterns.

In recording the results of the test, we are interested primarily in the extreme variations from the performances of the average child, and since each homemade record will vary in this regard, normal individuals must be tested to determine some crude norms. Yet, so marked are the broken rhythms, blockings, and tremors of certain stutterers that the abnormality is obvious. We usually give the jaw-bite first, then the panting, and finally the tongue-protrusion.

Breathing. Whenever possible, it is wise to record the breathing patterns during the stuttering blocks. Kymograph or polygraph records can often demonstrate symptoms which are difficult (though not impossible) to detect by careful observation. The breathing of a stutterer often reflects his efforts and struggles to break the hard contacts of the tongue, lips, or vocal cords, which are so characteristic of secondary stuttering. It also can demonstrate the presence of fear in the form of a suspension of silent breathing or a slowness of inhalation. When simultaneous records of thoracic and abdominal breathing are made, the stutterer often shows that his chest cavity is expanding or inhaling at the same time that his abdomen is contracting in the effort to speak. Tremors of the breathing musculature are also noticeable in some cases. In others, the stutterer's attempts to interrupt his blocks or to time the speech attempt will be reflected in sudden inhalations or gasps. One of the most common of secondary symptoms is the stutterer's attempt to speak on residual air. He exhales suddenly and much more thoroughly than during normal speech and then makes the speech attempt on the very "end of his breath."

In adults, stereotyped and consistent patterns of breathing abnormality are found, and these are occasionally rehearsed prior to speech attempt. Many stuttering blocks do not manifest themselves in any respiratory irregularity. The breathing disturbances in stuttering are probably the result of the vocal struggle rather than its cause. Devices such as an initiatory gasp, used deliberately for timing the speech attempt on a feared word, produce many of the above symptoms. The use of breathing exercises in the treatment of stuttering has been generally discarded by most clinicians.[41, 42, 43, 44]

[41] Dodds, G. and Lickley, J. D., *The Control of the Breath,* London, Oxford University Press, 1935.

[42] Fossler, H. R., "Disturbances of Breathing During Stuttering," *Psychological Monograph,* 1930, Vol. 40, pages 1–32.

[43] Judson, L. and Weaver, A. T., *Basic Voice and Speech Science,* Madison, College Typing Co., 1933, pages 212–216.

[44] Van Riper, C., "Study of Thoracic Breathing of Stutterers During Expectancy and Occurrence of Stuttering Spasm," *Journal of Speech Disorders,* September, 1936, pages 61–72.

Symptom analysis. This part of the stuttering examination is of great importance and must never be slighted. Much of the abnormality of stuttering consists of habitual reactions associated with the fear or block, and these must be carefully identified. This is frequently more difficult than might be expected. Severe secondary stutterers often have a whole series of devices or habitual approaches to the speech attempt on a feared word. Some of these devices seem to be reserved for conditions of extreme panic and only make their appearance under that condition. The first examination seldom provokes the entire ·gamut of secondary symptoms. We therefore provide the adult stutterer with a check list of these symptoms so that he can supplement our observation. In examining a stutterer, however, we must be careful to test him under conditions of stress in order to get a true picture of the manner in which he approaches a hard word or attempts to release himself from the blocking. Phonograph recording, phoning, speaking before an audience, paraphrasing, narrating anecdotes about unpleasant stuttering experiences, all can be used to provoke severe enough symptoms to permit diagnosis. The general classes of symptoms which must be checked are: symptoms of avoidance, postponement, "starters," antiexpectancy, release, and the postspasm reactions. These can be underlined on a stuttering history blank as they are noticed, or written on a special blank provided for the purpose. Special notation should be made of the symptoms that appear most frequently.

1. *Symptoms of avoidance.* Some of the means by which a stutterer may avoid a feared word are: giving up the speech attempt altogether, substituting a different word for the one feared, changing the order of the words (circumlocution), waiting for help on the word, pretending to have to think, and using very condensed or telegrammic speech.

2. *Symptoms of postponement.* Stutterers often postpone the attempt on a feared word either because their fear is so great that they feel there is no possibility that they can say it at the moment, or because they feel that they may say it without any difficulty if they wait for a few seconds. Some of the techniques which they use to accomplish such a delay are: pausing, using accessory vocalization (such as saying "a . . . a . . . a . . . ," "why," or "er" before a word), repeating preceding words, repeating preceding sounds, prolonging the last part of the preceding word, repeating entire phrases preceding the feared word, or slowing down the rate at which the preceding words

298 STUTTERING: ITS NATURE AND CAUSES

are spoken. Here the stutterer is avoiding the feared word in time, though he does not intend to avoid it completely.

3. *Symptoms of starting.* Stutterers sometimes feel that most of their difficulty comes when they are attempting to start a word and that, if they can just start it some way, they will be able to say it successfully. Some of the more common types of these starting devices are: use of a starting word, sound, or phrase (such as "um," "well," or "you see"), use of some particular stereotyped movement just before the word is attempted (such as a body jerk, throat clearing, swallowing, or eye blink), repetition of preceding phrase at increased rate (sometimes called "getting a running start"), suddenly changed pitch of the voice, suddenly changed intensity of the voice, suddenly increased tension, suddenly decreased tension, and use of some movement to time the actual moment of speech attempt (and not before that moment, as was suggested in the above technique), such as tapping the foot, blinking the eyes, or jerking the head.

4. *Symptoms of antiexpectancy.* The relationship of fear to stuttering is so great that stutterers often feel that, if they could destroy the fear of approaching words, they would be able to say them without any difficulty. The three major ways of doing this are: using a kind of speech in which no word stands out enough to be feared, filling the mind with other things so that the expectancy of stuttering is kept out (distraction), and assuming an evident attitude of self-confidence. In the first-mentioned class, we find these types of devices: use of a monotone, slow and deliberate speech, singsong speech, very rapid speech, and slurred speech. In the second class, we find: unnatural speech which demands strict attention, voluntary movements of the body which serve as a distraction, visualization of words, a sequence of breathing or vocalization patterns, and overattentiveness to phonetic drill positions. In the third class, among those devices which are used to attain self-confidence, we may see: assumption of aggressive, belligerent, or clowning behavior, whispered rehearsal, compensatory behavior of various kinds, and the use of coughing, or some such obvious activity, to prove to the stutterer that he is still able to control his speech organs.

5. *Symptoms of release.* After a stutterer finds himself in a block, he does certain things to release it. Some of these more commonly used techniques of release are: to stop immediately and try again on the same word, to pause when the block is felt and then to finish the rest of the word, to stop and postpone a new attempt for some time,

to stop and wait until almost all breath is gone and then to say the word on residual air, to stop and avoid the word entirely, to stop and use some distraction, to stop and assume a confident behavior (to change the attitude), to continue the word and increase the tension, to continue the word and change the pitch of the voice, and to change the pattern of breathing by speaking the rest of the word on inhalation.

Sequences. While discovering what secondary symptoms are manifested, notations must be made of the sequences in which these symptoms occur. Does the stutterer follow a stereotyped pattern? Does he always pause first before a feared word, then start it by swallowing? Or does he usually postpone the attempt on a feared word by repeating the preceding word, and, if that fails, by repeating the whole preceding phrase? Does he try to release a spasm first by forcing, and, if that fails, does he attempt a release through stopping and starting again? Most stutterers follow some definite sequence in the secondary symptoms which they utilize in the attempt to speak. Sometimes a sequence will contain four or five secondary reactions. Many of these patterns have become very strong through their continued use, and the definite sequence must be recognized before any work can be done upon its disintegration.

The clinician must familiarize himself with evidences of these secondary symptoms in the speech of the stutterers whom he examines. It is also desirable to find out what methods for the alleviation or cure of the speech defect have been suggested to the stutterer and have been tried subsequently by him. (Examples of such suggested methods are: talking slowly, swinging the arm when talking, taking a deep breath before feared words, using monotone, stopping and starting the speech attempt again, and so on.) Since there is often a positive relationship between these tricks and the spasm pattern which the stutterer has developed, the development of the reactions must be clarified for him.

Cues—specific expectancy. After a symptom diagnosis has been made of the stutterer, one must discover, through questioning, what the cues are which set off the actual stuttering block. For every stutterer who is aware of his speech difference, certain features of communicative material stand out as being invested with stuttering threat. These words, or parts of words, which stand out are the centers and subcenters of the configuration of communication. Some of the stuttering landmarks in a sentence upon which word fear is experienced are: the first words in a sentence, the last words in a sentence, the unfamiliar word, the word which is difficult to pronounce, and the inexact word. Often the accented syllables also serve as cues which arouse specific fear of a certain part of a word. In addition to the cues that are dependent upon the actual content of the communicative material, there are the more artificial cues which arise from the stuttering experience of the individual. If special sounds or words have been stuttered upon sufficiently enough and vividly enough in the past to leave an indelible impression upon the stutterer, they, too, may subsequently set off specific fear of stuttering. The clinician must find which of these cues are responsible for precipitating specific fears in the stutterer.

General expectancy. In addition to discovering the cues which set off specific expectancy in the stutterer, the situation, or general fears, must be found. Does the stutterer have blocks when talking or reading aloud when alone? Does he stutter when he sings or whispers? Which people in the home situation are the most difficult to talk to and why? What school situations are most difficult? Are there any playground or business situations which are greatly feared? What situations does he avoid? Does he avoid the use of the telephone? What situations does he recall as having been very unpleasant because of his stuttering?

Prior to entering a feared situation, does he rehearse what he is going to say or does he visualize himself stuttering? How does he attempt to change a feared speech situation so that he will have less trouble? Does he brood over speech failures? Is his characteristic reaction to a feared situation one of retreat or one of attack? Is he prone to have reactions of absolute panic? Question the stutterer as to each of the above.

Request the stutterer to give examples of any of the following penalties which have been inflicted upon him. Which are most common?

The penalties are of three types: social, sexual, and economic. All of these penalties are expressed through audience behavior. Some of the most common audience reactions that fall under the category of social penalties are:

1. Attack by, or rejection from, a social group.
2. Underestimation of stutterer's intelligence.
3. Expression of dislike, discomfort, anger, irritation, disgust, or impatience.
4. Expression of amusement.

5. Interruption, anticipation, or thwarting of communication.

6. Ridicule.

7. Pity and tolerance.

The most common sexual penalty is rejection of companionship by members of the opposite sex.

Economic penalties which are interpreted from audience reactions are:

1. Peremptory rejection of application for employment.

2. Unwillingness to place stutterer in a position of responsibility.

3. Overprotection.

4. Demand for speech improvement under threat of losing economic security.

5. Impatience with communication limitation.

Attitude toward stuttering. After the specific and general fears have been determined, the clinician must discover the general attitude of the stutterer toward his speech handicap. Does he obviously suffer whenever he has a spasm? Is he able to watch one of his blocks? Does he accept his defect optimistically or does he have a pessimistic view of life because of it? The following simple tests may be given, during which the tester notes the reaction of the stutterer. 1. Ask the stutterer to imitate one of his blocks, looking in the mirror as he does it. 2. Ask the stutterer to relate some incident concerning his speech, and see whether or not he is able to look at you during a block. 3. Bring a stranger into the room, and see whether or not the stutterer will speak to him when asked a question. Did he look at the stranger?

In addition to these observations, it is well to ask the individual to answer a few such questions as: 1. Do you think there is any advantage in being a stutterer? 2. Does stuttering make it difficult or embarrassing for you to buy something in a store? 3. Is the average person as friendly with a stutterer as he is with a normal speaker? 4. Does stuttering make it difficult for you to keep friends? 5. Are you ashamed of your stuttering? 6. Does your stuttering make life seem worthless to you? 7. Would you rather be blind than stutter? (Ask same question substituting deaf, fat, having a large birthmark on face, and feeble-minded, for first handicap.) The obvious reactions of the stutterer to these questions, combined with his reactions to the other tests and his blocks in general, will give quite an adequate picture of his attitude toward his speech difference.

References

The literature on stuttering is so scattered and the titles of the articles are so misleading that the beginning student in speech correction often feels utterly helpless in attempting to understand the problem. The various points of view are often conflicting. One authority declares one thing; another rejects it in favor of his own pet theory. So far as stuttering is concerned, speech correction is in the same state that medicine was before Pasteur's discovery of bacteria. Fortunately, some research has been done, but it has not been conclusive. We are therefore providing the student with brief abstracts of most of the important work done in this field. He may thereby be spared some of the confusion which bedevils the beginner who tries to understand stuttering.

General References

1. Ainsworth, S., "Integrating Theories of Stuttering," *Journal of Speech Disorders*, 1945, Vol. 10, pages 205–210.
The author attempts to sort all the theories of stuttering into three classes: the dysphemic, the developmental, and the neurotic. Opposing points of view are contrasted.

2. Bender, J. F., "Do You Know Someone Who Stutters," *Scientific Monthly*, 1944, Vol. 59, pages 221–224.
Some interesting case material which brings out the essential nature of stuttering.

3. Bender, J. F., *The Personality Structure of Stuttering*, New York, Pitman, 1939.
Summary of concepts of stuttering; research on stuttering; the stuttering personality. A good source book for the findings of experiments on the personalities of stutterers.

4. Bender, J. F. and Kleinfeld, V. M., *Principles and Practices of Speech Correction*, New York, Pitman, 1938.
Fifteen of the various theories concerning the nature of stuttering are clearly presented.

5. Blanton, S. and M. G., *For Stutterers*, New York, D. Appleton-Century, 1936.
A book based on the thesis that stuttering originates in emotional disturbances and is maintained by them. Emotional patterns, theories of stuttering, theories of treatment, and suggestions for parents, teachers, and stutterers are discussed.

6. Bluemel, C. S., *Stammering and Allied Disorders*, New York, Macmillan, 1935.
A consideration of primary and secondary stammering and other speech defects from the viewpoint of Pavlov's theory of conditioning and inhibition. Other theories of stammering are reviewed, and some of the author's own therapeutic suggestions are given.

7. Boome, E. J. and Richardson, M. A., *The Nature and Treatment of Stuttering*, New York, Dutton, 1932.

A book discussing the two causes of stammering—endogenous or constitutional, and exogenous or environmental, with examples supporting both. The authors emphasize the study of the child from all angles, and suggest relaxation, breathing, suggestion, and the solution of emotional difficulties as therapy.

8. Coriat, I. H., "The Psychoanalytic Conception of Stuttering," *The Nervous Child*, 1943, Vol. 2, pages 167–171.
A description of stuttering as a neurosis and in psychoanalytic terminology.

9. Fletcher, J. M., *The Problem of Stuttering*, New York, Longmans, Green, 1928.
Includes the classification of speech defects, statistical data on stuttering, various theories of the causes of stuttering, physiological symptoms of stuttering, explanation of the author's belief that stuttering is a morbid social maladjustment, and suggested environmental therapy.

10. Gifford, H. M., *How to Overcome Stammering*, New York, Prentice-Hall, 1940.
Stuttering considered as a symptom of an emotional conflict and treated as such by correcting the maladjustment and using suggestion and relaxation.

11. Hahn, E. H., *Stuttering: Significant Theories and Therapies*, Stanford University: Stanford University Press, 1943.
Probably the best compendium of the theories and treatments of stuttering available to the student.

12. Heltman, H., *First Aids for Stutterers*, Boston, Expression Co., 1943.
Well-written description of the nature of stuttering, the theories of its cause, and its prevention. The author also discusses self-help for the stutterer, stuttering in the school, and speech hygiene.

13. Hill, H., "An Interbehavioral Analysis of Several Aspects of Stuttering," *Journal of General Psychology*, 1945, Vol. 32, pages 289–316.
Stuttering as emotional blocking of the speech sequences. The article is stimulating but not for the beginning student, since it is couched in Kantorian terminology.

14. Johnson, W., *Because I Stutter*, New York, D. Appleton-Century, 1930.
Written on the basis of the author's own experiences and deals particularly with the effect of the stutterer's experiences upon the development of his personality.

15. Krout, M. H., "Emotional Factors in the Etiology of Stuttering," *Journal of Abnormal and Social Psychology*, 1936, Vol. 31, pages 174–181.
Three college stutterers have their emotional conflicts analyzed.

16. Travis, L. E., *Speech Pathology*, D. Appleton-Century, 1931.
Explains fully the neuromuscular basis of speech and the other speech disorders, as well as stuttering. In pages 95–190, the author discusses the symptomatology and causes of stuttering, the nature of stuttering, the meaning of stuttering symptoms, and the management of the stutterer.

17. West, R., "The Pathology of Stuttering," *The Nervous Child*, 1943, Vol. 2, pages 96–106.
An interesting summary of the problem of stuttering with little theoretical bias. Lists 13 facts which any theory of stuttering must take into account.

Causes of Stuttering: Dysphemia

18. Anderson, J. and Whealdon, M. L., "A Study of the Blood Group Distribution Among Stutterers," *Journal of Speech Disorders*, 1941, Vol. 6, pages 23–28.
No differences between stutterers and nonstutterers.
19. Backus, O. L., "Incidence of Stuttering Among the Deaf," *Annals of Oto-rhino-laryngology*, 1938, Vol. 47, pages 632–635.
There were 55 stutterers in schools for the deaf; six were congenitally deaf.
20. Berman, A. B. and Train, G. J., "A Genetic Approach to the Problem of Stuttering," *Journal of Nervous and Mental Diseases*, 1940, Vol. 91, pages 580–590.
The nature of the stuttering "inheritance" does not follow Mendelian laws.
21. Berry, M. F., "A Study of the Medical Histories of Stuttering Children," *Speech Monographs*, 1939, Vol. 5, pages 97–114.
More diseases of the nervous system among stutterers: encephalitis, etc.
22. Berry, M. F., "A Common Denominator in Twinning and Stuttering," *Journal of Speech Disorders*, 1938, Vol. 3, pages 51–57.
Stuttering, twinning, and left-handedness are produced by the same generic factors.
23. Bilto, E. W., "A Comparative Study of Certain Physical Abilities of Children with Speech Defects and Children with Normal Speech," *Journal of Speech Disorders*, 1941, Vol. 6, pages 187–203.
Both stutterers and articulation cases are inferior to normal speakers in large bodily co-ordinations.
24. Bryngelson, B., "A Study of Laterality of Stutterers and Normal Speakers," *Journal of Social Psychology*, 1940, Vol. 11, pages 151–155.
Seventy-eight stutterers were matched with nonstutterers. Group differences in confused or shifted laterality were found to be statistically significant.
25. Bryngelson, B. and Clark, T. B., "Left-Handedness and Stuttering," *Journal of Heredity*, 1933, Vol. 24, pages 387–390.
The results of this study seemed to indicate that left-handedness is a sex-limited characteristic, most often transmitted from the male through the female and back to the male.
26. Bryngelson, B. and Rutherford, B., "A Comparative Study of Laterality of Stutterers and Non-Stutterers," *Journal of Speech Disorders*, 1937, Vol. 2, pages 15–16.
A study of the handedness history of 74 stutterers and 74 nonstutterers, showing 4 times as much ambidexterity and 8 times as much shifting in the stuttering group.
27. Cobb, S. and Cole, E. N., "Stuttering," *Physiological Review*, 1939, Vol. 19, pages 49–62.
A summary of neurological findings on stutterers to indicate that the disorder may be due to a variation in cerebral structure.
28. Cross, H. M., "The Motor Capacities of Stutterers," *Archives of Speech*, 1936, Vol. 1, pages 112–132.

Stutterers are significantly inferior to normal speakers in bimanual movements but not in unimanual ones.

29. Daniels, E. M., "An Analysis of the Relation Between Handedness and Stuttering with Special Reference to the Orton-Travis Theory of Cerebral Dominance," *Journal of Speech Disorders*, 1940, Vol. 5, pages 309–326.
No evidence was found that shift of handedness, or ambidexterity or left-handedness, produces stuttering.

30. Douglass, L. C., "A Study of Bilaterally Recorded Electroencephalograms of Adult Stutterers," *Journal of Experimental Psychology*, 1943, Vol. 32, pages 247–265.
Bilateral occipital blocking is significantly greater in stutterers during stuttering.

31. Fink, W. H. and Bryngelson, B., "The Relation of Strabismus to Right or Left Sidedness," *Transactions of the American Academy of Ophthalmology and Otolaryngology*, 1934, pages 3–12.
Strabismus, left-handedness, and stuttering seem to be associated.

32. Freestone, N. W., "A Brain-wave Interpretation of Stuttering," *Quarterly Journal of Speech*, 1942, Vol. 28, pages 466–468.
Stutterers had more alpha waves and larger waves than did normals. The author's discussion of the findings and their interpretation is especially worth while.

33. Gray, M., "The X Family: A Clinical and Laboratory Study of a 'Stuttering' Family," *Journal of Speech Disorders*, 1940, Vol. 5, pages 343–348.
Two branches of a stuttering family were studied. One branch was "stuttering conscious." The other was not. In the first family branch 40 per cent stuttered; in the other, only 6 per cent did.

34. Greene, J. S., "Functional Speech and Voice Disorders," *Journal of Nervous and Mental Diseases*, 1942, Vol. 95, pages 299–309.
The author declares that there are hereditary factors in 50 per cent of cases.

35. Hill, H., "Stuttering: I. A Critical Review and Evaluation of Biochemical Investigations," *Journal of Speech Disorders*, 1944, Vol. 9, pages 245–261.
An excellent and critical summary of most of these investigations.

36. Hill, H., "Stuttering: A Review and Integration of Physiological Data," *Journal of Speech Disorders*, 1944, Vol. 9, pages 289–324.
The physiological data reviewed in this summary of investigations include researches on: breathing, blood pressure and other cardiovascular changes, tonus and tetanus, reflexes, eye movements and pupilary changes.

37. Hogewind, F., "Medical Treatment of Stuttering," *Journal of Speech Disorders*, 1940, Vol. 5, pages 203–208.
Stutterers present symptoms of somatic as well as psychogenic disorders.

38. Hunsley, Y. L., "Dysintegration in the Speech Musculature of Stutterers During the Production of a Non-vocal Temporal Pattern," *Psychological Monographs*, 1937, Vol. 49, No. 1, pages 32–49.
Stutterers who tried to follow a rhythmic pattern of clicks by biting, tongue protruding, and panting were inferior in these skills to normals.

39. Johnson, W. and Duke, L., "Change of Handedness Associated with Onset or Disappearance of Stuttering," *Journal of Experimental Education*, Dec., 1935, Vol. 4, No. 2.
Case studies illustrating the effect of a shift of handedness on the onset or the disappearance of stuttering.

40. Kopp, H., "The Relationship of Stuttering to Motor Disturbances," *The Nervous Child*, 1943, Vol. 2, pages 107–116.
Oseretzky's tests on 450 stutterers reveals that stuttering "is not a psychologic but a neurologic disorder characterized by a profound disturbance of the motor function."

41. Lindsley, D. B., "Bilateral Differences in Brain Potentials from the Two Cerebral Hemispheres in Relation to Laterality and Stuttering," *Journal of Experimental Psychology*, 1940, Vol. 26, pages 211–225.
More blocking and unsynchronized brain waves in stutterers than in normals.

42. Milisen, R. and Johnson, W., "A Comparative Study of Stutterers, Former Stutterers and Normal Speakers Whose Handedness Has Been Changed," *Archives of Speech*, 1936, Vol. 1, pages 61–86.
A study of causes, age of onset, and causes of the disappearance, showing the average onset of stuttering at the age of three, and 40 per cent outgrowing stuttering before eight years of age.

43. Nelson, S. E., "Personal Contact as a Factor in the Transfer of Stuttering," *Human Biology*, 1939, Vol. 11, pages 393–418.
Personal contact or imitation must be only a slight factor in causing stuttering to run in families.

44. Nelson, S. E., "The Role of Heredity in Stuttering," *Journal of Pediatrics*, 1939, Vol. 14, pages 642–654.
The author compared 204 stutterers with equal number of nonstutterers and found much more stuttering in the families of the former.

45. Rheinberger, M. B., Karlin, I. W., and Bergman, A. B., "Electroencephalographic and Laterality Studies of Stuttering and Non-stuttering Children," *The Nervous Child*, 1943, Vol. 2, pages 117–133.
The authors compared ten stutterers with ten nonstutterers and found no differences in brain waves, but the nonstutterers were more unilateral.

46. Scarborough, H. E., "A Quantitative and Qualitative Analysis of the Electroencephalograms of Stutterers and Non-stutterers," *Journal of Experimental Psychology*, 1943, Vol. 32, pages 156–167.
No differences between 20 normal speakers and 20 stutterers.

47. Spadino, E. J., "Writing and Laterality Characteristics of Stuttering Children," *Columbia University Teachers College Contributions to Education*, No. 837, New York, 1941.
Few, if any, differences between stutterers and nonstutterers.

48. Strother, C., "A Study of the Extent of Dyssynergia Occurring during Stuttering Spasm," *Psychological Monograph*, 1937, Vol. 49, pages 108–128.
A study of action-current, breathing, and eye-movement abnormalities during the overt stuttering spasm. Among other conclusions, it was found that no one type of abnormality always occurred on all of the blocks.

49. Strother, C. R. and Kriegman, L. S., "Diadochokinesis in Stutterers and Non-stutterers," *Journal of Speech Disorders*, 1943, Vol. 8, pages 323–335.
A review of other studies of diadochokinesis and an experiment showing no essential differences between stutterers and nonstutterers.

50. Strother, C. R. and Kriegman, L. S., "Rhythmokinesis in Stutterers and Non-stutterers," *Journal of Speech Disorders*, 1944, Vol. 9, pages 239–244.
No differences were found between the two groups.

51. Travis, L. E., "Dissociation of the Homologous Muscle Function in Stuttering," *Archives of Neurology and Psychiatry*, 1934, Vol. 31, pages 127–131.
Action currents were taken from masseter muscles of stutterers and normal speakers during stuttering and during free speech. In general, the currents were identical in normal speech, and in stuttering those of one masseter muscle were much different from the action currents of the other.

52. Travis, L. E., *Speech Pathology*, New York, D. Appleton-Century, 1931.
Reviews the earlier research on dysphemia from the point of view of cerebral dominance.

53. Travis, L. E. and Knott, J. R., "Brain Potentials from Normal Speakers and Stutterers," *Journal of Psychology*, 1936, Vol. 2, pages 137-150.
Statistically significant differences were found.

54. Van Riper, C., "The Quantitative Measurement of Laterality," *Journal of Experimental Psychology*, 1935, Vol. 18, pages 372–382.
A description of a laterality test employing the simultaneous drawing of patterns on two writing boards which can be converged at varying angles. The angle at which one hand produced mirrored patterning was shown to differentiate between thoroughly right- or left-handed and ambidextrous groups. Stutterers were shown to have a high degree of ambilaterality.

55. West, R., "A Neurological Test for Stutterers," *Journal of Neurology and Psychopathology*, 1929, Vol. 10, pages 114–118.
A test using jaw-brow movements in repetitive acts, showing stutterers inferior to normals in such neuromuscular co-ordinations.

Causes of Stuttering: Developmental

56. Berry, M. F., "A Study of the Medical Histories of Stuttering Children," *Speech Monographs*, 1938, Vol. 5, pages 97–114.
More diseases of the nervous system among stutterers: encephalitis, convulsions, epilepsy.

57. Davis, D. M., "The Relation of Repetitions in the Speech of Young Children to Certain Measures of Language Maturity and Situational Factors," *Journal of Speech Disorders*, 1940, Vol. 5, pages 235–246.
The author examined children 2, 3, and 4 years old. Repetition of words and phrases decreased with age; syllable repetitions did not. Four syllable repetitions per thousand words; 14 word repetitions per thousand; 24 phrase repetitions per thousand. Boys had more syllable repetitions than girls. These were normal-speaking children.

58. Fröschels, E., "Stuttering and Nystagmus," *Monatschrift für Ohrenh.*, 1915, Vol. 49, pages 161–167.

This old reference expresses the author's present views but more clearly. "A speech act in its normal course is suddenly interrupted through lack of an idea or word or through a psychological repression such as embarrassment, fright or great joy." "If during the period of initial stuttering, the child is not made conscious of it through incorrect educational methods or fearful attitudes in some person over him, this initial stuttering vanishes as soon as the stream of thought becomes more regular and vocabulary is available." Two of Froeschel's recent articles which express the same point of view are: "Pathology and Therapy of Stuttering," *The Nervous Child*, 1943, Vol. 2, pages 148–161; and "Survey of the Early Literature on Stuttering, Chiefly European," *The Nervous Child*, 1943, Vol. 2, pages 86–95.

59. Heltman, H., "Psycho-social Phenomena of Stuttering and Their Etiological and Therapeutic Implications," *Journal of Social Psychology*, 1938, Vol. 9, pages 79–96.

Hesitation and repetition are common to most, if not all, children during the years of developing speech; and this may be due to an inadequate vocabulary or to general confusion. "But whatever the cause, if the physical aspects of this lack of fluency in childhood were observed in adults it would be diagnosed as stuttering."

60. Johnson, W., "Stuttering in the Pre-school Child," *University of Iowa Child Welfare Pamphlets*, No. 37, 1934.

"Parents differ (*a*) in the degree to which they pay attention to their children's speech, and (*b*) in the way they define 'stuttering.' Some parents label almost any repetition or hesitation in a child's speech as stuttering. Other parents either do not notice the child's non-fluency or do not think of it as stuttering even when it is extremely conspicuous. Also, some parents, having decided their child is stuttering, become extraordinarily worried; other parents, having made the decision, simply forget it." Johnson expresses the developmental etiology of stuttering very clearly in another article: "The Indians Have No Word for It," *Quarterly Journal of Speech*, 1944, Vol. 30, pages 330–337.

61. Johnson, W. (and others), "A Study of the Onset and Development of Stuttering," *Journal of Speech Disorders*, 1942, Vol. 7, pages 251–257.

Careful summaries of case histories show that in some cases stuttering develops after the diagnosis. Summarizes the developmental factors present and finds few differences between stutterers and a group of matched normal children.

62. Milisen, R. and Johnson, W., "Comparative Study of Stutterers, Former Stutterers, and Normal Speakers Whose Handedness Had Been Changed," *Archives of Speech*, 1936, Vol. 1, pages 61–86.

Shows the relationship between birth injuries, illnesses, accidents, and other developmental factors and the onset of stuttering. There are also some interesting observations on how children "outgrew" their stuttering.

63. Steer, M. D., "Symptomatologies of Young Stutterers," *Journal of Speech Disorders*, 1937, Vol. 2, pages 3–13.

"If the child's speech pattern emphasized the deviations recognized as symptoms, he would be recognized as a stutterer; but he might manifest the deviations without undue emphasis or consistency and still be normal as to speech." "On the other hand, if the generally accepted symptoms of stuttering are really indicative, then their presence in the speech patterns of children of both types, stuttering and non-stuttering, would indicate that children in general do stutter. In other words, stuttering might be defined as a function of the maturation of the mechanism used in speaking. And therefore adults who stutter do so because of a condition of arrested development in their speech."

64. Voelker, C. H., "A Preliminary Investigation for a Normative Study of Fluency; a Clinical Index to the Severity of Stuttering," *American Journal of Orthopsychiatry*, 1944, Vol. 14, pages 285–294.
Children 12 to 19 were tested: Average speaker showed no syllable repetitions per 100 words, less than 1 word repetition, 10 hesitations, 3 to 6 pauses which were conspicuous. A fluency break occurred every 5 or 6 seconds. Stutterers differed from normals only in prolongations and word and syllable repetitions.

Causes of Stuttering: Emotional Conflicts

65. Brown, F. W., "Viewpoints on Stuttering," *American Journal of Orthopsychiatry*, 1932, Vol. 2, pages 1–24.
Suggested procedures for a rational method of attempting to solve the problem of stuttering, including the study of each stutterer as an individual personality, use of mental hygiene, the instruction of parents and teachers in mental hygiene, and research into therapeutic techniques.

66. Coriat, I. H., "The Psychoanalytic Conception of Stuttering," *The Nervous Child*, 1943, Vol. 2, pages 167–171.
"Stammerers are narcissistic infants who have compulsively retained the original equivalents of nursing and biting." Exposition and some illustration.

67. Cooper, C. A., "Discussion on the Relationship Between Speech Disorders and Personality Defects in Children, and How Stuttering May Unfavorably Affect Children's Personality Development," *Journal of Pediatrics*, 1942, Vol. 21, pages 418–421.
Parents are likely to overvalue the importance of the speech defect and to underestimate the importance of the personality conflicts which produce or result from stuttering.

68. Despert, J. L., "A Therapeutic Approach to the Problem of Stuttering in Children," *The Nervous Child*, 1943, Vol. 2, pages 134–147.
The importance of neurotic maternal attitudes when they are focused on the child's social and speech behavior is clearly presented.

69. Dunlap, K., "Stammering: Its Nature, Etiology and Therapy," *Journal of Comparative Psychology*, 1944, Vol. 37, pages 187–202.
Tension and frustration are the predisposing cause of stuttering. Emotional shock precipitates the disorder.

70. Gifford, M. F., *How to Overcome Stammering*, New York, Prentice-Hall, 1940.
"Since stammering usually begins in childhood, the reason for this maladjustment is usually found in this period. Some situation which the stammerer could not control because of his immaturity gave rise to a problem which he could not solve. His resulting emotional frustration was expressed in stammering."

71. Greene, J. S. and Small, S. M., "Psychosomatic Factors in Stuttering," *Medical Clinics of North America*, 1944, Vol. 28, pages 615–628.
From 30 to 40 per cent had Rorschach indications of marked emotional instability.

72. Heilpern, E., "A Case of Stuttering," *Psychoanalytic Quarterly*, 1941, Vol. 10, 95–115.
A summary of a case of stuttering due to "oral eroticism."

73. Krausz, E. O., "Is Stuttering Primarily a Speech Disorder?" *Journal of Speech Disorders*, 1940, Vol. 5, pages 227–231.
Stuttering is not a speech disorder but a negative compulsive behavior focusing on the social aspect of speech.

74. Meltzer, H., "Personality Differences Between Stuttering and Non-stuttering Children as Indicated by the Rorschach Test," *Journal of Psychology*, 1944, Vol. 17, pages 39–59.
Fifty cases of each group were tested with Rorschach. "In practically all factors which implicate emotional instability the scores of stuttering children exceed those of the control group."

75. Rotter, J. B., "The Nature and Treatment of Stuttering: A Clinical Approach," *Journal of Abnormal and Social Psychology*, 1944.
Case histories are presented to show that stuttering cannot be understood apart from the environmental and emotional conditions under which it occurs. Eliminate the cause, not the symptoms.

76. Solomon, M., "Stuttering as an Emotional and Personality Disorder," *Journal of Speech Disorders*, 1939, Vol. 4, pages 347–357.
Stuttering is the reflection in speech of a struggle to get some equilibrium during social interaction. The stutterer is one who lives in a relatively constant state of emotional strain and whose speech breaks down under this pressure.

77. Spring, W. J., "Words and Masses: A Pictorial Contribution to the Psychology of Stuttering," *Psychoanalytic Quarterly*, 1935, Vol. 4, pages 244–258.
The verbal and painting activities of a young boy are analyzed to clarify the reasons for his mother-hatred.

78. Thorpe, L. P., "Psychobiological Mechanisms of Stammering," *Journal of General Psychology*, 1938, Vol. 19, pages 97–109.

79. Usher, R. D., "A Case of Stammering," *International Journal of Psycho-Analysis*, 1944, Vol. 25, pages 61–70.
In rather difficult terminology, the case of a stutterer whose symptoms concealed unjustified fears, depression, and anxiety.

Development of Stuttering

80. Bluemel, C. S., *Stammering and Allied Disorders*, New York, Macmillan, 1935.
A consideration of primary and secondary stammering and other speech defects from the viewpoint of Pavlov's theory of conditioning and inhibition. Other theories of stammering are reviewed, and some of the author's own therapeutic suggestions are given.

81. Fröschels, E., "A Study of the Symptomatology of Stuttering," *Monatschrift für Ohrenheilk.*, 1921, Vol. 55, page 1109. .
Describes the sequence of development as follows: 1. nonforced repetitions, normal tempo; 2. nonforced repetitions, irregular tempo; 3. forced repetitions, normal tempo; 4. forced repetitions, irregular tempo; 5. forced repetitions, abnormally fast; 6. forced repetitions, abnormally fast, then inhibited; 7. forced repetitions, abnormally fast, then inhibited and slowed down; 8. slow repetitions, obviously postponement devices.

82. Fröschels, E., "Differences in the Symptomatology in the United States and in Europe," *Journal of Speech Disorders*, 1941, Vol. 6, pages 45–46.
American stutterers are more skeptical and need a belief in an organic cause. They develop secondary symptoms more readily.

83. Gray, M., "The X Family: A Clinical and Laboratory Study of a 'Stuttering' Family," *Journal of Speech Disorders*, 1940, Vol. 5, pages 343–348.
Describes the types of parental attitudes which tend to make the stutterer highly conscious of his disorder and lead to secondary symptoms.

84. Johnson, W., "The Indians Have No Word for It," I. *Quarterly Journal of Speech*, 1944, Vol. 30, pages 330–337.
Describes the growth of the secondary symptoms and the fears and struggle reactions which result.

85. Solomon, M., "Stuttering as an Emotional Disorder," *Proceedings of the American Speech Correction Association*, 1932, Vol. 2, pages 118–121.
A description of the three clinical stages of stuttering, all of which the author believes to be caused by emotion: 1. the basic stage of pure habit; 2. the fear or fright stage; 3. the stage of distortion of the personality. Some principles of treatment are suggested.

86. Van Riper, C., "The Growth of the Stuttering Spasm," *Quarterly Journal of Speech*, 1937, Vol. 23, pages 70–73.
An article showing the difference between the primary stuttering blocks of children who have just begun to stutter and the elaborate superstructure of habit reactions present in secondary stuttering blocks. A description of how these secondary reactions are built up is given.

Secondary Stuttering: Its Symptoms

87. Ammons, R. and Johnson, W., "Studies in the Psychology of Stuttering: XVII, The Construction and Application of a Test of Attitude

Toward Stuttering," *Journal of Speech Disorders*, 1944, Vol. 9, pages 39–49.
The test is described and shown to be important in determining how morbid a stutterer feels about his speech defect.

88. Brown, S. F., "The Loci of Stutterings in the Speech Sequence," *Journal of Speech Disorders*, 1945, Vol. 10, pages 181–192.
The author summarizes the results of other studies concerning the word cues which the stutterer interprets as threatening stuttering or which produce it. Stutterers have more difficulty on certain words than on others, on words beginning a sentence than on other words, on longer words than on shorter, on accented syllables than on those unaccented, and on meaningful material than on nonsense material containing the same words.

89. Brown, S. F. and Hull, H. C., "A Study of Some Social Attitudes of a Group of 59 Stutterers," *Journal of Speech Disorders*, 1942, Vol. 7, pages 323–324.
Stutterers are more poorly adjusted in social situations.

90. Eisenson, J. and Horowitz, E., "The Influence of Propositionality on Stuttering," *Journal of Speech Disorders*, 1945, Vol. 10, pages 193–198.
The more meaningful the stutterer's utterance, the more stuttering.

91. Eisenson, J. and Wells, C., "A Study of the Influence of Communicative Responsibility in a Choral Reading Speech Situation for Stutterers," *Journal of Speech Disorders*, 1942, Vol. 7, pages 259–262.
When stutterers shifted from choral reading with normal speakers to solo reading, stuttering spasms increased 60 per cent.

92. Harris, W. E., "Studies in the Psychology of Stuttering: XVII, A Study of the Transfer of the Adaptation Effect in Stuttering," *Journal of Speech Disorders*, 1942, Vol. 7, pages 209–221.
When stutterers read and reread a passage, the number of spasms decrease, but there is no transfer of this lessened stuttering to other situations.

93. Heltman, H. J., "Psycho-social Phenomena of Stuttering and Their Etiological and Therapeutic Implications," *Journal of Social Psychology*, 1938, Vol. 9, pages 79–96.
Stuttering is perfectly correlated with expectancy of stuttering. No experimental evidence, however, is offered.

94. Hendrickson, E. H., "Simultaneously Recorded Breathing and Vocal Disturbances of Stutterers," *Archives of Speech*, 1936, Vol. 1, pages 133–149.
A summary of the literature on breathing plus an analysis of the breathing abnormalities and vocal abnormalities found in stuttering.

95. Johnson, W., "The Indians Have No Word for It: II. Stuttering in Adults," *Quarterly Journal of Speech*, 1944, Vol. 30, pages 456–465.
A good description of how the stutterer reacts to his nonfluency.

96. Johnson, W., *The Influence of Stuttering on the Personality*, University of Iowa Studies in Child Welfare, Iowa City, Iowa, 1932.
Autobiographical material to show the effect of stuttering on the social adjustments of the stutterer.

97. Johnson, W. and Ainsworth, S., "Studies in the Psychology of Stuttering: X., Constancy of Loci of Expectancy of Stuttering," *Journal of Speech Disorders*, 1938, Vol. 3, pages 101–104.

The stutterer expects to stutter on the same words of a reading passage when he rereads it.

98. Johnson, W. and Colley, W. H., "The Relationship Between Frequency and Duration of Moments of Stuttering," *Journal of Speech Disorders*, 1945, Vol. 10, pages 35–38.
Neither frequency of stuttering nor duration of stuttering can by themselves be regarded as the true measure of severity.

99. Johnson, W., Knott, J., Webster, M. J., Larson, R. P., Solomon, A., Sinn, A., Millsapps, L., and Rosen, L., "Studies in the Psychology of Stuttering," *Journal of Speech Disorders*, 1937, Vol. 2, Studies 1–7.
A series of seven studies showing: 1. That moments of stuttering are distributed in a nonrandom order among words spoken. 2. Eighty-eight per cent of the words on which stuttering was expected were stuttered upon. 3. When a cue which had been associated with a difficult situation was introduced into a situation previously considered "easy," the stuttering increased significantly in the latter situation. 4. Expectation of stuttering need not operate on a highly conscious level. 5. Stuttering is reduced 98 per cent when expectation of stuttering is eliminated. 6. When words previously stuttered upon in a passage were omitted, future stuttering occurred on words closely associated with those omitted. 7. The use of changes of speech patterns serves as a distraction which decreases the frequency of spasms.

100. Koepp-Baker, H., *Handbook of Clinical Speech*, Ann Arbor, Edwards Brothers, 1937, Vol. 1, pages 147–154.
This reference discusses other factors, mainly psychological, which affect a stutterer, and gives suggestions to a stutterer for "managing himself."

101. Kimmell, H., "Studies in the Psychology of Stuttering: The Nature and Effect of a Stutterer's Avoidance Reactions," *Journal of Speech Disorders*, 1938, Vol. 3, pages 95–100.
Autobiographies from 39 stutterers were examined to determine the kinds of avoidance reactions shown by stutterers and the effect these had on their adjustment.

102. Knott, J. R. and Johnson, W., "The Factor of Attention in Relation to the Moment of Stuttering," *Journal of Genetic Psychology*, 1936, Vol. 48, pages 479–480.
The stronger the attention to stuttering, the more stuttering; the greater the need to avoid, the more frequent the stuttering.

103. Maddox, J., "The Role of Visual Cues in the Precipitation of Stuttering," *Proceedings of the American Speech Correction Association*, 1938, Vol. 8, pages 49–51.
An experimental study showing that the frequency of stuttering was increased when the stutterer observed himself in a mirror when reading aloud.

104. Milisen, R., "Frequency of Stuttering with Anticipation of Stuttering Controlled," *Proceedings of the American Speech Correction Association*, 1938, Vol. 8, pages 44–46.
A study concluding that the median stutterer was unable to predict more than 61 per cent of his spasms, and that the occurrence of spasms tends to bring an increase in spasm frequency.

105. Milisen, R. and Van Riper, C., "A Study of the Predicted Duration of the Stutterer's Blocks as Related to Their Actual Duration," *Journal of Speech Disorders*, 1939, Vol. 4, pages 339–345.
The stutterer can successfully predict the duration of his stuttering blocks.

106. Pittenger, K., "A Study of the Duration of the Temporal Intervals Between Successive Moments of Stuttering," *Journal of Speech Disorders*, 1940, Vol. 5, pages 333–341.
Stuttering does not occur in cyclic patterns. There are no rhythms of occurrence.

107. Porter, H. v. K., "Studies in the Psychology of Stuttering: XIV, Stuttering Phenomena in Relation to Size and Personnel of Audience," *Journal of Speech Disorders*, 1939, Vol. 4, pages 323–333.
There is a significant increase in the frequency of stuttering with increase in the number of auditors up to four. A close agreement exists between actual stuttering and its anticipation.

108. Richardson, L. H., "The Personality of Stutterers," *Psychological Monographs*, 1944, Vol. 56, No. 7, pages 1–41.
Stutterers are more depressed, introvertive. Several tests were given.

109. Robbins, S. D., "Relative Attention Paid to Vowels and Consonants by Stammerers and Normal Speakers," *Proceedings of the American Speech Correction Association*, 1936, Vol. 6, pages 7–23.
The conclusions from a study comparing the most prominent letter, the most prominent-looking letter, the most prominent-sounding letter, and the most prominent-feeling letter of stammerers and normals.

110. Solomon, M., "Stuttering, Emotion, and the Struggle for Equilibrium," *Proceedings of the American Speech Correction Association*, 1936, Vol. 6, pages 221–239.
One of the clearest descriptions of the way a stutterer feels about his stuttering, the development of the secondary symptoms of avoidance and struggle, and the fears and shames which accompany the disorder.

111. Steer, M. D. and Johnson, W., "An Objective Study of the Relationship Between Psychological Factors and the Severity of Stuttering," *Journal of Abnormal Psychology*, 1936, Vol. 31, pages 36–46.
An objective study of the frequency of stuttering as related to different speaking situations.

112. Van Riper, C., "The Influence of Empathic Response on the Frequency of Stuttering," *Psychological Monograph*, 1937, Vol. 49, No. 1, pages 244–246.
Stutterers were asked to repeat words pronounced by another stutterer, and the results showed that stutterers had more blocks upon words which the pronouncer stuttered upon than on the words which the pronouncer said with no difficulty.

113. Van Riper, C., "The Effect of Penalty Upon Frequency of Stuttering," *Journal of Genetic Psychology*, 1937, Vol. 50, pages 193–195.
A study to investigate the relationship of expected or felt penalty to the actual number of spasms, showing that a positive relationship exists.

114. Van Riper, C., "A Study of the Thoracic Breathing of Stutterers

During Expectancy and Occurrence of Stuttering Spasm," *Journal of Speech Disorders*, 1936, Vol. 1, pages 61–72.

A study of stutterer's breathing during expectancy and actual block, showing that there is generally a high correspondence and that some stutterers present constant breathing abnormalities.

115. Voelker, C. H., "A Preliminary Investigation for a Normative Study of Fluency; a Clinical Index to the Severity of Stuttering," *American Journal of Orthopsychiatry*, 1944, Vol. 14, pages 285–294.

The differences in the types of fluency break between stutterers and normal speakers. The former had more prolongations, syllable and word repetitions. The average normal-speaking child had no syllabic repetitions per one hundred words.

XI

The Treatment of Stuttering

We know of no better way to begin a chapter on the treatment of stuttering than to give the beginning student of speech correction a little historical background on the subject. Stuttering has presented a difficult problem to physicians and teachers for thousands of years, and we are still far from finding an easy solution. Stutterers have been "cured" by a thousand different techniques. We know of one who never stuttered again after his father, in a fit of irritation, dumped a bushel of herring over his head. In our own chase of the will-o'-the-wisp—an easy, reliable method for eliminating stuttering—we have tried many different techniques but have never found one which entirely satisfied us. Many of these techniques produce excellent temporary results, but relapse seems to occur so frequently that a conscientious speech correctionist refuses to use them. In view of the conflicting therapies now in use, many workers in the field of speech correction hesitate to adopt any systematic approach to the problem. They use, however, any method which decreases the fears or interruptions. Such a policy often leads to hit-and-miss, trial-and-error treatment. In this book we describe a systematic re-educational therapy for stuttering, which, when combined with personality readjustment, has proved more successful than any other we have used.

The treatment of primary stuttering is dealt with by most speech correctionists in about the same fashion, but secondary stuttering has been subjected to everything from cathartics to clavicular breathing exercises. Let us consider samples from a list of 150 described by Klingbell (38).

Herodotus (*ca.* 484–424 B.C.), the Greek historian, records treatment of Battos, son of Polymnestos, by a Pythian priestess, who recommended emigration south, to Libya.

Satyrus, the Greek actor, is said, by Plutarch, to have been responsible for the cure of *Demosthenes* (*ca.* 383–322 B.C.), who not only had a harsh and tuneless voice, but stuttered and had difficulty with the pronunciation of *r*. Satyrus prescribed voice exercises for him, in which the use of a mirror and pebbles in his mouth were part of the treatment and which called also for declaiming while going uphill.

Johann 'Konrad Amman (1667–1724) was a Swiss physician and one of the earliest writers on the instruction of the deaf and dumb. He practiced in Holland and also treated stutterers. He believed "hesitantia," as he called stuttering, to be due simply to vicious habit. He directed his treatment for it chiefly to the tongue.

Moses Mendelssohn (1729–1786) was born at Dessau and is noted for his attempts to find good reasons for opinions currently held. He insisted that the chief reason for stuttering was physical and that it was due to a collision between many ideas flowing simultaneously from the brain. He recommended slow reading aloud, the succeeding words being kept covered so as not to be seen until they were required to be enunciated.

Erasmus Darwin (1731–1802), English physician and naturalist, keen and philosophic observer of nature, believed that sensations or emotions such as awe or bashfulness caused interrupted association of the movements of the organs of speech. He advocated constant practice of the difficult sounds with as much softening of the initial consonants as possible.

J. M. G. Itard was a French doctor who died in Paris in 1838. He was a surgeon and later doctor for the Institute for Deaf and Dumb in Paris. He maintained that stuttering was due to muscular debility, and used a golden or ivory fork, placed in the cavity of the alveolar arch of the lower jaw, for the purpose of supporting the tongue. He reported but two cures, neither of which was permanent according to other accounts.

Dupuytren, who lived about the same time as Itard (*ca.* 1817), made his patients speak in a singing tone, marking certain intervals by a slight movement of the foot. *Colombat* is incorrectly regarded as being the originator of this technique.

Yates, early 1800, was a New York doctor and, according to some, the inventor of the system known at that time as "the American Method." His treatment was carried out in an institute under the direction of "the *widow Leigh*," governess of Yates' daughter, this being done to avoid professional disrepute. Another version attributes the invention to *Mrs. Leigh* herself, whose husband had been a stutterer. Yates believed that stuttering was caused by spasm of the glottis, and treated it by advocating the raising of the tip of the tongue to the palate and holding it there while speaking. The secret was bought by *Malebouche* who made it "scientific" and traded on it, selling it to the Prussian and Belgian governments. *Baussmann* was made "professor" of the system by the Prussian Ecclesiastical Minister of State, and *Dr. Zitterland* and *M. Charlier* were also prominent in its application throughout Europe. It was made the subject of a report by *Magendie*, to the French Academy in 1828, and died a natural death shortly after, having excited a phenomenal amount of attention.

Canon Kingsley states that this method was secretly peddled by an English quack many years before.

Henry McCormac was a doctor who announced a curative method for which he claimed infallibility. It consisted of using deep inspirations and forcible expirations, for he believed stuttering was caused by the attempt to speak with nearly emptied lungs.

Neil Arnott (1788–1874), a Scottish physician, attributed the cause to spasm of the glottis and recommended the use of a continuous *e* sound between each word to keep the glottis open.

Johann Frederick Dieffenbach (1795–1847) was a German surgeon who became famous as an operator and later professor and director of clinical surgery in Berlin. He began the surgical treatment for speech defects, which became fashionable in Europe for several years. His favorite operation was to make a horizontal section at the root of the tongue, excising a triangular wedge completely across and nearly through it, with the object of dividing the lingual muscles, and thereby interrupting their innervation, in order to modify or cure the muscular spasm. His method was the result of a fancied connection between defective articulation and strabismus.

James Hunt treated stuttering successfully in England for many years, under the commendation of such observers as *Canon Kingsley* and Mr. Liston, the eminent surgeon. His treatment, according to Kingsley, was "naturally, and without dodge or trick, to teach the patient to speak consciously, as other men spoke unconsciously." By comparing the normal with the abnormal use of the organs of speech, he reduced the complicated phenomena to abuses of the action of the lip, tongue, jaw, and breath, either singly or combined. (London, 1870.)

Canon Charles Kingsley (1819–1875), the celebrated English orator, writer, and chaplain to the Queen, was himself a stutterer until he was 40 years of age. He believed that the cause of stuttering could be traced in three cases out of four to conscious or unconscious imitation. In a letter to a young lady he tells her that she stutters because her upper teeth, like his, shut over the lower ones, and prescribes a set of rules for her guidance in reading and speaking, the chief of which were opening her mouth widely, reading or speaking from a full lung, breathing inward at every stop, and keeping her tongue down. He advocated the use of dumbbell exercises to help breathing, and he also advised the placing of a bit of cork between the back teeth when speaking, keeping the upper lip drawn tightly down. He considered that childhood was an unsuitable time for treating the defect, and considered boxing as being "over and above a healing art" for stammerers.

C. Wyneken held stuttering to be a neurosis, all the manifestations of which depend on the psychical condition of the patient, and that the larynx is the chief seat of the disturbance. The proximate psychical cause he held to be the defective influence of the will, produced by doubt. His treatment was based largely on imbuing the patient with faith in his preceptor and in himself. He believed also in exercises for respiration, the voice, and speech, accompanied by the rhythmical beating of time.

Robert Bates was an American who treated stuttering with a variety of appliances: (1) a narrow flattened tube of silver applied to the median line of the roof of the mouth. This was used to aid the formation of the linguo palatal letters. (2) A hollow biconvex disc with a projecting silver tube placed between the lips to help labials and dental labials. (3) A belt and spring adjusted on the neck over the thyroid cartilage to help the gutturals.

Steckel called stuttering one of the worst forms of fear hysteria and believed stuttering to be as much a psychological betrayal as are slips of the tongue and pen. The neurosis begins always in childhood, generally as a pure anxiety neurosis. He used psychoanalysis in treatment. (1908.)

Treatment of the Young Stutterer in the Primary Stage

The young stutterer in the primary stage of the disorder presents a situation which calls for an entirely different type of therapy from that employed when the stuttering has developed into the advanced, or secondary, stage. The primary stutterer reacts unconsciously and automatically to his blocks, and hence his symptoms are the short, effortless, rapid repetitions or the equally short, easy prolongations.

Since the primary stutterer is not aware of any existing speech abnormality, he has developed none of the anticipatory reactions which result from fear of approaching word difficulty. His attitude toward his speech is normal, for not only is he unaware of his handicap, but also he is unconscious of any attendant social penalty. He may feel the blocks, but he accepts them as his normal way of communication and not as an unacceptable method of speaking. The stuttering is not a constant experience but comes in waves. At some times a great many blocks occur, and at other times there is no evidence of interruption. Most of the stutterers in this stage are young children who have just begun to stutter, although we find a few adults who have not developed any other reactions toward their blocks except these easy, automatic ones, and who have built no insecurities around that difference.

The object of treating the young primary stutterer, then, is to handle the speech problem in such a way that he will not develop any of the reactions to his blocks which would send him into the secondary stage. If he can be kept in the primary stage, where only brief repetitions and prolongations occur, his chances of outgrowing the disorder will be much greater.

The primary symptoms of stuttering—repetitions, prolongations, and hesitations—are not uncommon even among adults and are found much more frequently in almost all children. Any condition which produces communicative pressure, excitement, fear, or stress of any kind increases the number of these symptoms. Any subjective condition such as fatigue or nervousness tends to do likewise. If this is true, can all children be said to stutter? Certain investigators make this statement. The author prefers to consider primary stuttering according to his definition of a speech defect. If the repetitions, prolongations, or hesitations are so frequent or peculiar that they command attention and interfere with communication, they may be called symptoms of stuttering. If not, they are part of the wide rhythmic variation permitted to normal speech. To put it in another way, children vary in nervous stability, in cerebral dominance, in their ability to resist disturbing influences, in their ability to send properly timed impulses down to the paired-speech musculatures, in their ability to carry out a pattern of movements in time, and in a great many other integrative capacities. Children who possess these abilities and capacities to a high degree and who are not bombarded by a host of disturbing influences seldom show any repetitions, hesitations, or prolongations in their speech. On the other hand, children who inherit or acquire an unstable nervous system, a narrow margin of cerebral dominance, and inferior co-ordinative and integrative abilities will probably have a great many repetitions and prolongations even under slight environmental pressures. Many oversolicitous parents bring to the speech correctionist children who have fewer symptoms than the parents themselves. Before a child is diagnosed as a primary stutterer, the speech correctionist must know how often the primary symptoms occur and under what conditions.

"Outgrowing" stuttering, the term so frequently applied to the gradual disappearance of the handicap, is really a matter of maturation. The first symptoms appear when the child is in a state of developmental confusion. He is learning to speak while he is also giving his attention to the acquisition of walking and many other motor skills. His environment bombards him with hundreds of stimuli, and he responds to all of them, having learned experimentally no process of selection. Many simultaneous reactions, therefore, tend to create a nervous instability, which is often evidenced in an instability in the operation of the speech mechanism.   As the process of maturation proceeds, the child learns his motor skills, and, when they become automatic, he does not need to concentrate upon them.   He also learns to select stimuli from the barrage thrust upon him, and consequently much confusion disappears.   He learns to erect barriers against environmental excitement and does not respond to all disturbances.   Thus the child's entire mechanism becomes more stable, and, with increasing stability, the speech blocks often vanish.   However, they disappear only if, during this period of instability, the child has not become aware of them as a definite handicap.   If he can be prevented from reacting to his stuttering, he will develop none of the tricks for hiding blocks or for making speech attempts easier.   Thus he will be spared the abnormal communication which these habitual tricks and techniques ultimately bring.   Treatment of the young primary stutterer consists primarily of prevention.

This prevention is accomplished chiefly through the education and co-operation of the parents and teachers.   It can truthfully be said that the way to treat a young stutterer in the primary stage is to let him alone and treat his parents and teachers.   Nothing must be done to call his disorder to his attention or to point it out to him as an abnormality that he must eradicate.   Such techniques only serve to develop awareness of the abnormality and subsequent sensitivity concerning it.   But much can be done in the home and school to keep him from developing the useless and handicapping secondary symptoms.   The most important remedial methods for helping a young primary stutterer follow.

First, and of the greatest importance, all speech conflicts must be removed.   Whenever a child in the first phase of stuttering experiences a speech block, some attendant pressure exists which precipitates that interruption.   Therefore, his experiences and his environment must be analyzed to determine what these pressures are.   One satisfactory way of making this analysis is to keep a list of all words on which blocks occur, the situations in which they are found, and the possible pressure that caused them.   Parents often go just this far—they determine the pressure, and then do nothing about it.   It is not enough to recognize the precipitating factors; definite steps must be taken to remove or minimize them.   Some of the common speech conflicts which should be checked and removed are: interrupting the child; talking for the child whenever communicative difficulty is evident; suggesting other methods of talking which you think will make speech easier for him (such as talking slowly, taking a deep breath before words, thinking what he will say before he starts to talk, substituting another word for one on which trouble occurs, and so forth); ridiculing the child whenever blocks appear; requiring oral confession of guilt (whereby emotionality becomes attached to the speech act); too high speech standards in the home or school; penalizing or punishing the child when abnormality occurs (such as telling him to remain silent until he can say the word correctly); requiring the child to talk when he is fatigued or excited; attempting to make the child hurry when he is talking slowly; and forcing the child to "show off" by speaking pieces or reading to strangers when he is unwilling to do it. Each of these may seem of minor importance, but each is a potential force for increasing the number of primary blocks and for developing subsequent secondary reactions.

Second, the child must be kept in as good a physical condition as is possible. A stutterer needs more rest than the average child. We have mentioned that stuttering seems to come in waves of increased frequency and severity. Periods of good speech alternate with bad periods. When the stuttering is at the height of a frequency wave, fatigue will greatly increase the actual number of blocks, and, when stuttering is at the bottom of that wave, fatigue will precipitate blocks which otherwise would not occur. The child must also have a well-balanced diet, and all sources of physical infection or irritation should be removed. He must have as much physical stability as it is possible for him to attain.

Third, the child must have a pleasant home situation. All possible family conflicts should be cleared. This will be very difficult for some parents to accomplish, for a child reacts to implied attitudes, even though those attitudes are not discussed openly before him. Any implication of them reflects in his emotional adjustments, and anything so vital to the child's future welfare should be well worth any difficulty of accomplishment. In some homes, too, the tempo of living is so fast that it creates instability in the child. The members of the family act impetuously and under great tension, and the child will naturally acquire the same type of reactions. A stuttering child needs a home life devoid of such tension and full of calm activity, and this is another problem for his parents to solve as soon as they can. Use of a good routine is a very effective way of destroying nervous, useless activity in a home and of supplying much-needed stability. Finally, the rest of the family should accept the child's stuttering unemotionally as his particular way of talking.

Fourth, the parents and teachers must learn not to react emotionally to the child's stuttering blocks. Because of the principle of empathic response previously discussed in this text, the reactions of others to the abnormality will help to determine the stutterer's own reactions. If you are surprised, embarrassed, or impatient, he will become aware that his communication is not normal and will react likewise. If you tell him to hurry, to say words over and say them correctly, or if you say words for him because you don't want to wait for him or because you don't want others to see his handicap, he will become confused and ashamed and will begin to struggle and force in an attempt to speak normally. If you blush or seem embarrassed when he has difficulty in the presence of others, he will realize that there is something about his speech which makes others uncomfortable. One of the greatest needs in stuttering therapy is to train others in nonreaction to the speech block. Even though it be painful, the normal individual should discipline himself to look the stutterer directly in the eye while he is talking, to show no signs of impatience, and to make no attempt to help him speak. These attempts to help a stutterer talk only develop feelings of inadequacy and dependence in him. Understanding one's own emotional reactions, and a course of self-discipline in reacting intelligently rather than emotionally to one's personal problems, will greatly facilitate the development of nonreacting attitudes toward those who have more obvious differences. When the primary stutterer repeats and prolongs, the parents should wait quietly for the blocks to pass, and the stutterer should feel that he has all the time in the world to finish the sentence.

Fifth, the parents and teachers should seek to cancel all the child's unpleasant memories or experiences of stuttering. One of the best ways of doing this is to distract his attention to something else immediately after a block occurs, so that the block will not linger in his consciousness. Another way is to have the parents and teachers fake a stuttering block occasionally when talking to the child, so that he will not think such speech is peculiar only to him. Still another valuable technique is to manipulate the conversation so that the child can successfully say words with which he previously experienced difficulty, so that the final memory will be one of normal utterance of those words. If forcing begins to appear in the speech, the parents can show the child that he made the word difficult by "pushing it out," and that they, too, would experience the same difficulty if they forced the words out as they uttered them.   Great care should be taken to erase memories of speech difficulty, for if a stutterer retains impressions of unpleasantness, he will build up fears of such occurrences in the future.

Sixth, try to establish favorable speech conditions in the school and on the playground.   The teacher can help the classroom situation to a great degree if she ignores the stuttering and refuses to react to it, for she determines the attitude of many of the children.   She should tactfully explain to the other children in the room that the stutterer just has a different way of talking, that it is only temporary, and that he will get over it sooner if they all give him plenty of time to talk and pay no attention to the different kind of speech.   She should encourage the child to recite, and should never call attention to any evidence of speech abnormality in the recitation.   The classroom situation can be made much more favorable if all other problems are settled in an unemotional way.   If the teacher is easily provoked to anger, easily embarrassed, and shows her own emotionality often, it will be much more difficult to establish a nonemotional attitude in the children.   If the stutterer is teased on the playground, the teacher should discuss that problem with the other children, attempting to solve it not by threats or punishment, but by the explanation that all of the others have differences, too, and that they will actually harm the stutterer if they taunt him because of his different speech.   The attitude in the school is of vital importance, because children can be ruthless in their attitude toward a handicap.   But a wise teacher can create an understanding attitude of acceptance and unemotionality, even though she may be unable to recognize the actual techniques with which it is accomplished.

Seventh, the child should be given as many ideal speech situations as possible.   He can strengthen his normal speech by exercising it. Let him tell stories, recite verses, and read aloud in situations in which there is no pressure or tension.   Let him have the responsibility, and do not interrupt or correct him.   Encourage him to talk in family situations in which there is no tension—at the dinner table or in informal recitals of his day's activity.   Have the other children in the family, or the parents, play speech games with him which emphasize slow, distinct speaking and rhythmic speech.   Little dramatizations of stories can be arranged in the home, in which the stutterer is given parts which call for slow, smooth speech. Above all, the child should not be placed on exhibition. He should be encouraged to volunteer in informal situations, and should be accepted as part of the group when there is no attendant speech tension. It is usually unwise to place a young primary stutterer in any speech-correction class, as it only tends to point out his abnormality. Treatment of the young primary stutterer is always indirect. On those days when few blocks occur, he should be stimulated to speak as much as possible. On the days when he has a great deal of trouble, he should be so handled that he talks very little.

Eighth, insist upon unilaterality in most of the child's activities. Let him determine his own hand preference and eliminate all effort to change this preference. When the child is able to write easily, teach him to talk and write at the same time, using the technique described in the next sections of this chapter. Give him many new one-handed skills and do not permit him to engage in such activities as typing or piano-playing.

Ninth, train the child to perform temporal patterns with the paired musculatures. The parent and teacher can play little games in which the child beats out simple rhythms. Thus the parent can tap out a simple iambic rhythm, or play it on one piano key, while the child claps his hands, or kicks with both feet, or protrudes his tongue, or blows through a straw into water. The old nursery game of "patty-cake" is an excellent device. Various rhythms may be used. Both limbs and both of each pair of speech structures must act simultaneously in similar or mirrored ways.

Tenth, increase the child's personality assets in every way and decrease his liabilities. The solution of his emotional conflicts and behavior problems will often reflect itself in better speech. Many a primary stutterer has been "cured" by giving him mastery of new skills and greater social adequacy.

Eleventh, if it is impossible to keep the child from being dubbed a stutterer and penalized because of his speech difference, it is wise to tell him that he does indeed have some hesitations and repetitions in his speech, but that these are not at all serious, that he will probably outgrow them, and that almost every person has them. The parent and teacher may point out those that occur in their own speech or they may occasionally fake a few of them so that the child will attach no importance to them. If he is being teased about the disorder, he should be taught to admit it casually by saying, "Sure, I stutter a little. Everybody does. What of it?" Most teasing stops when confronted by such an attitude.

It is also possible to stop much of the teasing by calling in the ring-leader of the group doing the teasing and informing him of the conse-quences of his actions. For some odd reason, teasing usually stops when it is realized that it leaves a permanent effect. If the ringleader is also given the responsibility for preventing any playground teasing, he will usually co-operate enthusiastically.

CASE STUDY OF A PRIMARY STUTTERER

At the time of examination Tommy Buckton was four years old. An only child, reared in a prosperous but childless section of the city, he pre-sented the picture of unhappy forced maturity. His manners were adult. His conversation during our first meeting concerned electricity, badminton, and brontosauri as well as the more normal interests of his age. He in-sisted from the first on demonstrating his knowledge. He could say the ABC's; he could print his name and several other words; he could sing; he owned a typewriter; he had built a bridge "with very little assistance." He had "eighty-three dollars in the bank" and three war bonds. He "col-lected paper match folders." He had gone to the cafeteria all by himself and had paid for his own meal. He uttered these statements of his prowess politely and almost as though defining his status as an adult individual was obvious but necessary.

Unfortunately, the effect of precocity was marred by frequent repeti-tions of initial syllables of his long words, and by prolongations of the first sound or vowels of the short words. He seemed to be entirely unaware of these symptoms. They did not alter the swift, tense flow of his sentences. No forcing was apparent even when a syllable was repeated ten or twelve times. No eye-shift or avoidance mechanisms were present. The primary symptoms were especially prevalent at the beginning of sentences after a pause. They also occurred when he was interrupted or misunderstood or corrected. No breathing abnormalities were present. His articulation was perfect. He was thoroughly right handed. When he was asked to keep time to the rhythm record, he did unusually well, but was very much upset because he made errors on the more difficult series. He stuttered much more when trying to give excuses for these errors.

The interview with the mother disclosed that the child's father had stuttered as a boy, and that the paternal grandfather had stuttered until his death. The child had never seen this grandfather, however. Two severe illnesses had occurred during the boy's second year, and he had begun to stutter rather gradually "just before his third birthday" and "about the time he recovered from the last siege of pneumonia." The parents had not been concerned about the boy's hesitations and repetitions at first, ascribing them to his "lowered vitality" and to the fact "that all children go through some of this hesitating." The periods of nonfluency alternated with others of speech "so good that we were sure he was going to be a lawyer when he grew up." The mother was the first to become concerned about his symptoms and the first to label it "stuttering." This diagnosis was made after an old school friend of the mother's had visited their home for several days and had brought along her son of about the same age as Tommy. During this entire visit, Tommy's speech was "terribly broken." He "repeated all over the place. He could hardly say anything without trying eight or nine times." According to the mother, he did not play well with his visitor. He clung to his playthings and refused to share them. He continually asked how long the visitors were going to stay. He constantly interrupted his mother's conversations with her friend. "All in all, he was just a terrible child. We couldn't understand it because he's generally so well behaved."

It was difficult to get the mother to give us a clear picture of the subsequent behavior. She used such phrases as "He began to resent our leaving him, although we had always done so before without provoking any tears or protests." "It finally got to the point where my husband and I could not talk to each other at the table without his constant interruptions." "He grew more and more demanding of my attention." "When our maid left and Mrs. Brown came, he resented her efforts to discipline or manage him. He wasn't particularly mean; he just refused to co-operate or just ignored her." "He always stuttered much more when he knew we were going to leave him in her charge for an evening or a week end."

An interview with the father helped to clarify the picture somewhat. "My wife hates housework or the responsibility of a home. She wants to be always on the go. Quite a club woman. She doesn't know how to handle the kid, and admits it in front of him. Not that he's hard to handle either. But she gets excited and upset and the boy seems to feel it. She's got a lot worse since Tom began to stutter, and we've had a little trouble about it. I can't reason with her, and you'll find you can't either. So far as his stuttering is concerned, I'm not worried. I had a little myself when I was young, and he'll get over it all right. But she gets rattled about it and would drag him all over the place trying to get him examined."

We visited the home one late afternoon and stayed for dinner to observe the conditions there. Two very important facts came to light. First, the parents both treated the child exactly as though he were an adult. Their demands upon him for social conformity were far out of line. They also devoted much of the attention they gave to the boy to evoking exhibition of the intellectual sort. They displayed his interest in prehistoric animals, his ability to play a tune on the grand piano, his anagram blocks. The boy obviously enjoyed their approval of his intellectual prowess. Second, the dominant method used for discipline was a threat of leaving him. For instance, the mother asked him to wash his hands, a request he ignored. Whereupon, she stated that if he did not do so immediately, she, his father, and their guest would refuse to eat with him. "We shall probably have to eat downtown again, Tommy." Tommy hastily washed his hands. The mother boasted that this technique plus the isolation was always effective.

"We have never had any real difficulty with Tommy ourselves, but Mrs. Brown finds him very difficult at times." The boy was well behaved, according to her criteria.

The boy showed many of the repetitions on the long words during his exhibitionism and his interruptions at the table. The father ignored them, but the mother always stopped and became tense and nervous. Several times she supplied the word the boy was attempting to say. He showed no reaction.

Treatment consisted of (1) five one-hour interviews with the mother. In them we were able to lead her to see that the boy was being forced to attain verbal and social achievements far beyond his natural capacities. She also attained insight into the destructive effect of her methods of discipline and her reactions to his stuttering. In addition, she began to understand that she was resenting the child's interference with her own desires and comfort, and that she was rejecting her responsibilities as a mother.

In order to provide sufficient motivation for the change which had to be made in the child's environment we had her observe a class of very severe adult stutterers who told of their unhappy experiences. She left the class very much shaken but determined to do anything that would keep her child from having to undergo such a handicap. We then gave her some material to read on the nature and treatment of primary stuttering and asked her to discuss the whole problem with her husband, but to accept full responsibility herself for its solution.

We then suggested the following: (1) Eliminate the demand for speech exhibition of any kind. (Throw away the book of Brontosauri, and so on.) (2) Ignore all forms of exhibitionism or react to them with perfunctory interest. (3) Familiarize herself, through visits to pre-schools and kindergartens, with the interests and behavior patterns of other children of Tommy's age and then expect no more of him. (4) Make arrangements to have him play with other children of his own age occasionally and to enter pre-school within three months. (5) Dismiss Mrs. Brown and adopt the role of the perfect intelligent mother for three months. (6) Cease threatening to leave the boy, and curtail drastically those activities which required her to leave him even for a few hours. (7) Give the boy a lot of obvious affection and "babying" and spend several hours a day in playing with him. The play activities should be those of other children his age, and with physical or mechanical or exploratory play predominating. The former emphasis on intellectual activities should be gradually decreased. (8) The parents should speak to the child in short simple sentences without being obvious about it. Long or unfamiliar words should be avoided. The speech in the home should be quiet and unhurried. (9) When Tommy had one of his fluent periods he should be stimulated to speak a great deal. On his bad days, he should have little necessity to speak at all. (10) All disturbing influences such as confession of guilt, interruption, confusion, misunderstanding, should be minimized as much as possible. (11) All attempts at correction or finishing his troublesome words should be eliminated.

The parents should look at him calmly and wait for him to say the word. He should feel no necessity for hurry. The mother should train herself to remain relaxed when he is stuttering. (12) Use a good deal of speech play. Echo games, rhythmic vocalization, relaxed speech, and other relatively easy forms of speech activity were demonstrated to the mother and she was asked to try some each day.

The mother was then given a set of blanks with headings for each of the above twelve items on each, and she was urged to make a daily report to us of her efforts to solve the problem by filling out the blanks. We also arranged for a weekly conference to iron out any difficulties which did arise. Somewhat to our surprise, the mother was very conscientious and did an excellent job.

The stuttering symptoms gradually disappeared. The periods of fluency became longer and the bad periods much shorter. Within six months the boy was in nursery school and no symptoms were ever noted there. The mother, interestingly enough, was more grateful for the change in her own personality and life than she was for the boy's release. The father laughed at the whole program and said, "I told you he would outgrow it just like I did."

The Treatment of the Stutterer in the Secondary Stage

This stage of the disorder, it will be remembered, is reached when the individual has developed fears of words and situations, habitual or conscious reactions to the fear of or occurrence of block, and mal-attitudes toward his stuttering. It is marked by the appearance of the secondary symptoms of avoidance, postponement, antiexpectancy, starters, release, and disguise. Social maladjustment usually develops. The disorder, to use some of the older terminology, has become "chronic," or self-perpetuating. The more the individual stutters, the greater grow his fears, and the more frequent and severe his blocks become. A vicious circle of reaction has been established.

The various methods for treating secondary stuttering. In an earlier section we have described several of the many conflicting theories concerning the nature of stuttering. From a consideration of these theories, it might be concluded that there would be many contrasting kinds of treatment. Yet, when the actual therapies now in use are scrutinized, one is impressed by the large number of similar methods used in common by the majority of speech correctionists. Terminologies, emphasis, and theoretical justifications differ; the activity remains the same. This rather curious agreement is even more evident in terms of the subgoals set up for the stutterer. No matter to what theoretical schools they belong, all clinicians attempt to reduce the stutterer's fears, forcings, and inadequate social behavior. All speech correctionists carry out some etiological therapy, depending on the theory of causation to which they subscribe or on the causal factors present in any given case; and this part of the therapy differs widely. However, few clinicians actually working with stutterers confine their efforts to eliminating the causes. All of them work with symptoms—with the situation and word fears and with the repetitions, prolongations, facial contortions, and other typical stuttering reactions. There seem to be two major schools of thought in terms of actual therapy.

One school of speech correctionists, numbering among its adherents many of the older workers in the field, attempts to teach the stutterer methods for *avoiding* or preventing *fear* and *occurrence* of stuttering blocks. It aims to eliminate the emotional factors which precipitate the symptoms. The stutterer is urged to believe in the theory advanced by the clinician, and nothing is left undone to convince him that he can be cured. Strong clinical suggestion and even hypnosis are used to strengthen his confidence in the remedial techniques. Routine breathing and vocalization exercises and rituals are employed. Through the use of distractions of all kinds, the fear of stuttering is kept from consciousness. Gestures, head movements, and other forms of muscular reinforcement are used as starters. Strange methods of vocalization—preceding all consonants by a vowel, singsong speech, the "octave-twist," stereotyped rhythms of stress or phrasing, slurring of the consonants, and many other similar devices— are used to keep the fear from becoming potent enough to precipitate stuttering. Every effort is made to get the stutterer to forget his fears and symptoms. He is urged to consider himself a normal speaker. By the use of speech situations and types of communication arranged according to graduated levels of difficulty, his confidence is nursed along until it becomes sufficient to enable him to speak without fear or stuttering at each successive level. Group techniques help to decrease the fear and increase the suggestion.

In most cases, this type of treatment produces immediate release from fear and stuttering. The stutterer believes that at last a miracle has happened. Hesitantly he applies the formula and lo! it seems to work. His confidence grows by leaps and bounds, and, as it does, his fears decrease. He writes his clinician a glowing letter of praise and thankfulness and departs for his home. Occasionally, his new speech fluency continues for the rest of his life. Whenever fears arise, and they are inevitable, he applies the formulas given to him by the speech correctionist. If the environmental pressures are not too great, and novelty, suggestion, and faith are still effective, the formulas successfully dispel the fear. He realizes that he can still speak without stuttering.

Unfortunately, like most of the devices the stutterers themselves have invented, the formula devices soon become habitual and relatively unconscious. When this happens, they no longer are able to take the place of fear in the stutterer's mind, and relapse usually occurs. Giving the stutterer a period of free speech does not solve his problem if, and when, fear returns. Nevertheless, in the safe haven of the speech clinic, where belief and novelty are important factors and both group and clinical suggestion are everywhere, the stutterer finds great relief. Under such conditions, few stutterers experience much trouble, but unfortunately such conditions do not exist in ordinary life. When the stutterer returns to his home or former environment, or meets situations which remind him of past failures, there is no one around to tell him that his fears and blocks are mere bugaboos which will disappear if he follows the formula. Life is not made up of easy speech situations or optimal conditions for communication. He finds that he cannot remain relaxed when he applies for a position. He finds it impossible to remain permanently unemotional. The self-confidence, so carefully and painstakingly nurtured by the speech correctionist, collapses like a house of cards. The formula suddenly seems to have lost its charm. Faith crumbles. The stuttering returns in all its viciousness, often with greater frequency and severity than before. The stutterer attempts to relax, but fear and panic prevent relaxation. He starts his arm swing, or "octave twist," or whatnot, and finds that suddenly it does not keep out the blocks. After repeated failure, he finally gives up and resumes his hunt for a new miracle worker to cast out his "stuttering devil." Meanwhile, the speech correctionist has new stutterers to whom the formula may be taught.

The second major school of speech correctionists is relatively young. While most of the devices used by the other school have been employed for centuries, those of the new school have evolved in the last ten or twenty years. Although its adherents quarrel among themselves about the etiology of stuttering and fail to agree with regard to the nature of the primary symptoms, they all doubt that the secondary stutterer can ever entirely free himself from fears of certain situations and certain words.   They feel that an individual who has developed habits of avoidance, postponement, timing, and disguise as reactions to the fear of stuttering will never break those habits by merely experiencing a period of free speech.   They doubt that faith in any formula will eliminate the fear in the majority of stutterers.   They feel that the effects of suggestion and distraction are temporary and that self-confidence is affected by 'too many other factors to render it a permanent foundation for fear-free speech.   In other words, this school believes that it is impossible to keep out all fears or occurrences of stuttering blocks for any great length of time, and that no abnormal form of rhythm or utterance will provide permanent relief.

The adherents of this school point out that it is possible to modify the form of the stutterer's speech abnormality without preventing its occurrence.   They call attention to the wide variation in secondary symptoms found in different stutterers as a sign of the fact that it is possible to stutter in many different ways.   They claim that it is possible to stutter with a minimum of abnormality and interruption and that, when this is done, the fear of stuttering and most of the blocks disappear.   They insist that most of the abnormality and interruption is produced by the stutterer's conscious or habitual devices to avoid, minimize, disguise, or release himself from the blocks he feels.   They believe that these devices can be disrupted and eradicated.   They attempt to use the fear of stuttering as a signal to warn the stutterer to modify and control the form of any symptoms which might ensue, and as a signal to adopt new preparatory sets which can prevent the occurrence of the old secondary symptoms.   They insist that the stutterer acquire an objective attitude toward his speech difference— that he admit its existence and refuse to pose as a normal speaker, but that he control his fears and blocks so that only a minimum of interruption and abnormality will occur.   They feel that such an attitude so diminishes the social penalties placed upon the disorder that the fear of stuttering is greatly reduced.   They declare that these principles not only will decrease the duration and severity of the individual blocks but that those blocks will diminish in number.   Fluency and release from fear are thus considered to be by-products of *controlled stuttering* rather than the results of *avoided stuttering*.   The adherents of this school argue that their methods provide security for the stutterer when fears or blocks do reoccur.   We may summarize the point of view by saying that this school teaches the stutterer not to keep out or avoid his blocks and fears, but to control them so that they can occur with a minimum of interference to communication.

Outline of treatment for modifying the form of stuttering. It is probably obvious that the author belongs to the latter school. The method for treating the secondary stutterer, which will be described in this text, po'nts its therapy at the following goals: (1) Eliminate the neuromuscular blocks through establishing unilaterality of motor lead control and simultaneous talking-and-writing techniques. (2) Help the stutterer solve as many of his emotional conflicts as possible and change, if we can, the environmental conditions which tend to keep him a fundamentally hesitant person. (3) Decrease the fears and malattitudes by teaching the stutterer to admit and accept his stuttering as a temporary problem which must be faced and conquered. (4) Modify and lessen the severity of the stuttering blocks by eliminating the secondary symptoms of stuttering. (5) Teach the stutterer not to avoid fears or blocks, but to use them in learning how to stutter in an easy, effortless fashion, with a minimum of interruption or abnormality. With this therapy it usually takes longer to achieve speech free from blockings, but relapse is much less frequent, and the stutterer always has a method for controlling his fears and stuttering reactions if they do return.

The treatment of the secondary stutterer is largely carried out through individual conferences with the speech correctionist, through the use of carefully prepared speech assignments, and through cooperative projects involving groups of stutterers. Like all speech defectives, each stutterer presents an individual problem and must be treated as such. Certain individuals require much more work on one phase of the treatment than do others. Personality readjustment such as that sketched in Chapter IV is frequently necessary. Adequate motivation is important, for this treatment makes such a strong demand on the individual that perfunctory co-operation dooms it to immediate defeat. It is usually wise to let the student see the exact sequence of the treatment so that he may appreciate the importance of attaining the subgoals in order to attain the final goal of free speech.

Therapy is carried out through a series of successive periods or levels, each of which involves the use of new subgoals and techniques. The techniques, however, overlap, and those of prior levels continue throughout all later ones. Thus the assignments and projects of the second stage include not only the new techniques specific to that level but also all those used in the first stage. New subgoals and new techniques are added to, not substituted for, former ones. During the work on each of these levels, the speech correctionist should use every effort to prevent speech fluency due to the influence of suggestion or attitudes of self-confidence. These factors are too unstable to be relied upon for permanent relief. Instead, all clinical emphasis should be placed upon the attainment of good mental hygiene, the ability to disrupt the old habitual reactions of avoidance or release, and the ability to control the form of speech abnormality. Speech free from all stuttering is a by-product and an end-product, not the immediate goal. Stress is not placed on the absence of stuttering blocks or fears, but upon those blocks and fears that are controlled. The student is encouraged to stutter, but to stutter without the old abnormalities of emotion and behavior.

The First Period of Therapy

The activities which characterize the first period of treatment for the secondary stutterer may be enumerated as follows: (1) training in unilaterality; (2) training in the performance of temporal patterns with the paired musculatures; (3) eliminating the stutterer's tendency to avoid feared words and difficult speech situations; (4) initiating a program of general self-improvement, which includes the eradication of those other differences and inadequate reactions which provoke social penalty or interfere with efficient therapy; (5) changing the malattitudes of shame, embarrassment, and unpleasantness which are associated with the experience of stuttering; (6) training in the erection of psychological barriers against disturbing influences; (7) analyzing and understanding the stutterer's fears and symptoms through self-study during the stuttering act; (8) systematically studying stuttering as a speech disorder, including all other points of view, and culminating in an understanding of the entire sequence of treatment and an evaluation of the modifications of the general therapy necessitated by the characteristics of the stutterer's own individual problem.

Individual therapy. It is usually necessary to clarify for the stutterer the general policy governing his co-operation. The author's policy is to terminate all treatment for a period of two weeks as a penalty for failing to make a daily achievement in each of these eight phases of the therapy. This system is understood by each stutterer before he is accepted as a case, and few excuses are considered ade-

quate. The clinician devises all the assignments for five days of each
week, and the stutterer constructs his own assignments for the sixth
day. One day of the week is set aside as a day of "relapse," during
which the stutterer need not apply any of the principles or methods
that he has learned. It might be thought that the latter policy would
undo all the progress of the week, but clinical experience is all to the
contrary. The stutterer needs the rest from the regime; he needs an
opportunity to express the old habitual urges of avoidance that he has
repressed during the week. Interestingly enough, he often finds it
difficult and even unpleasant to refrain from using his new adjustments and techniques, and each new week is greeted with eagerness.

In making the assignments, the clinician always tries to fit them
to the peculiar needs of the stutterer. He constructs them so that
they are simple, easily understood, and possible of being performed
without too much inconvenience. They must always be pertinent to
the purpose they are alleged to serve. They must permit some objective check or report. The stutterer must be able to state the purpose
behind the assignment. While the clinician always attempts to keep
the difficulty of the assignment within the limit of the stutterer's
ability to carry it out, certain fluctuations in mood which cannot always be sensed by the clinician make it necessary to provide for refusal. Thus, the stutterer may protest any assignment, but he must
state his reasons. The clinician must always evaluate these protests
very carefully, and, if the reasons seem legitimate, the assignment is
revised. If the stutterer's objections are not psychologically valid,
he is told that the assignment must be fulfilled under penalty of the
two-weeks' dismissal. During the first weeks of therapy, a close
check must be made to determine whether or not the assignment has
actually been performed, for most secondary stutterers have an infinite
capacity for wish fulfillment. The speech correctionist, his assistants,
or some other speech defective should occasionally supervise the
stutterer on some of the assignments to provide assistance, analysis of
reactions, and morale.

Group therapy. When it is necessary to work with groups of stutterers, certain periods may be set aside for each of the eight phases of
the work, although the assignments should still be fitted to the individual stutterer. In certain clinics, report sessions are held at the
beginning of each day. The stutterers all meet together and report in
turn their achievements of the previous day. New assignments are
then given and explained by the speech correctionist. Individual

conferences with each stutterer are held throughout the day to take up any special problems needing solution, explanation, or emphasis. During these conferences, the clinician also requires the stutterer to carry out short assignments representative of each of the eight phases of the work. Modifications of the assignments can be made. Usually, at some other period during the day, a group meeting is held during which the speech correctionist can lecture on various phases of stuttering and encourage general discussion. When such group meetings cannot be held during the day owing to the demands of the stutterer's work or class schedules, a stutterer's club, meeting in the evening, can serve the same function.

Plan for a Group Meeting

1. Work on delayed response under pressure. Each person to talk on subject "My Most Humorous Experience as a Result of my Speech." Audience to take turns asking questions directed to the speaker. Not more than four questions should be asked of any one speaker and these should be timed to surprise if possible. Speaker is to respond to these interruptions by using delayed response—count to ten silently, then answer question before proceeding with speech.

Audience Check

1. Eye contact shifted during silent count?
2. Is stuttering more severe after interruptions?
3. Does speaker appear confused and rattled when interruptions come?

2. Prewrite five sentences. Before saying sentences before the group, set a maximum number of blocks you intend having for each sentence. Tell the group the number for each sentence. Penalty for exceeding number of predicted blocks before whole sentence is spoken will be to *shout* the remaining words.

Audience Check

1. Success in predicting blocks.
2. To make certain penalty is fulfilled.
3. Were any tricks used to prevent blocks? Record.

3. Give a speech on "People I Have Fooled About Myself." Your task is to stutter voluntarily (using the repetitive pattern) on the first word after every pause, whether it is feared or not, and to cancel each appearance of your old form of stuttering by using the same word in the next sentence.

Audience Check

1. One person to record number of times syllables were repeated in each use of voluntary stuttering.
2. One person to observe whether or not any of these became involuntary.
3. One person to observe the speaker's post-spasm reactions.

In some clinics, the students are required to spend all of their time on speech therapy, but the author does not feel this necessary or wise. Speech therapy should be made a part of normal life as far as possible. Speech assignments should carry the student into all types of situations and should not be confined to the school or clinic but performed throughout the city. The stutterer should work on his speech especially in those situations which were formerly most difficult. He should try to duplicate those situations in which his stuttering was most severely penalized and apply his therapy therein. The stutterer must learn to control his fears and blocks, not in the quiet haven of a tolerant speech clinic, but in the situations of normal life.

Training in unilaterality. The author's theoretical bias and clinical experience have led him to insist upon a strict unilaterality in the stutterer's motor skills, whether or not any shift of handedness seems to have been a potent dominant factor in causing the disorder. He requires his stutterers to give up the two-handed skills involved in the playing of musical instruments or in typewriting, although some musical instruments necessitate only unilateral skills and it is possible to attain sufficient one-handed speed in typewriting for all ordinary purposes. If the stutterer has a history of having been shifted in his handedness and demonstrates an essential ambidexterity or dominance of the usually nonpreferred hand despite years of use and training of the other hand, he should be required to effect a complete change of sidedness. All activities should be modified so as to produce a complete unilaterality of motor control. The stutterer must learn to eat, write, play tennis, dress himself, and do all the other things with the designated hand. The larger activities, such as throwing, should be emphasized early and the finer skills later. New activities closely related to speech, such as shorthand or telegraphy, may be learned on the new unilateral basis. When no shift of handedness is required, the student should do his utmost to maintain a similar unilaterality in these activities and to acquire increased skill in them, using the hand he naturally prefers.

One of the most effective ways of ensuring unilateral motor lead control of speech is that of simultaneous talking-and-writing. Using the proper hand, the student should endeavor to "tie up" talking and writing in the following manner. Initiating the script attempt first, he should make the speech attempt simultaneously with the dominant stroke of the first letter of the word. These dominant strokes vary with different individuals, but they may be easily ascertained through analysis. Speech attempt should be sudden and exactly timed with this stroke, without previous rehearsal in whispered or implicit form. No mumbling should be permitted, and articulation should be as clear as possible. At first the whole word should be written out, and the teacher should closely supervise the speech and script attempts to ensure proper timing. Later on, only the first letter of the word need be written, and the student may perform the activity by himself, although frequent rechecks by the teacher are usually necessary. Reading, memorized material, and some occasional conversation may be used for this simultaneous talking-and-writing.

In addition to the above type of simultaneous talking-and-writing, using only one hand, another type using both hands is also employed. This form is called *vertical board writing*, and the stutterer uses a board similar to that used for testing handedness. The proper hand is watched by the stutterer, and the other hand is allowed to follow automatically. Unilateral control of a bilateral performance is thereby achieved. The unwatched hand usually writes mirror-script as the watched hand is directed in normal writing. Movement of both hands should be as unified as possible, but always under the dominance of the proper hand. The same timing and clear articulation demanded by unilateral talking-and-writing is also required for vertical board writing.

In most clinical practice, the stutterer is required to turn in a certain number of pages of simultaneous talking-and-writing each day, to record on a chart his progress in mastering some new unimanual skill, to report what bimanual activities he performed with one hand, and to show the clinician the check list of times he used the wrong hand during a certain designated period or nucleus situation.

When examination of the case history and special tests convinces the speech correctionist that a shift of handedness has occurred, it is usually necessary to insist upon a complete return to the former type of handedness. It must be realized that such a shift back to a former hand is not to be effected without a great deal of difficulty. The student must be willing to co-operate. All of his bimanual activities should be changed to unimanual ones, at least during the period of treatment. He must learn to button his clothes, to eat, and to write with the other hand. Sometimes, the use of a cotton wrapping about the hand will prevent its unconscious activity. Most important of all, he must learn to write with the other hand, and, while doing so, should attempt to keep the original writing hand from making little simultaneous writing movements. The slant should not reverse itself. Care is usually taken to provide a good clear script, since the coordinations are thereby improved.

Training in performing rhythmic patterns with the paired musculatures. Since stutterers are notoriously weak in their ability to perform temporal patterns using paired musculatures, training in such activities is provided as part of the daily routine, and the stutterer is required to report his achievement in this phase of the work. All types of what West calls "diadochokinesis" are used. Lifting and lowering the eyebrows, biting, tongue protrusion, panting, and the use of the upper or lower limbs in simultaneous mirror-movements are among the activities employed in this training. Among the latter limb exercises are clapping, squeezing, slapping, lifting, marking, pulling, pushing, kicking and stamping, and depressing signal keys or levers.

Phonograph records are used to provide a stimulus pattern. The stimuli are tones or buzzer noises arranged according to some arbitrary pattern. The author produces his own stimulus patterns by means of a simple rhythmic variator constructed on the principles of that described in Hunsley's research.[1] Three records, graduated according to complexity of the stimulus pattern, are used. Each record consists of a temporal stimulus pattern, repeated five times at each of ten different speeds. The rhythm of the first or easiest record may be shown graphically by the spacing of the following period marks: (. ..), and that of the most difficult record by: (... ..). The stutterer is required to listen to the first two repetitions of the stimulus pattern. He then carries out his activity in unison with the last three occurrences of the stimulus pattern. At certain speeds, little difficulty is experienced, but as the pattern is speeded up, clonic and tonic blockings are noticed. Training, however, can greatly improve the

---

[1] Hunsley, Y., "Dysintegration in the Speech Musculature of the Stutterer During the Production of a Non-vocal Temporal Pattern," *Psychological Monographs*, 1937, Vol. 49, pages 32–49.

stutterer's ability in performing these patterns, and the author believes that the activity has a distinct clinical value.   When more complex rhythms are necessary, those of the Seashore tests are employed.

In order to provide an objective check on the subject's ability to approximate the stimulus pattern, the author employs a polygraph or kymograph setup, similar to that described by Hunsley.   The stutterer can depress keys, levers, or bulbs with the hands or feet, or use biting tubes or other apparatus.   These are connected to the tambour carrying the writing lever, and the subject's performance is thus recorded.   The stimulus pattern is usually recorded on the same polygraph when the phonograph record is made, in this way providing the necessary model.   If the speech correctionist has a good ear for rhythm, he can dispense with the apparatus.   The author prefers the apparatus because it allows the stutterer to work by himself.

The objection might be raised that these bimanual or bilateral performances are contrary to the training in unilaterality sketched in the last section.   However, in following the temporal pattern, the paired structures act as units rather than independently, and hence some unilateral dominance in timing must be effective in order to achieve the integration.   In order to facilitate this integration, all movements of the jaws, tongue, and other speech structures are timed by the tapping of one finger or by a movement of the preferred hand. It is interesting that stutterers perform better when using this unilateral timing in conjunction with the biting, tongue protrusion, and other similar activities than they do when it is omitted.

Eliminating avoidance of feared words and speech situations.   The secondary stage of stuttering is always characterized by word and situation fears, which range in intensity from a slight uncertainty or doubtful premonition to a state of panic so extreme as to leave the stutterer glassy-eyed and incapable of any intelligent effort.   The pulse rate has been known to increase from 75 to 120.   All the other physiological and psychological characteristics of extreme fear have been noted.   Since fear always entails the expectation or anticipation of unpleasantness, the stutterer always feels a strong urge to avoid that unpleasantness.   This avoidance manifests itself in many ways, but especially in the substitution of another word for the feared word and in the refusal to enter situations in which stuttering is likely to be experienced.   Circumlocution, cessation of speech attempt, attempts to get the listener to say the word, and speech in short phrases or monosyllables are some of the other ways in which the stutterer avoids his feared words. Also, he uses hundreds of tricks and approaches to alter the feared speech situations so that they are no longer the ones which frightened him. His mind is filled with rehearsal and revision of what he plans to say. Frequently he shifts the word order so as to minimize the expected difficulty. On his way to the feared situation, he visualizes his future agony over and over again. Many stutterers have few overt blocks and yet suffer extremely from the necessity of maintaining the constant vigilance that avoidance demands. The tragedy of avoidance is that in the long run it defeats its own purpose and increases the fear. Avoidance begets fear and makes it cumulative. The author knows from his own past experience as a severe stutterer and from his dealings with many other stutterers that it is better to have a five-minute blocking than to avoid a word successfully. We never conquer fear by running away; we only increase it.

In eliminating the avoidance reactions, the speech correctionist must teach the stutterer to understand why he avoids feared words and situations, to recognize when and how he avoids them, and to realize the future consequences of this avoidance. In achieving these aims, it is wise to go with the stutterer into some situation that might produce an avoidance. After it has occurred, the clinician should analyze the situation to determine what benefit actually resulted from the avoidance. Often the stutterer will have blocks on other words. Indeed, he often has them on the circumlocution or the substitution itself. The listener may be interviewed to discover what his actual reaction really was. The stutterer may be asked to keep track of fifty situations in which he avoided the block and to note in how many of them no other stuttering occurred. The speech correctionist and all of the stutterer's other associates who know of his therapy should penalize all avoidances and accept the stuttering. The stutterer should develop a conscience which itself will penalize the tendency to avoid. Association with other stutterers will often provide, through examples, the rejection of avoidance taught by the clinician. The strongest clinical pressure should be placed upon nonavoidance as the cardinal principle of the therapy. Nothing is so debilitating as refusal to make an attempt or reacting to a challenge by retreat. No stutterer can give up avoidance immediately, but if a month's therapy still finds him frequently substituting and avoiding, he is banned from the clinic for a time. Since many of these substitutions are relatively unconscious as well as habitual, the clinician must use some judgment in his accusations and penalties. In general, however, a general intolerance toward this type of weakness should characterize the clinic atmosphere.

In the daily conferences with the clinician, the stutterer should report on the previous day's progress in eliminating avoidances and should receive the next day's assignments concerning this phase of the therapy.   After a few weeks of preliminary work, the stutterer is required to write out a detailed account of every avoidance that occurs, describing the feared word or situation and the reason for the failure. The clinician should always assign some task to cancel the failure. This usually consists of sending the stutterer into a similar situation or one of equivalent difficulty and requiring him to use the same feared word or to avoid it purposely, confessing to the audience the trick he had employed.   All words which the stutterer has avoided are posted on the bulletin board and the other stutterers and clinicians try to direct his conversation and speech activities so as to include them. These words may be worked up into a reading passage of rather absurd meaning and repeated at intervals throughout the day.   An effective device is that which requires the stutterer to avoid certain nonfeared words in a given speech situation.   The subsequent circumlocution and hesitant phrasing become very detestable, and occasionally these formerly nonfeared words will become feared, thus showing the stutterer the consequences of avoidance.

Some other typical assignments in eliminating word avoidance are as follows:

1. Record and post on your progress chart in the clinic the exact time at which your first word avoidance occurred. Do this daily for a week.

2. Say, "D-D-D-Doggone it, I substituted just then," and make a check mark on a card whenever you avoid a word during mealtime.

3. Make three phone calls and hang up the receiver the moment you find yourself substituting or using circumlocution to avoid a word.

4. Fake a long effortless repetition on the next word after you have caught yourself substituting.   Record the situation in which this occurred.

5. Ask some other stutterer to draw up a list of ten speech situations. Perform three consecutive situations without word substitutions.

In order to get rid of the tendency to avoid difficult situations, it is useful, during the first few weeks of treatment, to give the stutterer what, in clinic parlance, is called a "bath of stuttering."   A list of one hundred or more speech situations is handed to the stutterer, and he is required to perform them within a certain number of days. These situations range from the stopping of a stranger to request a direction or a match to the procuring of information concerning the prices, advantages, and disadvantages of portable boats. The stutterer is asked to study any tendencies to avoid or alter the situations and to report them as well as his actual experiences. It is also useful to assign a certain quota of stuttering blocks per day. If this quota is set at five hundred, and the student is instructed to collect them in speech with strangers, the average stutterer will have to work hard to get that many. To the young clinician, these assignments may seem of doubtful value, but they effect profound alterations in the stutterer's characteristic dread and urge to avoid the words and situations that frighten him. Such experiences teach him that direct attack on his bugaboos tends to dissipate the fears. The threat of stuttering no longer throws him into a state of utter panic. A stuttering fear or a stuttering block becomes something to work with; it becomes objectified. Thus the stutterer prepares himself for that control of the form of his stuttering which is the immediate goal of this type of treatment. Avoidance can never give a stutterer the permanent speech security that the ability to control his stuttering blocks will guarantee.

The program of general self-improvement. Since the frequency and severity of the secondary stutterer's blocks are usually proportional to his feelings of insecurity and inadequacy, it is vitally necessary to carry out a program of general improvement. This program includes the elimination of those differences other than his speech defect which society penalizes, and also the destruction of those characteristic behavior patterns which are not adequate to a normal life. All speech correctionists, no matter to what school they belong, recognize the importance of this general self-improvement and provide remedial measures to accomplish it. The stutterer should be given opportunity to develop as many new social assets as possible. Daily assignments in self-improvement are always given as a part of the clinical program arranged. The general principles of this personal re-education have been sketched at some length in a previous chapter, and the actual techniques vary so much with the stutterer's individual problem that it is impossible to give more than a few examples here.

C. Y., a boy of fourteen, constantly subjected to bullying by a playmate, was given three months of boxing lessons and coaching in baseball technique. He made the high-school team and whipped the associate who had bullied him. After these achievements, he showed a great improvement, not only in the lessening of his fears, but also in his general approach to stuttering therapy.

J. S., a woman of thirty, with no previous success in securing male friends and with few female associates, was referred to a counsellor who instituted beauty treatments, taught her to dance, compelled her to enter new church groups and social organizations, and guided her awkward mastery of social skills. Day-dreaming and extensive reading were eliminated as reactions to social penalty. She became overaggressive, but her speech defect rapidly cleared as the program of general self-improvement took effect.

B. W., a cleft-palate and stuttering boy, seemed to make no progress whatever until he was given a chum who was also working on a speech defect and until intensive tutoring allowed him to satisfy the demands of his parents for high educational achievement.

Eradicating the malattitudes of shame and embarrassment. One of the most important phases of the treatment of the secondary stutterer is that which attempts to change the shame and embarrassment that are associated with the act of stuttering. We have previously sketched the manner in which these attitudes develop from the penalties and the attitudes of the stutterer's associates. The secondary stutterers usually seen by the speech correctionist possess these malattitudes to a high degree, and they probably can never be eradicated in their entirety. It is usually wise to ask the stutterer to recall his most unpleasant experiences and to recount them to a group of fellow stutterers. When these formerly traumatic situations are re-experienced on an adult and objective level, much of the attendant emotionality tends to disappear. The clinician must be careful to prevent overdramatization.

The stutterer must be taught to recognize the part played by these attitudes in perpetuating and intensifying his handicap. He must come to understand that these attitudes are ever-present obstacles in the path of his future progress. He must see that they foster much of the fear and panicky unintelligent struggle which increase the number and duration of his blocks. As soon as the stutterer realizes that shame and embarrassment are not inevitable concomitants of his symptoms, half the battle is won. The attitudes themselves are unpleasant enough to help the stutterer in his attempts to reject them. It is vitally important that another attitude be substituted in their place. Otherwise, little progress will be made.

The attitude taught to the stutterer as a substitute for the old reactions to his blocks is that of unemotional admission of his speech difference as a problem to be solved. For the time being, he is a stutterer in his own eyes and in the eyes of his associates. It is odd that a shallow pretense of normal speech is a common trait of even very severe stutterers. They commonly go to extreme lengths to hide their disability; they struggle to disguise it even after it has been clearly demonstrated. This pose must be rejected. *The stutterer must freely admit his speech difference for what it is.* In the meantime, his task is to solve a difficult problem, to learn to master his stuttering, to learn to speak without interruptions and abnormality sufficient to provoke social penalties. If he is ever able to do so, he needs to free himself from those old attitudes, poses, and reactions which will interfere with his attempts to control his fears and blocks. In summary, we may say that the stutterer must (1) learn to adopt an objective attitude toward his disorder, and (2) gradually diminish the shameful and embarrassed reactions which accompany it. *Each day during the first period of therapy for the secondary stutterer, assignments designed to fulfill these aims should be given to him.*

The objective attitude is taught by precept and example, by verbalization and exhibition, by pseudo-stuttering, and by mirror work. The speech correctionist should give frequent talks to his stutterers on the function of and necessity for the objective attitude. The stutterer can be required to write a summary of these talks. Examples of the use of the objective attitude by other handicapped individuals seem to help a great deal. The basic reasonableness of the new attitude should always be emphasized, and the speech correctionist must adopt a similar attitude toward his own differences or insecurities. Other stutterers who have become fairly well adjusted to their speech differences should be used as models and should accompany the new stutterer in his first outside speech assignments. Attitudes are best learned empathically. Often the speech correctionist can accompany the stutterer into some feared situation and, by pretending to stutter viciously, accompany this pseudo-stuttering with calm objective attitudes.

Many stutterers find it extremely difficult to talk about their disorder, and yet this very verbalization is one of the most effective agents in acquiring an unemotional attitude toward it. Normal speakers find stuttering a strange and interesting subject and are always willing to discuss it, after the threat of mutual embarrassment has been removed. The stutterer should seize every opportunity to

educate the general public concerning the nature and causes of stuttering. Parents and old acquaintances especially should be used in
providing this discussion. The stutterer should be asked to comment
good-humoredly on an occasional stuttering block. A casual smiling
reference to a word that was uttered with difficulty often paves the
way for an interesting discussion, even with total strangers. The
stutterer should be required to admit his stuttering as a daily routine.
Thus, whenever the author's stutterers enter the door of the clinic,
they are required to say to themselves, "For the time being,
Mister ——, you're a stutterer. No use posing as something else.
Better get to work on your problem if you want to get rid of the
handicap." The stutterer should be given assignments which require
him to run errands or to enter certain business places in quest of
information. He should exhibit the objective attitude in a certain
number of these tasks each day. Failures may occur, but success is
assured if the stutterer is persistent. At first, the stutterer may find
the new attitude unnatural and transparently false. Nevertheless,
if it is exhibited consistently, it will soon become a true reaction.

Another excellent device for teaching the stutterer to use the objective attitude and to get rid of his shame and embarrassment is that
of pseudo-stuttering. When employing this pseudo-stuttering (also
known as "voluntary stuttering" or "faking spasms") for improving
his mental hygiene, the stutterer voluntarily imitates some obvious
type of stuttering symptoms in his speech attempt on a nonfeared
word. Usually a long repetition or prolongation is used. All forcing
and facial contortion should be kept out, and the pretended blocks
should be easy, obvious, and direct. As he performs this pseudo-
stuttering, the stutterer must look his auditor in the eye, and, as soon
as the pretended block is completed, he should continue without
hurrying or showing any other sign of shame or embarrassment. He
should practice the new attitude with the pretended symptoms. Occasionally, he may comment casually on the apparent difficulty experienced in producing the word in order to let his listener know that
he feels no embarrassment. Stutterers often protest such assignments
at first, but they soon come to realize how effectively the pseudo-
stuttering eliminates shame and embarrassment, decreases audience
penalty, and produces a sense of mastery and control of their fears and
post-spasm reactions. The objective attitude can often be learned
through pseudo-stuttering and then associated with the true involuntary symptoms themselves. Pseudo-stuttering often dissipates the

fear of true stuttering to an amazing degree. Daily assignments in "faking spasms" are thus an important part of the secondary stutterer's therapy. Some typical examples follow:

1. Prewrite the first sentence of three phone calls. Underline one non-feared word in each. Fake an easy prolongation on the underlined word for five seconds before continuing. Rate yourself on a five-step scale of attitude toward stuttering.

2. Fake three repetitions on the first sound of the first nonfeared word in asking five strangers the way to the speech clinic. In how many of these situations did you look your listener in the eye?

3. Collect fifty perfect examples of pseudo-stuttering. Record the word, the type of symptom used, and the situation.

4. Go with some other stutterer into five stores. Ask him to tell you what to say in each. Select one word upon which to fake a stuttering block. Arrange to continue the faked block until he gives you the signal to continue. Do the same for him.

5. Fake a block on the first word spoken to the first three of your acquaintances you meet this afternoon. Record the amount of emotional tension on a five-step scale. Write up your report.

Another excellent clinical technique for teaching the objective attitude is that of observing one's stuttering in the mirror. The necessity for confronting oneself, and especially one's greatest insecurity, is no easy adjustment. Many stutterers find it extremely distressing at first. If the clinician sits down in front of the mirror with the new stutterer and does some pseudo-stuttering himself, the shock is not so great. The more advanced stutterers can also help the newcomer through the first traumatic experiences. The stutterer should watch himself as carefully as possible, noting all the symptoms and emotional reactions that occur. He should then write a description of what he has observed. He should also attempt to duplicate on nonfeared words some of the contortions and abnormalities that accompany his real blocks, taking care that the faking is kept on a voluntary level. He should verbalize his observations as he watches himself. Some assignments typical of those required daily of each stutterer are:

1. Have some other stutterer watch you as you read for one minute. Ask him to imitate you as carefully as possible. Be able to report what reactions he imitated.

2. Read silently, then paraphrase orally in front of the mirror. As soon as you block, stop and attempt to imitate, as exactly as possible, the symptoms that occurred.

3. Verbalize the thoughts of a stutterer feeling sorry for himself as you observe your reactions in the mirror. Exaggerate the self-pity.

4. Explain to yourself in the mirror the necessity for acquiring an objective attitude. Then repeat your arguments to another stutterer, who should attempt to take the other side. Make a mark on a sheet of paper every time you have a block.

Teaching the objective attitude to a secondary stutterer will do much to eliminate the old shameful and embarrassed reactions by a mere process of substitution. More rapid progress will be made, however, if these older reactions are attacked directly. This may be done by analysis, by penalty, and by the removal of the environmental intolerances that cause them. The stutterer should keep a diary of all situations in which his stuttering produces marked shame or embarrassment. He should present this diary to the speech correctionist during his daily conference so that the psychological analysis can be effected. Usually, the stutterer is reacting not in terms of the actual situation but in terms of some past unpleasantness. Alternative reactions are suggested. If the embarrassment has some justification, the speech correctionist devises means to cancel it. The clinician may penalize shame and embarrassment by exaggerating them in a verbal way and by requiring the stutterer to do likewise. The stutterer may be asked to read his woebegone account of the situation over and over again, until it loses meaning or importance. In altering the environmental intolerance toward any stuttering symptoms, the clinician should attempt to educate the stutterer's associates with respect to the remedial methods employed. When they understand what the stutterer is doing and why he is doing it, the intolerance usually disappears. The stutterer himself can do much to alter his environment in this regard.

Training in the erection of psychological barriers against disturbing influences. Anyone who has associated with severe secondary stutterers realizes how quickly they are affected by any disturbing influence. The mere threat of interruption reduces them to a paroxysm of unintelligent random behavior. They are the victims of every communicative pressure. They feel the need to respond instantly to every question. They scrutinize their auditors for any hint of penalizing response and exaggerate whatever they see. They constantly accept the listener's evaluation of their behavior and are therefore at the mercy of anyone to whom they talk. This helpless state is naturally one which greatly interferes with treatment. For these reasons, the speech correctionist insists upon the stutterer's making some daily achievement in the erection of psychological barriers against these disturbing influences.

This phase of the treatment seeks to train the stutterer: (1) to use the delayed response whenever confronted by a pressure for immediate communication; (2) to ignore those audience reactions which tend to disturb him; (3) to master his environment by changing and controlling adverse audience reactions; and (4) to evaluate his behavior in terms of his own greater understanding of his speech problem rather than in terms of the audience's less insightful evaluation. Daily assignments are designed so as to create certain of these disturbing influences and to demand a resistant and well-controlled response.

1. Write the names of two people with whom you paused for a count of twenty before answering their questions.

2. Go to the Economy Cleaners and say, "I believe you have a package for me." This will cause the clerk to ask your name. Before you answer, observe her carefully so that you can describe her eyes, hair, and dress. Then say your name without hurrying.

3. This is what we call a "fool situation." It is devised to teach you that because a clerk thinks you are a fool, her opinion does not actually make you one. Go into a grocery, walk straight to a vacant place at the counter and wait until the clerk comes. Look her in the eye and say calmly and directly, "Can I leave my watch here to be fixed?" Observe the expression on her face without responding. If she asks you to repeat, do so very deliberately and without hurrying. When she answers you, with pity or anger or incredulity, observe her reaction as though you were studying that of a guinea pig, thank her, and leave. Be prepared to analyze your behavior and hers. If you perform the assignment successfully, you will find a great surge of self-respect and security. You will realize that you are no longer the victim of any person who wishes to think poorly of you. If you fail, ask some other stutterer who has performed these assignments successfully to show you how independent of disturbing influences one can be.

4. Collect the names of five people who have interrupted you without causing you to stop the rest of the sentence.

5. In the Postal Telegraph office, there is a girl who will laugh in your face whenever you stutter. Ask her where the post office is and fake a long repetitive spasm on "post office." When she laughs, ask her why she does so. Say that you are working on your speech and that people often laugh when you stutter, and that your teacher asked you to find out why they did. Report her answer.

6. Go downtown to the stores and price different articles, faking blocks on the word "price" until some clerk says the word for you. Thank her and ask her if she would mind if you tried the word again. Note whether her attitude changed after your request.

7. Write out a sentence you could say to change the attitude of a person who says, "Hurry up and say what you want to. I don't have all day."

8. Find some listener who consistently looks away when you stutter. Try to change this behavior by getting into a discussion of stuttering, during which you can point out that looking away is not usually relished by any handicapped person. Report your experience.

9. Fake a block or have a real one, and grin after the word comes out. Say, "That one sure got away from me, didn't it?" Smile again and continue without further comment. What was the audience reaction to this technique?

Analysis and understanding of the stutterer's fears and blocks during the stuttering act. People unacquainted with the phenomenology of stuttering might think that the stutterer, of all people, should know what he does when he gets blocked on a word. Oddly enough, this is seldom the case. Few stutterers who have not been trained in the analysis of their symptoms can tell what happened, even when the blocking has just occurred. The fears are too disturbing and the approach and release reactions are too habitual. Since our therapy is aimed at the control and modification of fears and symptoms, this vague and confusing experience must be clarified. The stutterer must come to know just what he does when he approaches a feared word or situation. He must study his anticipatory and release reactions before he can hope to eliminate them. It is interesting that this analysis itself reduces much of the fear and shame associated with the disorder.

In the chapter concerning speech tests, a detailed outline of such a symptom analysis is given. It is not sufficient that the speech correctionist make this analysis; the stutterer must also construct his own. He must come to recognize the avoidance, postponement, timing, disguise, and antiexpectancy devices that characterize his own particular type of stuttering, and he must do so experientially rather than theoretically. When he uses an interrupter device to release himself from block, he must recognize it immediately. He must know instantly when he perceives a word in terms of its first letter or some of its parts rather than as a whole. He must know what social penalty he dreads when he finds himself afraid of a certain speech situation. After he is able to accomplish these things, the confused, panicky state will no longer continue to exist and he will be able to reject and modify the old characteristic reactions that contribute so much to his handicap.

The speech correctionist must always guide the stutterer in the study and analysis of his stuttering symptoms. At first, the stutterer's attention should be called to the presence of these symptoms whenever they occur during the clinical conference. The speech correctionist should interrupt the stutterer and describe just what took place. Other stutterers more versed in symptom analysis should sit in front of a mirror with the student and comment on each device as it occurs. The stutterer should be taught to verbalize his thoughts as he approaches feared words and situations. He should be assigned to collect characteristic samples of his stuttering behavior and to duplicate them on demand. The clinician may imitate the stutterer's reactions and may objectify them by means of a phonograph recording. As a final culmination of this phase of the therapy, the stutterer should write out a detailed symptom analysis of his own stuttering. The work can be motivated by showing the stutterer that most of the therapy specific to the second period of treatment is based upon the disruption of these old reactions, and that he must therefore learn to recognize them when they occur. Daily assignments in the study of his symptoms are always given to the secondary stutterer in the first period of his treatment. Some typical examples follow.

1. Study the postponement devices of some other stutterer and use one of them on a feared word in a telephone conversation. Hand in a written account of the experience.

2. During the noon hour, record every variety of starter that you use to initiate speech attempt. Does a starter always follow a postponement?

3. Collect five examples of your attempts to disguise your stuttering. Be able to demonstrate them to your clinician.

4. Find out when the city bus company's franchise expires. Write a paper on what went on in your head prior to entering the situation. What visualization or rehearsal of the situation occurred?

5. Collect thirty words on which you used force sufficient to set up a tremor in your lips.

The systematic study of stuttering as a speech disorder. Although sheer faith in a theory concerning the nature, causes, or treatment of a disorder can diminish fear and motivate therapy, we believe that the best basis is a reasonable one. Confidence based on clinical suggestion and urging to believe is subject to devastating disruption when the stutterer is confronted by self-criticism or the criticism of others. For these reasons, we believe that free discussion and study of all points of view concerning stuttering are a necessary part of the therapy. Every assignment, every pronouncement of the speech correctionist, must be able to be justified. The stutterer is always urged to challenge anything that he does not understand. Free discussion and appeal to reason are the twin bases for this type of treatment. The more advanced and older stutterer should study the research, the history of treatment, and the etiology and development of stuttering. He should be able to talk intelligently concerning the disorder and attempt to dispel some of the ignorance concerning it. It might be thought that such a program would confuse the stutterer and interfere with treatment. Our experience, however, is all to the contrary. There is much we still do not know about stuttering, but the stutterer has a right to realize this. We know enough to carry out a successful therapy for the majority of secondary stutterers, and the individual stutterer will soon come to this conclusion despite the theoretical confusion that exists.

Daily assignments in the study of stuttering as a disorder are always given. The stutterer may be required to write synopses of articles or books. Questions concerning the material in certain selected references may be answered. He can prepare himself to give short talks on different phases of the disorder. Debates on the etiology of stuttering provide excellent motivation for group work. The lectures of the speech correctionist may be summarized. Statements of the clinician or of the authors of texts in speech correction may be challenged. Little experiments in stuttering may be formulated and performed. Misunderstandings or confusions can be expressed. There are many other ways in which stuttering as a disorder may be studied, and the speech correctionist will soon discover them.

Summary of the activities in the first period of treatment. In order to summarize the activities of this first period, a set of actual assignments for one day is given.

1. *Unilaterality.* Hand in three pages of talking-and-writing. Spend ten minutes in vertical board writing and record time and place. Thread a needle, held by some other person, within five seconds.

2. *Rhythmic training of paired muscles.* Protrude tongue and tap with forefinger of proper hand simultaneously with beating of metronome set at three speeds for thirty-second intervals. Record speeds used and number of clonic repetitions experienced.

3. *Eliminating avoidance.* Write down all words for which you substituted a nonfeared word during the three mealtimes. Go to a hotel and ask if a person by your own name is registered there. Take some other stutterer with you to watch avoidances.

4. *Self-improvement.* Make an appointment with the health service for a dental examination.

5. *Changing malattitudes.* Smile ruefully, though good-naturedly, after

three bad blocks and record the word on a card. Explain that you are working on your speech defect and are required to record all the hardest words. Note reaction of your audience.

6. *Erecting psychological barriers.* Ask your clinician to supervise one phone call today and to help you with each word on which you stutter. Refuse to become angry and thank him before continuing.

7. *Analysis of symptoms.* Record ten words beginning with a voiced consonant in which you put your mouth or tongue in position long before you bring in the voice. This is called *preformation.*

8. *Study of stuttering as a disorder.* Read the first two chapters in *The Nature and Treatment of Stammering,* by Boome and Richardson. Find three statements which you would like to challenge because of your own past experience.

The above assignments were all performed in less than two and a half hours of actual work. The stutterer attended three regular college classes, worked three hours for his board and room, and still had time for study and recreation. The assignments were reported and discussed in a conference lasting twenty minutes, and new assignments were then given.

The Second Period of Therapy

After the stutterer has had a good deal of experience in using the techniques and a good deal of success in attaining the goals of the first period as described in the preceding section of this chapter, he may be permitted to add a new goal and new techniques. This new goal may be described as the alteration of the spasm pattern, the modification of the form of stuttering. The secondary reactions of expectancy and release must be disrupted and largely eliminated. Reactions to the fear and occurrence of stuttering block must be discarded. The tricks of postponement, or initiation and release, must be eliminated. Since these reactions are usually habitual, the techniques consist mainly of assignments and projects to break those habits. As in the preceding period, the stutterer is urged to greet fear with speech attempt and without avoidance, no matter whether or not stuttering occurs; but he is urged to stutter without the tricks and habitual reactions of postponement, initiation, antiexpectancy, and release. He is shown, through study of the spasm patterns and symptoms of other stutterers, that it is possible to stutter in a great many ways and that a large share of his abnormality consists of particular reactions he has learned to use when fear or occurrence of block takes place. All of the preceding techniques are continued and constantly reinforced, but his new task is to get rid of the bad habits which he has developed because of his stuttering, to get rid of the secondary symptoms.

Most of these secondary symptoms are integrated into sequences called spasm patterns. Some stutterers have only one spasm pattern set off by all the cues causing fear of approaching words. Many stutterers have several, each set off by certain cues. Thus, one stutterer approached all feared vowel words by holding on to the last mouth posture of the preceding word, inhaling quickly, and making the speech attempt, which, if it resulted in block, was immediately stopped and the sequence repeated until no block occurred. On words beginning with a plosive, she began with a vocalized postponement device similar to the neutral vowel a, which usually terminated in a head jerk as an interruptor device. These spasm patterns are often very complex, but the stutterer must be able to identify and analyze them before he can hope to get rid of the individual reactions which are their components. Much of this is done through the self-study and analysis mentioned in the preceding section. Often the stutterer has a series of such spasm patterns at his command, using the least objectionable one first, then the next, and, finally, if neither of these provides release, using one that involves the most hypertension and abnormality. Thus, the first new therapy in this period should consist of the identification and variation of the stutterer's spasm patterns. They should be faked on nonfeared words and varied on feared words. New reactions may be interjected into their midst. The stutterer should attempt to stutter with spasm patterns used by other stutterers. Through these methods, the spasm patterns may be broken up into their components.

After the preliminary work of identifying and disrupting the stereotyped spasm patterns has been accomplished, the stutterer may proceed to the next step—that of getting rid of the individual reactions, one by one. It is wise to take the postponement reactions first, then the starters, and, finally, the release reactions. If the stutterer asks, as he often does, how he should stutter if he cannot use these reactions, the clinician should answer that it makes no difference, so long as they are kept out. Only one reaction should be worked on at a time, but, after it has been fairly well rejected, it must be kept out from then on, even though a second reaction is being worked upon.

Many individuals believe that a habitual reaction can be eliminated only through substitution of another reaction in its place, but we have found that a more efficient method is possible. Substitution of a new habit is used, but it is introduced only after the original habit has been weakened, and it will be described in the next section concerning the third period of treatment.

During the second period, a good share of the therapy is devoted to the weakening of the secondary symptoms. Often the system is so successful that the secondary symptoms are eliminated entirely. The procedure employs oral reading, conversation, or the pronouncing of feared words during the conference with the speech correctionist, and also the use of speech assignments to provide sufficient stuttering. It is important that the stutterer have enough stuttering blocks, or he will never learn to get rid of the reactions which constitute so large a share of his handicap.

Having closely identified the reaction to be eliminated or weakened, we plan a definite program for getting rid of it. We do this through the following methods: bringing the reaction up to consciousness, attacking the purpose of the reaction, eliminating the cues which set off the reaction, breaking up the pattern of the reaction, and penalizing the reaction. Illustrations of each are now given.

We bring reactions up to consciousness by: (1) checking one's own reactions; (2) having someone else check the occurrence of the reaction; (3) predicting the occurrence of the reaction; (4) faking the reaction on nonfeared words; (5) repeating the reaction, voluntarily, after it has occurred involuntarily; (6) associating the reaction with other attention-getting stimuli (as whistling); (7) collecting quotas of the reaction; (8) having the clinician point it out in situations where it will be very vivid; (9) using mirror work, phonograph recording, and so on.

We attack the purpose of the reaction by: (1) identifying the purpose the reaction serves; (2) showing how much the reaction contributes to the handicap (breathing records, photographs, and phonographic records); (3) demonstrating that it is possible to stutter in other ways; (4) demonstrating that the reaction contributes a great deal to the fear and panic; (5) showing, by mental-hygiene assignments, that temporary fluency is insignificant when compared to future consequences, and showing that temporary expedients are no solution to the stutterer's real problem; (6) ruining the service performed by the reaction by having the stutterer fake a long bad spasm immediately after its occurrence; (8) building up, by self-suggestion assignments and strong clinician attitudes, a feeling that the presence of the reaction is a failure and a defect, and thus building up a conscience against it.

We eliminate the cues that set off the reaction by: (1) isolating and identifying the cues—words, sounds, sound combinations, word length, word familiarity, speech situations, confusions, chain reactions, and emotional states—which commonly precede the use of the reaction and set it off; (2) demonstrating how often the cues are followed by the reaction (focus attention on this obvious lack of correlation); (3) using drills which present the cue material (words, situations, and so on) which the stutterer attempts to utter without the use of the reaction, and employing penalties if failures still occur; (4) associating other, and incompatible, reactions with the same cues; (5) attaching absurdity to the cues; (6) presenting drills designed to get the stutterer to reconfigure the cue material; (7) teaching the philosophy of the objective attitude toward stuttering; (8) teaching the stutterer ways of controlling audience reaction to his stuttering; (9) teaching methods of decreasing situation difficulty; (10) reconditioning "Jonah" words and sounds.

We break up the pattern of the reaction by: (1) manipulating and varying the stereotyped reaction pattern, the sequence; (2) prolonging the reaction far beyond its expected and normal course; (3) exaggerating the reaction; (4) interjecting other abnormality; (5) reversing the sequence of the reaction and practice; (6) interrupting and rejecting in the middle of the reaction; (7) practicing a modified reaction.

We penalize occurrence of the reaction by: (1) speech penalties: (*a*) silence for rest of hour, (*b*) addition of greater abnormality, (*c*) faked repetition of the same reaction as closely as possible, (*d*) repetition of whole sentence, (*e*) restimulation; (2) physical penalties: (*a*) shock per spasm or group of spasms, (*b*) deprivation of pleasure; (3) ludicrous penalties.

The above techniques are illustrated by the assignments on the next page. They do not represent all of the day's speech-correction activities of the stutterer to whom they were given, since they do not include those representative of the first period of therapy. The stutterer in question had possessed three major secondary symptoms. He characteristically postponed by repeating preceding words two to six times, depending on the intensity of the fear. He also used a sudden quick head jerk to time the moment of speech attempt. Finally, he maintained and prolonged the original tongue or lip position on all plosive sounds, forcing and struggling until his face was convulsed and scarlet. At the time the assignments were given, the postponement device had almost entirely disappeared, thus freeing his speech of much abnormality, and the clinician had begun to work on the head jerk, which was used as a starter. The assignments used are as follows:

1. Bringing the reaction up to consciousness. Since you never fear the word "and," you are to use the head jerk to time the moment of speech attempt on this word whenever you say it in three phone calls and in requesting information of two strangers. Report whether it made you conscious of some of the involuntary head jerks on other words.

2. Attacking the purpose of the reaction. Ask Harris to tell you about his experience with various tricks for starting feared words. Be able to sketch the manner by which starters grow into tremendous contortions. Why is it that starters sometimes do not "start"? Collect ten feared words which you attempted without the head jerk and compare the amount of abnormality with that on those timed with the head jerk.

3. Eliminating the cues that set off the reaction. On words beginning with one of the following three sounds you never use the head jerk, no matter how badly you stutter: s, k, m. Discover which of these initial sounds does not serve as a cue for the head-jerk symptom. Write a short paper on "Is a head jerk truly a necessary part of my stuttering?"

4. Breaking up the pattern of the reaction. As you have seen in the mirror, you always press your lips together immediately before jerking your head upward. Collect ten feared words in which you jerk your head downward and five words in which the lip pressing does not occur.

5. Penalizing the reaction. Collect five instances of involuntary head jerks which you penalized by faking a very slow and abnormal prolongation immediately after the timing symptom was used.

The stutterer will soon find that a daily regime of this sort, when supplemented by the activities of the previous period, will eradicate almost any symptom that is subjected to such a thoroughgoing clinical attack. He will learn, much to his surprise, that these secondary symptoms are not an integral part of his disorder, that it is possible for him to stutter without using them, and that their disappearance greatly decreases the abnormality and interruption. He finds himself controlling the form of his stuttering. He realizes that he is master of the handicap. The disorder begins to disintegrate, and with it go the fears that caused him so much agony. He comes to welcome the fear of a word as a challenge to his ability to modify the form of his symptoms and as an opportunity to make further progress. When fear is welcomed, it begins to disappear. As it does so, the number and severity of the blocks diminish. Some stutterers become entirely free from their fears after going through this second period of treatment, and since their blocks are of short duration and possess little abnormality when they do occur, they are not perceived as being important enough to matter. These stutterers communicate freely, and that is sufficient. If, in the future, they do stutter, they insist upon a form of stuttering in which the old secondary symptoms do not occur, and they remain content. One of them said, "Sure, I get blocked once in a while, but I never force or postpone or make faces like I used to, and the block is over before I know it. I'm satisfied with my speech. I've licked the handicap." Other stutterers seem to require substitute reactions to the fear or occurrence of block, and, for these latter individuals, the third period of therapy will now be discussed.

The Third Period of Therapy

In the third period, a new goal and new techniques are again added. This new goal is the establishment of a new type of stuttering, a new spasm pattern. The new type of stuttering should be one of short duration and little abnormality, in either vocalization or associated movement. The previous goals and methods are still part of the therapy. Assignments are given daily to reinforce and review them. But in this third period, instead of negatively trying to eliminate and reject old reactions, the stutterer attempts to learn a new reaction, a new way of stuttering. Since old habitual reactions are also broken by substitution of new ones, this therapy serves a double purpose. It also reinforces the mental-hygiene aspect of the therapy, since stutterers will not be nearly so likely to avoid, disguise, or develop emotional maladjustment about stuttering which does not thwart or socially penalize them. It tends to shave the reactions to stuttering to a minimum, leaving little to handicap them. In every sense of the word, the stutterer can afford to stutter. Both the primary and secondary reactions which form so large a share of the handicap are usually eliminated. When this happens, the fears of words and situations largely disappear, since one cannot be afraid of that which is not unpleasant. Indeed, when the stutterer learns that it is possible to stutter in a way which carries no thwarting or social penalty, his successful control of the blockings is actually pleasant.

We may outline our methods for teaching the stutterer to stutter easily and effortlessly as follows: He must learn to (1) *react to the fear of stuttering by rehearsing the old spasm pattern and then rejecting it;* (2) *assume a new preparatory set to start the speech attempt from a state of rest, to prepare the second sound of the word, to make the first sound with loose contacts or relaxed positions, to make the first sound as a move-*

ment, and to make a gradual but voluntary shift from one sound to the next without retrial.

We train our stutterers to recognize the old preparatory set, and then to reject it in favor of an alternative plan of attack. They are taught to rehearse the old abnormality consciously (they will any-

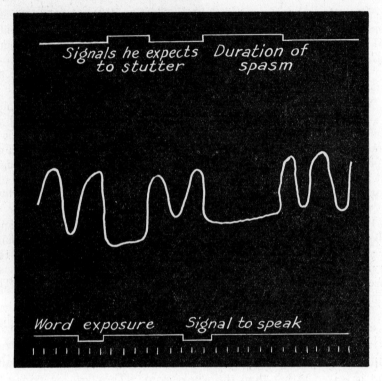

Fig. 15. Breathing record showing evidence of preparatory set to stutter on residual air.

way!) and then to reject it. Then they specifically plan to "hit the word in a new way." This new preparatory set has three dominant features: (1) to make the speech attempt from a state of articulatory quiescence rather than from a highly tensed musculature; (2) to initiate air flow—or voice flow—simultaneously with the speech attempt; (3) to make the feared sound of the word as a relaxed but highly voluntary *movement* leading directly into the succeeding sound.

It is apparent that what we have described is in essence merely a description of a speech attempt such as a nonstutterer might make. Each of the three features characterizes every normal utterance of a word.   Stutterers attempt their nonfeared words in this selfsame manner.   But when they expect stuttering, they attach the word in a totally different fashion.   They create a focus of tension in the tongue, lips, or throat long before they start the word.   Instead of initiating movements, they assume articulatory positions.   For example:

When I've got to say my name, Mary, in a hard situation, I know just what's going to happen.   My lips are going to clamp together suddenly, and I'll keep them glued there until the block is over and the word comes out.   I don't make a sound and there isn't a breath of air stirring, although I'm squeezing in with my abdomen as hard as possible to make the air burst open my lips.

My tongue is up in the back when I make a *k* sound at the beginning of a hard word.   It's stationary back there, but I'm pushing hard with it, trying to bore a hole through the roof of my mouth.   The speech bottle is corked tight.   I ought to have sense enough to open the cork, but all I do is press on the bottle down below.   Sometimes if I struggle hard enough, put all my effort into one sudden push, I can break the blockade and out comes the word, but usually the more I push with my stomach, the tighter I press my tongue.

I knew I would have to thank my hostess at the end of the party, and, believe it or not, I had my tongue between my teeth in a tight *th* sound for ten minutes before I gathered enough nerve to approach her.   The inevitable happened, and there I stood with my tongue still in its tooth-vise, frozen and motionless.   All I could think of was: "A zombie, I.   The living dead!"

In all of these descriptions, we can notice the production of a fixed articulatory position rather than the starting of a movement.   We can also observe that these stutterers are attempting to produce the sound that is feared rather than the whole word.   They are not trying to start a movement sequence.   The *m*, the *k*, and the *th* are so feared that they dominate the whole experience.   It is because of this morbid focus of attention that the stutterer is often unable to profit from releases that do occur.   Often the "Mary" will emerge as "Mmuh-mmmuh-mary."   This behavior may be explained as due to the stutterer's fear of the isolated *m* or *muh* sound.   The schwa vowel (ə) in a nonsense syllable is always used when the consonant is perceived as isolated.   Hence the use of *kuh* or *puh* to represent the isolated *k* and *p*.   The stutterer attempts feared words only in terms of their feared sounds.   Thus, he thinks he is having a great deal of trouble on the *s* sound of the word *stutter* even though he produces it as *sssssssss-stutter*.   To sum up these observations, the stutterer attempts his feared words much differently than his nonfeared words: because of his fear, he plans, and tries to produce, isolated sounds rather than total words; he attempts these sounds as though they were fixed, static positions instead of the flowing movements they should be; he uses these positions to constrict and block off the flow of air or voice, and then struggles to break the hard contacts above by excessive air pressure from below.

Our task, then, is to teach our stutterers to attempt their feared words exactly as they do their nonfeared ones. It is folly to expect them to do so at command, when they have such long-practiced abnormal methods of word attack. Instead, we must provide them with enough experiences in attacking feared words with the lips or tongue held loosely and quietly. We must help them find out that it is possible to "keep the mouth in motion" even when attempting the feared sound of a feared word. We must enable them to learn that it is possible to start a feared p word, for example, without pressing the lips together with compulsive force. Once they learn how short and effortless their blocks are when the air flow and speech attempt are made simultaneously, we have little need to motivate our stutterers. Once they learn how much easier it is to loosen the tongue in its contact with the palate than to blow it down with a sudden blast of air, they will try to find ways of approaching their feared words and releasing themselves from their blockings.

Despite the wide variety of ways of stuttering, it is difficult to convince any one case that he can stutter in other and easier ways. We must get him to experiment with his own stuttering. Our task is to suggest alternative approaches or methods of release that will tend to decrease the abnormality and interruption. We must also provide him with opportunities to stutter in these new ways and guide him in the learning process. For this part of the therapy is not only unlearning; it is learning as well. There will be failures, of course. The old familiar habits are strong; the new ones are vague, weak, and ill-formed. But failures are always necessary to learning. If we consider them analytically and understand their nature, the new skills will be bound to improve. It is vital however, that the attempts to learn to stutter without hard contacts, without tension, without preformation, be carried out in feared situations. The stutterer will learn much faster under these conditions, since a few unexpected successes will contribute more to learning than the familiar failures. Actually, all that the stutterer really needs to solve his problem are enough fears and moments of stuttering to experiment upon, and the idea that it is possible to stutter easily and effortlessly. If he will then vary his approach to the feared words, his symptoms also will vary. We have known stutterers, with no more clinical help than the statements in this paragraph, who got to work by themselves and learned to stutter so easily and effortlessly that the largest share of the handicap was eliminated. They were not cured. They continued to have what they called stuttering blocks, but the latter did not interfere with communication or provoke social penalties. This is no small achievement. The difficulties are great, especially when the stutterer works alone and without guidance. But it is possible to stutter in many ways, and one of those ways is with a minimum of interruption or abnormality.

In some clinics stutterers are deliberately taught a new way of stuttering, a new "spasm pattern." Two of these ways are in common use: (1) the voluntary repetition of the first sound or syllable of the word ("voluntary stuttering," or the "bounce" pattern) and (2) effortless prolongation of the first sound or syllable. Johnson (33) describes these two patterns thus:

. . . the nonfluency pattern is adopted and used *instead* of stuttering. Probably a simple repetition, like "tha-tha-tha-this" is most preferable, partly because it was just such behavior as this which was first diagnosed as stuttering and needs, therefore, to be re-evaluated as normal and acceptable. However, a simple, effortless prolongation of the first sounds of words will, in some cases, prove satisfactory, although considerable practice is required in prolonging the *p* and *t*. Also, care must be exercised lest the prolonging become a complete stoppage reaction, which would be merely another way of stuttering.

Bryngelson (13) recommends that the "voluntary stuttering" (repetition pattern) be first taught in reading and speaking before the mirror, but then extended to all activities. Johnson (33) likewise uses this mirror practice, but he also says:

If a dictaphone, or better, a mirrorphone is available, it is helpful to record one's speech, using the new repetition pattern and then listen to it over and over again, in order to become thoroughly accustomed to it and to learn to do it as smoothly and effortlessly as possible.

Gradually, then, the stutterer should introduce this pattern of nonfluency into his everyday speech, trying it out first in the easier situations and then introducing it in more and more difficult situations. He should employ it whenever he would otherwise stutter and he should also feign it liberally in saying certain words on which he would not otherwise stutter.

Another quotation may help to illustrate the teaching of these stuttering substitutes. Travis says:

With the idea that he is not to hide his stuttering, he is trained not only to change his mental set toward the defect but to stutter in a forward, flowing, easy "bouncy" pattern, as in "ba-ba-ba-ball." The purpose of the bouncy type of stuttering and of the objective viewpoint is to lessen the tension and strain on the speech organs, to overcome individual objectionable habits accompanying the spasm, to free the person of fear, dread, or shame, and to promote physical and mental adjustment to the stuttering. After the bouncy pattern is perfected, the smooth pattern, in which the spasm is translated, is encouraged, the effort being to develop forward, flowing vocalization without repetition. (52)

We do not advocate the use of either of these patterns as a substitute for the old stuttering abnormality. We doubt very much that any person will ever be entirely willing to "bounce" his syllabic way through life. A stutterer may be able to accept such a "method of stuttering" or such a "type of nonfluency" for the time being, while he is in the speech clinic, but in the crucial speech situations of normal existence, he must be able to stutter with much less conspicuousness than either voluntary repetition or prolongation can provide. If it is possible to approach feared words so that they sound like "th-th-th-th-this" or "lllllllllllike" that, why not go one step farther, and find out how to utter them "*like th*is." We can see no virtue in the demonstration of abnormality as such, if it is possible to stutter without it. Clinicians no doubt have insisted on some demonstrable repetitive or prolonged abnormality in order to keep the stutterer from falling into his old avoidances. But there are many dangers in the use of these patterns, too. The bounce can, and usually does, turn into a postponement trick. On a mildly feared word the stutterer will repeat the first syllable three times; on a badly feared word eight or ten times. Moreover, the sheer repetition of a sound has nothing to do with the necessity for making a transition to the second (or next) sound of the feared word. One might as well say "tra-la-la-la-boy" as to say "ba-ba-ba-boy." Stutterers often bounce fluently until they start the actual speech attempt. Then they go into the old contortion, or resignedly start bouncing again. The same criticisms may be leveled against the use of the smooth-prolongation pattern.

The above criticisms are not meant to imply that we do not use voluntary stuttering or smooth prolongation in our therapy for stutterers. We use both types. But we use them primarily as mental-hygiene and teaching devices. We feel that the "bounce" or repetitive form of pseudo-stuttering is one of the best agents for teaching the stutterer to face his problem as a problem rather than a curse. It is tolerated by society much more than is his old gasping, grunting, horrible abnormality. The stutterer who looks his listener in the eye and voluntarily repeats the first syllables of his feared words in a calm and effortless fashion becomes a totally different person so far as his speech defect is concerned. Instead of the random struggling or the craven hesitant approach to the attempt of feared words, we find purposive integrated speech attempts. The stutterer can learn to re-evaluate his disorder through the use of these forms of pseudo-stuttering. We use these forms of pseudo-stuttering, then, in attaining the following goals: (1) to teach the stutterer to attack the feared word without hesitancy; (2) to teach him to begin the word with its first sound instead of prefacing the speech attempt with a ritual of gasping, mouth opening, tongue protrusion, or other unnecessary movement; (3) to help him experience a symptomatology different from his old form, and one which is socially and personally preferable; (4) to give him a form of speech behavior which will enable him to say to the world, "Yes, I stutter. It's my problem, and I am attempting to solve it. I'm not emotional about it and you need not be upset either"; (5) to keep his speech on a highly voluntary level.

We ask our stutterers to use these forms of pseudo-stuttering first on nonfeared words but in feared speech situations. In this way, the mental hygiene value of the technique is especially effective. After the stutterer has learned to use the bounce or effortless prolongation calmly and with excellent attitudes, we then ask him to attempt his most-feared words in the same manner. Often the stutterer experiences great surprise when a badly feared word emerges as an easy, effortless repetition or prolongation rather than as the old contortion he had expected. A few of these experiences will teach him the usefulness of altering his preparatory sets prior to speech attempt. They will help him to realize that he can stutter in a much less abnormal fashion.

It is at this point that we start teaching the stutterer to attempt his feared words by starting the air flow simultaneously with the movement sequence necessary to the production of the word. We continue to use the bounce and the effortless prolongation, but only as evidence of good mental hygiene.   Thus:

Whenever anyone compliments you on your fluency or freedom from stuttering be sure to say something like this: "I have d-d-d-done pretty wwwwwell so far, but I sti-sti-still am working on it."   Then, when you meet that person in the future you will not be tempted to avoid or postpone in order to keep his good opinion.   You ought to know by this time that those tricks only increase the fear and will sooner or later precipitate more trouble.   After all, you are still working on your problem, so demonstrate it by using some calm pseudo-stuttering.

We teach our stutterers to continue to use these patterns whenever they are tempted to hide or disguise or avoid their stuttering.   They are taught to employ them on nonfeared words at the first sign of panic.   But we do not think it necessary to use them as approaches to feared words.   As we have said, they are likely to be used as postponement devices, and their duration is likely to be proportional to the fear.   As a mental-hygiene or teaching device they are excellent.   As a method of stuttering they leave much to be desired.

Teaching the speech attempt from a state of rest.   In teaching the stutterer to attack his feared words so as to produce a minimum of interruption and abnormality, we direct his efforts so that they bear on only one feature of the preparatory set at a time.   Our first goal is to teach the stutterer that it is possible to make the speech attempt from a state of rest, even though he is full of fear and certain that he will stutter.   Thus, we ask him to hunt for a feared situation and a feared word.   We point out to him the fact that formerly he would make the speech attempt on this word from a highly tensed speech musculature.   From our past study of his symptoms, we point out just what area seems to be the most tense—the lips, the tongue, and so on.   We ask him to keep this area, this focus of tension, as relaxed as possible.   He may become as strained as he wishes in any other area, but the focus area, wherever it may be, must be kept loose during the moment of speech attempt.

Relaxation has been used in treating stuttering for a hundred years, but we feel that it has been wrongly used.   The stutterer usually has been asked to remain generally relaxed, to become limp, to "play rag doll."   Such a condition helps to prevent the struggle reactions so characteristic of severe stuttering, to avoid hard contacts and tension tremors.   But the demands of normal existence prevent

an individual from existing in a flaccid state. Fears, sudden challenges, insecurity will all set off sudden involuntary tension states.
To ask the stutterer to remain entirely relaxed is to ask him to have
no fear of stuttering.

It is possible, however, as the work of Jacobson has shown, to use
some differential relaxation *especially when no major voluntary activity
is being performed*. We do not ask the stutterer to maintain an attitude of general bodily relaxation while uttering his feared words. We
merely ask him to keep his lips loose until he actually makes the
speech attempt on such a word as "please." Or we suggest that he
experiment to see whether he can keep from tightening his tongue (if
that is the focus of tension) until he starts to say such a word as
"look." In other words, the stutterer must learn to make his speech
attempts from a state of resting speech musculatures. We say, in
effect: "Stutter or not on this word, but make the speech attempt
without getting your mouth all tightened up. Keep your mouth and
throat loose until you actually begin the word. You must learn to
start feared words as you do nonfeared words. Why tie yourself up
in a knot of tension before you even start?"

This, then, is our first goal in learning to stutter with a minimum
of effort and abnormality. We insist that the stutterer confine his
efforts to its attainment until he has demonstrated his ability to make
the speech attempt from a state of rest in eight or nine very feared
situations and on feared words. We do not judge this ability in terms
of its resultant effect on speech. For the time being, we do not care
whether or not he stutters badly after he makes the speech attempt.
But we do want him to learn to start the feared words without preliminary tension. By doing so, he is destroying the old preparatory
sets, since one of their dominant features is this selfsame preliminary
hypertension.

Starting the air flow or voice flow simultaneously with speech attempt.
If you will watch any severe stutterer carefully during his blocks, you
will notice how often he places his mouth in position for the first sound
of a word before starting the vocalization or air flow. Voiced consonants such as *b* are produced as "puh"; the words beginning with *v*
are pronounced with a prolonged or intermittent *f*; the mouth for-
mations for the vowels are produced long before the voice begins.
These symptoms probably arose originally from the stutterer's desire
to hide his blocks, to suffer their tensions and struggles in silence.
But their effect is a baleful one. They break up the precise timing

which characterizes normal speech. The speech attempt is made fractionally: first the position is assumed, and second, the air flow or voice flow is started. This process of *preformation* is a secondary symptom. We have never observed it in primary stutterers. It occurs as a part of the stutterer's characteristic windup for his speech attempt on a feared word. It engenders much of his difficulty "in getting started." It facilitates tremors and spasms of the glottis, or false-vocal-cord occlusion, or ventricular phonation. Stutterers must be taught to replace this preformation by carefully initiating the air flow or voice flow with speech attempt. In producing a voiced plosive, such as begins the word *goat*, the stutterer must learn to start the vocal-cord vibration simultaneously with the raising of the back of the tongue. In producing a word like *shoot*, the voiceless air flow is timed to coincide with the movements which comprise the (*sh-*) phoneme. The stutterer must learn to do this under conditions of fear. Even when he is afraid he "will get stuck" he must learn how to time the voice and the tongue movement simultaneously. It is not difficult, since he does it regularly when uttering *g* words which he does not fear. A few experiences in attacking feared words in this way not only enables him to reject the preformation of which he was formerly unaware, but also teaches him that air flow and speech attempt can be accomplished simultaneously even when afraid.

Teaching the speech attempt as a voluntary movement sequence. It is interesting that three eminent authorities in the field of speech correction, Froeschels (26), Despert (22), and Robbins (49), with totally different clinical backgrounds, all advocate the use of "speech-chewing" or "breath-chewing" as a technique for eliminating stuttering. They have different reasons for attributing its efficacy, however. One of them uses it to induce relaxation; another, to free the person from a childhood emotional conflict based on the eating-speaking situation. We feel that if chewing-speaking exercises have any value it must lie in the fact that during chewing the mouth is continually in motion. The stutterer who chews as he speaks his feared words will not attempt them in terms of their first sounds alone. He will not assume a fixed position of the tongue or jaws or lips while "chewing" out his words. He will not make such hard contacts or tense positions of the articulators. All these values are good, but they may be achieved directly and much less bizarrely.

The stutterer must prepare himself to make initial or feared sounds of a feared word as a movement. This entails some training in perception.   Stutterers, like everyone else, tend to think of sounds as alphabetic letters, as fixed entities.   They think of the *f* sound as the sound produced by assuming the position of lip-biting and then blowing out the air.   When this sound is carefully observed, however, in its natural habitat, that is, within words, the sound is produced by a continuous upward and downward movement of the lower lip and jaw. The movement never stops when the lip strokes the upper teeth.   The contacts are so loose as scarcely to deserve the name.   The movement then flows into sound.   From this description we see the three criteria of a dynamic speech attempt: (1) the mouth must be kept in motion; (2) the contacts must be light, lest the movement be interrupted; and (3) the succeeding sound must be prepared for in mouth and mind so that the movement may have direction.

In teaching the stutterer to accomplish these ends, we dwell on only one of them at a time.   For example, we ask him to make a pre-written phone call, and have him underline one word on which he expects to stutter badly.   We ask him to rehearse aloud the old preparatory set to assume a fixed position, and then to reject it.   He then attempts the word from a state of rest, but endeavors to keep his lips, tongue, or jaws moving slowly and voluntarily as they produce the succession of sounds that make up the word.   The movements should be flowing rather than suddenly jerked.   Once they are begun they should not cease until the word has been uttered.

The contacts should be made lightly and dynamically rather than statically.   They should be brushed or stroked rather than pressed. One of the best uses of the smooth-prolongation pattern previously described is to teach the stutterer that it is possible to make these light contacts even when a plosive such as the *k* or *p* are prolonged.   However, we urge the stutterer to use this effortless prolongation only to learn what loose contacts are.   Once he understands, he must use the prolongation only for purposes of good mental hygiene.   In attempting feared words, he should use the light contacts merely as part of the flowing movement sequence.

At this point it should be said that the use of light contacts prevents the stutterer from building up the hypertension and struggle which mark the use of hard contacts.   Tremors require tight contacts or tense muscles in order to function, and so they also are prevented. Since the air-way is not being blocked off by glued lips or a cleaving tongue, the stutterer need not strive to blast the obstacle away by sheer force of breath.   The use of light contacts and loose constrictions also facilitates the ability to attempt the word as a sequence of uninterrupted movements. In most stutterers, the movements which they do begin are interrupted whenever hard contacts occur. Keep the contacts light and the movement flows on unimpeded.

Finally, the movements must have direction. Most stutterers fail to realize that in stuttering it is not the sounds that are faulty but the transitions between sounds. Even after long struggle, the first syllable of the word *baby* may first emerge as *bbbbbbbbbbuh* (bʌ), rather than *bbbbbbbbba-* (be). The stutterer may find himself prolonging the same sound interminably or repeating it like a broken record. Why continue to make a sound when you have already produced it? The answer to this question is that the stutterer's attention is so focused on the one feared sound that he never thinks of the sound that should succeed it. He seldom thinks of the *oy* in the word *boy*, because he is too engrossed in breaking the barricade of his lips. We know that stutterers can be taught to reconfigure their feared words so as to give direction to their movements. In teaching the stutterers to keep the movement flowing in the direction of the succeeding sound, we often ask them to form this second sound prior to speech attempt, or to plan to emphasize it slightly. We must do something to break the stutterer's habitual tendency to stop and fixate at one point in his movement sequence. By making sure that the mouth keeps moving in the direction of the succeeding sound, we prevent the false releases (*ssspuh-spoon*) and the fixation on a single articulatory position.

The above description of the process of making a speech attempt so as to minimize the interruption or abnormality may seem far too complicated for the average stutterer. We have had to be analytical in describing it, but actually the process is one which every stutterer practices every time he utters a word without stuttering on it. We all time the moment of speech attempt with air flow or voice flow; we produce sequential movements rather than static positions when we say a word; we use light contacts and fairly relaxed musculatures when we speak. The stutterer has always used these methods—but not on his feared words. When uttering the latter, he does all the wrong things: tensing the muscles prior to speech attempt; assuming fixed positions with hard contacts; failing to time his air flow with the speech attempt; and trying to say the word as though it consisted of one isolated sound. Each of these reactions creates a great deal of abnormality and interruption. They constitute much of the stutterer's burden. If he can be shown that it is possible to approach a feared word in the fashion that he approaches a nonfeared word, much of his abnormality would disappear. We are sure that this can be done and with much less difficulty than might be expected from the description of the procedures sketched above. After all, we are merely teaching him to do consciously what he has usually done unconsciously. It might be objected that teaching the stutterer to do these things would tend to make him too conscious of his mechanics, too concerned with details. If·a stutterer has to go through such a rigmarole of preparation on every feared word, will he not prefer the well-worn grooves of his abnormality? An old ache is, after all, easier to bear than a new one. To this we would heartily agree, were it not that the new preparatory sets become habituated very swiftly *if they are taught under emotional conditions* and that they result in greatly improved fluency. Relatively few successful experiences are required. If one had to go through life alertly scrutinizing every word, rejecting old reactions and specifically preparing new ones, this therapy would be worthless. But the new preparatory sets soon become stronger than the old, and the moment a word is perceived as feared, they come into play. The stutterer's speech seems to handle itself. Almost unconsciously and without preformation, he makes the speech attempt from a state of rest and utters the word as a sequence of movements. We have observed stutterers using these preparatory sets without realizing that they were doing so. If some of these movements lag a little, the abnormality and interruption are slight. Any stutterer can afford to stutter in this way.

As soon as the stutterer has gained through experience a knowledge of how to attack his feared words through the substitution of new and better preparatory sets, he is sent out into normal situations involving much speech to perfect his new skills. He is asked to keep a success-failure ratio; to present an analysis of his failures and a program for their eventual conquest. When he finds himself stuttering in his old way, he attempts to bring his symptoms under control before effecting a release. He does not stop and start over again, nor attempt to jerk himself out of his hard contacts and tremors. Instead he continues the speech attempt but in a more intelligent fashion, by loosening his contacts, decreasing the tensions, bringing in the air flow or voice, and starting the movement into the second sound. Finally, after the word has been spoken, he arranges to "cancel" the failure by pausing deliberately and speaking the word again with better preparation, and, last of all, by using the word in another sentence as soon as possible.

Thus the stutterer always has the possibility of making some speech progress. If his preparatory sets are still too weak and the old spasm results, he can still bring his blocks under voluntary control. If he does not manage this, he can cancel. Only when he does nothing at all about his stuttering will he fail to gain some benefit from his fears or blocks. Few stutterers will be able to persist in their blind struggling spasms if they are exposed to as thoroughgoing a therapy as we have outlined in this chapter.

References

1. Ainsworth, S., *Manual of Speech Therapy and Public School Procedures* (Mimeographed), Special Education Clinics, Indiana State Teachers College, Terre Haute, Indiana, 1944.
An excellent outline of speech therapy for stutterers as it could be applied by the public-school speech correctionist.

2. Angell, C. S., "An Experimental Analysis of Some of the Methods of Relaxation Used in Speech," *Speech Abstracts*, Vol. 3, page 24.
Instruction to relax was compared with quiet music. No differences. After six minutes, the case is as relaxed as he will ever be.

3. Barber, V., "Studies in the Psychology of Stuttering: XV. Chorus Reading as a Distraction in Stuttering," *Journal of Speech Disorders*, 1939, Vol. 4, pages 371–383.
When stutterers read in unison they do not stutter as much. Reading the same material is easier than when the co-reader reads different material.

4. Belgum, D., "Stuttering," *Hygeia*, 1944, Vol. 22, pages 346–347; 391.
Therapy at the University of Minnesota Speech Clinic is described by a case.

5. Bender, J. F., "Do You Know Someone Who Stutters?" *Scientific Monthly*, 1944, Vol. 59, pages 221–224.
Describes two different types of treatment used by the same clinician. Emphasizes the importance of rapport between stutterer and clinician.

6. Bender, J. F., "The Prophylaxis of Stuttering," *The Nervous Child*, 1943, Vol. 2, pages 181–198.
An excellent summary of the nature of stuttering, with a fine discussion of its prevention.

7. Blanton, S. and Blanton, M., *For Stutterers*, New York, D. Appleton-Century, 1936.
The role of the parent, teacher, and the stutterer himself in therapy.

8. Bluemel, C. S., "Primary and Secondary Stammering," *Proceedings of the American Speech Correction Association*, 1932, Vol. 2, pages 91–102.
A good description of the development of stuttering, how to treat the primary form, and how to prevent the secondary form.

9. Brown, F. W., "The Permanent Cure of Stuttering," *Mental Hygiene*, 1933, Vol. 17, pages 266–277.
Personality problems of stutterers must be solved before permanent cure.

10. Brown, S. F. and Shulman, E. E., "Intra-muscular Pressure in Stutterers and Non-stutterers," *Speech Monographs*, 1940, Vol. 7, pages 67–74.
Stutterers are not any more tense than normal speakers. Relaxation therapy is not advisable in an etiological sense.

11. Bryngelson, B., "Prognosis of Stuttering," *Journal of Speech Disorders*, 1941, Vol. 6, pages 121–123.
Good prognosis for therapy requires: intelligence, determination, self-discipline, a good home life, youth, and good health.

12. Bryngelson, B., "Psychologic Factors in the Management of the Exceptional Child," *Journal of Exceptional Children*, 1938, Vol. 5, pages 65–67.
The teacher's function in helping the stutterer to adjust to his speech difference is clearly presented.

13. Bryngelson, B., "Psychological Problems in Stuttering," *Mental Hygiene*, 1937, Vol. 21, pages 631–639.
Outlines psychological and speech therapy. Recommends "voluntary stuttering."

14. Bryngelson, B., "Stuttering and Personality Development," *The Nervous Child*, 1943, Vol. 2, pages 162–171.
Describes some of the parental methods which produce secondary stuttering and maladjustment. Describes the "objective attitude toward stuttering."

15. Bryngelson, B., Chapman, M. E., and Hansen, O. K., *Know Yourself—A Workbook for Those Who Stutter*, Minneapolis, Burgess, 1944, page 53.
A series of discussions and projects which progressively help the stutterer to understand his problem and to solve it. Useful in public-school work.

16. Bullwinkle, B. A., "Methods and Outcome of Treatment of Stutterers in a Child Guidance Clinic," *Smith College Studies of Social Work*, 1933, pages 107–138.
The seven cases who showed no improvement were shy, sensitive, mother-attached, and rejected.

17. Buckholtz, C. A., "Indigenous Confidence for Stutterers," *Quarterly Journal of Speech*, 1933, Vol. 20, pages 60–64.
Build up the stutterer's confidence by any means and you solve his problem.

18. Burkhart, E. J., "History and Present Status of the Correction of Stuttering," M. A. Thesis, Unpublished, Marquette University, 1941.
There seems to be a wide divergence in theories of stuttering but a great similarity in the methods used for treating it.

19. Carhart, R., "An Experimental Evaluation of Suggestion Relaxation," *Speech Monographs*, 1943, Vol. 10, pages 29–40.
Simple instructions to relax are better than suggestion relaxation, but there is no carry-over into life situations involving speech.

20. Carhart, R., "The Two-Room Technique in the Treatment of Stuttering," *Journal of Speech Disorders*, 1941, Vol. 6, pages 105–112.
Building up of confidence through use of a trick microphone connection.

21. Chittenden, G. E., "A Stutterer Is What You Make Him," *Hygeia*, 1943, Vol. 21, pages 68–69.
Describes a case who was harmed most by his parents' well-intentioned but harmful methods of correction.

22. Despert, J. L., "A Therapeutic Approach to the Problem of Stuttering in Children," *The Nervous Child*, 1943, Vol. 2, pages 134–147.
Two cases of stuttering children are intensively explored and treated by psychiatric and speech therapy. Advocates "chewing" of speech.

23. Dow, C. W., "Stuttering: A Tentative Outline of an Hypothesis and Therapy," *Journal of Speech Disorders*, 1941, Vol. 6, pages 40–45.
Teaches his cases to form the speech sounds voluntarily and in proper sequence without forcing.

24. Fletcher, J. M., *The Problem of Stuttering*, New York, Longmans, Green, 1928.
Includes the classification of speech defects, statistical data on stuttering, various theories of the causes of stuttering, physiological symptoms of stuttering, explanation of the author's belief that stuttering is a morbid social maladjustment, and suggested environmental therapy.

25. Fogerty, E., *Stammering*, New York, Greenberg, 1936.
Advocates removal of emotional causes, use of breathing exercises, suggestion, and relaxation.

26. Fröschels, E., "Pathology and Therapy of Stuttering," *The Nervous Child*, 1942, Vol. 2, pages 146–161.
Discusses other methods of therapy, and recommends his own "chewing speech."

27. Gifford, M. F., *How to Overcome Stammering*, New York, Prentice-Hall, 1940.
Recommends relaxation, suggestion, and distractions as well as psychotherapy.

28. Greene, J. S., "Stuttering: What About It?" *Proceedings of the American Speech Correction Association*, 1931, Vol. 1, pages 165–176.
Declares strongly against using distractions. Maintains that they only work temporarily and that in the long run they harm the stutterer more than they help him.

29. Hahn, E. F., "A Study of the Effect of Remedial Treatment on the Frequency of Stuttering in Oral Reading," *Journal of Speech Disorders*, 1941, Vol. 6, pages 29–38.
Outlines a treatment which involves: relaxation, breathy tone, silent recall of how the sound was made, beginning with simple material and proceeding to complex, conscious phrasing, prolonging the vowels, rate control, beginning with easy and going gradually into difficult situations, building up confidence, carrying fluency into outside situations, and using some psychotherapy.

30. Heltman, H. J., "History of Recurrent Stuttering in a 25-Year-Old Post-graduate College Student," *Journal of Speech Disorders*, 1941, Vol. 6, pages 49–50.
Eighteen years of intermittent stuttering; frequent relapse; final cure.

31. Hollingsworth, H. L., "Chewing as a Technique of Relaxation," *Science*, 1939, Vol. 90, pages 385–387.
Summary of experiments on relaxation, showing value of chewing.

32. Johnson, W., "The Indians Have No Word for It: I. Stuttering in Children," *Quarterly Journal of Speech*, 1944, Vol. 30, pages 330–337.
One of the best articles to put in the hands of the parents of a primary stutterer. The treatment of primary stuttering or nonfluency is described.

33. Johnson, W., "The Indians Have No Word for It: II. Stuttering in Adults," *Quarterly Journal of Speech*, 1944, Vol. 30, pages 456–465.
A very clear and very interesting application of semantics to stuttering. Recommends the voluntary bounce pattern, the disregard of the cues that set off fear, and the attempt to reduce stuttering to hesitant speech.

34. Johnson, W., "The Treatment of Stuttering," *Journal of Speech Disorders*, 1939, Vol. 3, pages 170–171.
Recommends using various methods, and tolerance for the points of view and therapies used by other clinicians.

35. Johnson, W. and Rosen, L., "Studies in the Psychology of Stuttering: VII. Effects of Certain Changes in Speech Pattern upon the Frequency of Stuttering," *Journal of Speech Disorders*, 1937, Vol. 2, pages 105–109.
The authors had their stutterers use many different forms of speech ranging from whispering to singing, and recorded number of spasms in each. They feel that distraction was responsible for the decrease in stuttering.

36. Kamm, B., "Resistance Problems," *Bulletin of the Meninger Clinic*, 1938, Vol. 2, pages 161–171.
A stutterer fights the efforts of those who try to help him. Sabotage in the clinic.

37. Kemble, R. P., "Constructive Use of the Ending of Treatment," *American Journal of Orthopsychiatry*, 1941, Vol. 11, pages 684–691.
Some excellent suggestions about how to end treatment.

38. Klingbell, G. M., "The Historical Background of the Modern Speech Clinic: Stuttering and Stammering," *Journal of Speech Disorders*, 1939, Vol. 4, pages 115–131.
Short descriptions of the theories and treatments of stuttering from ancient times to the present.

39. Knutson, T. A., "Oral Recitation Problems of Stutterers," *Elementary School Journal*, 1939, Vol. 39, pages 604–608.
Practices of teachers in calling on stutterers to recite are listed and recommendations are given.

40. Knutson, T. A., "What the Classroom Teacher Can Do for Stutterers," *Quarterly Journal of Speech*, 1940, Vol. 26, pages 207–212.
Outlines classroom policies and information the classroom teacher should possess about speech defects.

41. Kopp, G. A., "Treatment of Stuttering," *Journal of Speech Disorders*, 1939, Vol. 4, pages 166–168.
A famous passage on "No one has ever cured an adult stutterer."

42. Lane, R. R., "Suggestions for Handling Young Stutterers," *Elementary School Journal*, 1944, Vol. 44, pages 416–419.
Policies for classroom teachers. Do's and Don'ts.

43. Lemert, E. M. and Van Riper, C., "The Use of Psychodrama in the Treatment of Speech Defects," *Sociometry*, 1944, Vol. 7, pages 190–195. Psychodrama, phonographic recordings of stutterer's experiences, and other dramatic devices are used in psychotherapy for stutterers.

44. Levbarg, J. J., "Hypnosis—Treatment Used on a Stammerer with Marked Mental Disturbance," *Eye, Ear, Nose and Throat Monthly*, 1941, Vol. 20, pages 55–56; 60.
Hypnosis was used to explore conflicts and to reduce the fear and blocks.

45. Louttit, C. M., *Clinical Psychology*, New York, Harper, 1936, pages 446–450.
Two very interesting case studies showing psychotherapy.

46. Obermann, C. E., "Steps in Overcoming Stuttering," *The Nation's Schools*, 1942, Vol. 30, pages 37–39.
Some very practical suggestions are given for treating secondary stuttering.

47. Peters, C., "Public Speaking; A Therapeutic Procedure," *Quarterly Journal of Speech*, 1933, Vol. 20, pages 64–67.
Helps to break up bad breathing habits and build good mental hygiene.

48. *Proceedings, American Speech Correction Association*, "A Symposium on Stuttering," 1931, Vol. 1.
A collection of the papers on the treatment of stuttering presented by 28 speech correctionists at the national convention.   Various techniques of visual treatment, psychological, breath control, mental hygiene, psychoanalysis, and cerebral dominance therapy are discussed and explained.

49. Robbins, S. D., "Distraction in Stuttering," *Proceedings of the American Speech Correction Association*, 1932, Vol. 2, pages 103–110.
A very comprehensive study of distraction as a device for eliminating the fear and the occurrence of stuttering.   Recommends its use.

50. Rutherford, B., "Prevention and Cure of Stuttering in Primary Grades," *Proceedings of the American Speech Correction Association*, 1932, Vol. 2, pages 28–34.
How the parents, teachers, and the child himself can carry out good mental hygiene principles and thereby prevent the maladjustments which occur.

51. Stoddard, C. B., "A Public School Approach to Treatment of Stuttering," *Journal of Speech Disorders*, 1939, Vol. 4, pages 219–222.
Public-school procedures involving voice training, visualization, phonetics, mental hygiene, and spontaneous speech.

52. Travis, L. E., "The Need for Stuttering," *Journal of Speech Disorders*, 1940, Vol. 5, pages 193–202.
The need for stuttering must be removed or barriers built, or the integration ability of the stutterer must be augmented so that the need will not be felt.

53. Van Riper, C., "Do You Stutter," *Atlantic Monthly*, 1939, Vol. 164, pages 601–609.
A popular history of the treatment of stuttering and the quest for a stuttering cure.

54. Van Riper, C., "A Symptomatic Treatment of Stuttering," *Proceedings of the American Speech Correction Association*, 1937, Vol. 7, pages 110–120.

Describes the importance of devices used by stutterers to avoid or minimize their speech difficulty. These devices are said to become habitual parts of the speech abnormality. Since they are habits, they may be broken, and a plea is made for symptomatic therapy.

55. Van Riper, C., "The Preparatory Set in Stuttering," *Journal of Speech Disorders*, 1937, Vol. 2, pages 149–154.
An outline of symptomatic therapy for stutterers, describing the preparatory set, and designed to tear down the old preparatory sets toward feared words, with a subsequent substitution of new sets for the old.

56. Voelker, C. H., "A New Therapy for Spasmophemia on Gestalt Principles," *Archives Pediatrics*, 1942, Vol. 69, pages 657–662.
Rather difficult to understand but results are said to be excellent.

57. Voelker, C. H., "The Visualization Treatment of Spasmophemia," *Medical Record*, 1935, pages 142, 272.
The greater the visualization of the words, the more he fears them and the more he stutters.

58. Wedberg, C. F., *The Stutterer Speaks*, Redlands, Calif., Valley Fine Arts Press, 1937.
An autobiographical account of how one stutterer "cured" himself.

59. Whitten, I. E., "Therapies Used for Stuttering: A Report of the Author's Own Case," *Quarterly Journal of Speech*, 1938, Vol. 24, pages 227–233.
A very interesting account of how preliminary psychiatric therapy was followed by successful speech therapy.

60. Will, N., "A Six-month Report on the Personality Development of a Thirteen Year Old Stuttering Boy," *Quarterly Journal of Speech*, 1944, Vol. 30, pages 88–95.
The interrelationship of speech and psychotherapy is clearly shown in this case report.

XII

Cleft-Palate Speech

Although cleft-palate speech, like foreign dialect, is characterized by articulatory and voice defects and hence could be classified under both disorders, the consonantal substitutions, omissions, and distortions and the qualities of the various vowels are so peculiar that they demand separate treatment. The disorder may vary from a slight nasal lisp to a form of speech in which the consonants and vowels are so distorted that even the parents of the child can seldom understand him. Profound disturbances of personality also often occur.

Causes. Cleft-palate speech may be the result of any one of three causes: imitation; a soft palate that is paralyzed or sluggish or too short; a cleft or opening along the midline of the soft or hard palate or of both palates. The latter condition is frequently accompanied by cleft or harelip. Cleft palate seems to have some hereditary factor, and since the speech accompanying it is usually strikingly different, young children who associate intimately with a parent, sibling, or playmate who possesses a cleft palate tend to acquire some of the defective sounds, particularly the nasal snort which is used for the sibilant sounds. Shortness, sluggishness, or paralysis of the soft palate may be due to injury, to the effect of diphtheria or some other infection, to adenoidal cushions which prevented normal palatal movement, or to congenital influences. When the speech disorder arises from an actual cleft, the latter is due to embryological maldevelopment. During one stage of the intrauterine life, the mouth and nasal cavities become separated from each other by the union of two shelves of tissue which meet along the midline to form the roof of the mouth. About once in every 2,200 instances, a complete joining does not take place, and a child is born with some form of cleft palate. Animals also suffer from this failure in embryological development.

Articulatory and phonatory aspects of the disorder. The most common articulatory error is the substitution of some nasal equivalent for the plosive and fricative sounds. The child often forms the lip or tongue position characteristic of the normal sound, but expels the majority of the air stream through the nose. Thus, the w, b, and d sounds have a peculiar m or n sound blended with them. The voiceless plosives p and t are usually preceded by a sharp nasal puff, which dominates and distorts the combined sound. The gutturals k and g are among the most difficult for the child to make, since it is difficult to create any air pressure behind the tongue when there is an open nasal channel. Some cleft-palate cases contract their nostrils when making these sounds. Other substitute a backward movement of the tongue toward the pharynx or a short sharp puff of air from the true or false vocal cords ("the glottal shock").

Almost all the fricatives are accompanied by a pronounced nasal snort, since narrowing the mouth cavity merely directs the air stream upward and out through the nostrils, which are usually constricted to produce some sort of fricative noise. Many of the more difficult sounds are deliberately omitted. Since lip and tongue movements have little effect on the sound, they are usually sluggish and poorly co-ordinated. Many vowels and nasals are added to words to prevent too swift a loss of air pressure, and this contributes to the general uncouth sloppiness of the speech. The vowels are very nasal, although generally they can be easily recognized. In some cases, however, even the vowels are badly distorted due to sluggish tongue, jaw, and lip movements. Frequent inhalations are necessary, and phrasing is jerky. Many infantile substitutions are found, since the speech standards are bound to be rather low, and the child often seems so resigned to his fate that he makes no attempt to produce speech that approximates normal standards. Instead, he talks as easily as he can, and hopes or demands that his parents and associates may learn his language.

Surgical treatment. Much can be done for the cleft-palate child through surgery if it is attempted early in life. Surgeons still argue about the proper age for operation, some recommending that the repair be accomplished when the child is from two or three weeks old, and others preferring to wait until the second year. The main objection to early repair is that the tissues do not hold so well; the objection to later operation is that the child has already developed many of his fundamental speech habits, and thus more re-education will be required. The trend seems to be in favor of postponing the operation until after the second birthday.

The purpose of the operation is to stop the nasal air leak by closing the open cleft and by lengthening and readjusting the muscular tissue so that the soft palate can be voluntarily activated in shutting off the upper nasopharynx. Clefts in the hard palate are often closed by a dental plate. Various operative techniques are used in lengthening the velum and displacing it toward the rear wall of the throat, and descriptions of them may be found in the references given at the end of this chapter. Since some of the older operative techniques are very unsatisfactory from the point of view of speech, the surgeon should be chosen with care. It must also be remembered that certain cleft-palate cases present so many difficulties that perfect functioning of the repaired palate is impossible. Occasionally, the surgical repair will clear up the speech defect immediately. However, Kenyon[1] declares: "In cleft-palate patients I have never seen such a completely successful operative result, although I understand that such patients exist." In most instances, speech retraining must be carried on for some time after the operation, treatment usually beginning about two months afterward. In other cases, where the operation is unsuccessful or cannot be performed, an obturator can be used. This appliance is usually constructed of a plastic plate which conforms to the arch of the hard palate, a tail-piece corresponding to the normal soft palate in its lowered position, and a bulb at the end of the tail-piece. The pharyngeal wall is constricted about the bulb, and closure is thus effected. Some individuals seem to have much difficulty in learning to use these appliances, while others achieve fairly normal speech with them. In any event, muscle-re-education and speech training are usually necessary.

Speech-correction procedures. The aims of treatment are: (1) to strengthen the muscles of the soft palate; (2) to teach the child to direct the air stream outward through the mouth opening; (3) to increase the mobility of the tongue, lips, and so forth; and (4) to teach the child to discriminate between the articulatory errors and the correct sounds and to learn to make those that are correct.

Strengthening the soft palate. Several methods are used in strengthening the palatal muscles. One of them is massage. The massage should be demonstrated by the physician and its amount designated by him. It is usually begun about five or six weeks after the final

---

[1] Kenyon, E. L., "A Suggestion for Coöperation in an Effort to Lessen the Degree of Nasality Found in Cleft Palate Patients," *Proceedings of the American Speech Correction Association*, 1938, Vol. 8, page 85.

 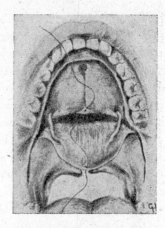

Fig. 16.   Fig. 17.

Fig. 16.   Line of incision and beginning elevation of mucoperiosteum.

Fig. 17.   Diagrammatic representation of palate completely detached from bone, both major palatine arteries intact, and preservation of a band of nasal mucosa to which the palate is attached with the first suture as shown.

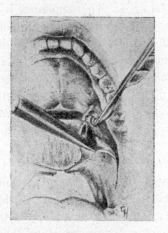 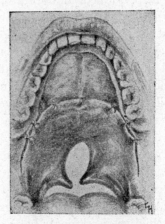

Fig. 18.   Fig. 19.

Fig. 18.   Detail diagram of deep separation of the soft tissues, exposure of the hamulus, freeing of the palate aponeurosis in this area behind the artery, section of the tensor tendon.

Fig. 19.   Completion of first stage. The palate has been set back and anchored with horsehair sutures as shown. Several layers of iodoform and balsam of Peru gauze are placed smoothly over the exposed bone and will be retained without sutures for several days.

The plates on these two pages are from the article in the Journal of Speech Disorders, 1939, Volume 4, pages 157–158, entitled "Cleft Palate Operative Technique," and they are published by special permission of the author and editor.

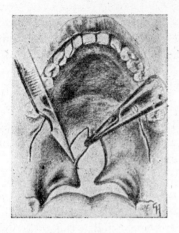

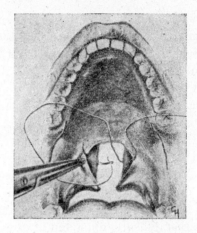

Fig. 20.   Fig. 21.

Fig. 20.   Beginning of second stage.   New openings through the former lateral incisions may or may not be thought necessary.   The edge is trimmed off from the tip of the uvula up into the palate substance about 2 mm.

Fig. 21.   A deep stay suture is usually placed to engage a good bulk of tissue.   This may be of catgut and tied on the nasal surface or it may be of nonabsorbable material and brought out into the mouth.   Extra muscle and nasal mucosa sutures may be put in at this stage.

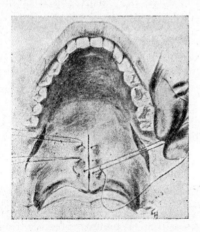

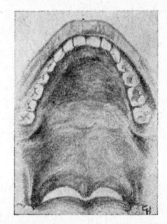

Fig. 22.   Fig. 23.

Fig. 22.   Closure of the cleft with vertical mattress sutures of horsehair.   The closure is carried entirely around the uvula and then up onto the nasal surface with fine catgut sutures.

Fig. 23.   Completed and healed palate.   Set back the distance of the original exposed bone shown in Fig. 19, minus the folding of the soft tissue and the contraction in healing. It is not possible to tell by looking at the palate whether or not it completely closes the nasopharynx, but, of course, the greater its length, the better is its chance of doing so, provided the levator muscles are functioning.

operation, and three or four short periods are given daily. A sterilized finger cot is placed on the teacher's or parent's forefinger. The hand is held supine, with the flat part of the forefinger in contact with the hard palate. The movement is a sliding one, toward the end of the soft palate. The pressure is slight at first, gradually increasing as the palate gains in strength. The student should then be given instructions to resist the pressure. No attempt should be made to massage the palate when the student has a cold or other respiratory infection, and care should always be taken to avoid gagging.

Another exercise similar to massage consists of placing the finger cot or tongue depressor in contact with the soft palate and requesting the student to break the contact without moving his head or jaw. This is rather difficult at first, but, if yawning is suggested at the same time, the student will learn the movement. By following the palate for part of its movement, the teacher can gradually increase the student's ability to contract the muscles.

Many cleft-palate cases find themselves unable to blow up ordinary toy balloons because the air escapes through the nose, but if soap bubbles and very thin-membraned balloons are used, the soft palate is unconsciously strengthened. Stiff balloons may also be used by having the student blow them up while holding his nose. He then releases his fingers and tries to keep the air from escaping through his nostrils by raising the palate. It is wise to remove the inflated balloon from the lips and yawn before reinserting it. If the balloon is returned to the lips at just the proper time, the air pressure will help the soft palate to effect its closure.

Other useful exercises are: clearing the nasal passages by velar sucking; repeated swallowing; filling the cheeks with compressed air without contracting the nostrils; yawning while reclining; gargling; fastening inflated balloons to nasal olives inserted in the nostrils, and attempting to keep the balloons from collapsing when the mouth is opened; panting through the open mouth; and blowing through tubes or constricted air passages against pressure. Whenever possible, these exercises should be used in a reclining position at first; the nostrils must be watched to prevent contraction there instead of at the velar opening; and the tongue should lie as flat in the mouth as the activity will permit.

When working with older children or adults, these exercises may be used as given; but with younger children they must be disguised as games. Frequent shifts of presentation must be made to maintain interest.   The adult or older child should understand clearly just what is desired in terms of palatal functioning.   By observing the teacher's mouth as she yawns or utters a whispered "ah," and by comparing the action of her soft palate with that of his as seen in a mirror, he will begin to comprehend the nature of his problem.   Models of the mouth and nasal passage are likewise useful.   Even younger children can be made to understand something of their problem, by telling them about the "little red door to the nose-attic" and using frequent contacts with a tongue depressor or spoon to create a sense of its location.   When he realizes that he must shut that door and knows where it is, half the battle is won.   Tactual sensations seem to be very effective in provoking movement in younger children.

Directing the air flow through the mouth.   The second major aim of cleft-palate therapy is to direct the air stream outward through the mouth.   As Young [2] says: "The center of the child's speech consciousness will be in the nose and will stick there long after the operation."   The object of this phase of the treatment is to make the child very much aware of the mouth as the major outlet for voluntarily expired air.   Many types of blowing exercises are used for this purpose. Generally, they involve the overcoming of friction or elasticity, the directing of the air stream toward a narrow goal, or the comparison of the amount of nasal or oral air expelled.   Some typical exercises are given.

1. Place a sheet of tissue paper against a wall mirror and hold it there by blowing a thin stream of air against it.   Be sure not to contract the nostrils.

2. Blow ping-pong balls across a table in a game similar to polo.

3. Play the game of wind-bowling, using paper ninepins.

4. Have a sailboat race, blowing tiny boats across a basin of water.

5. Use an apparatus made with two little platforms, one above the other.   This is held in such a fashion that the upper platform is projected outward beneath the nostrils and the lower platform outward below the lower lip.   By placing wisps of feather on the two platforms, the student is required to blow the feathers off the lower platform without disturbing the upper.

6. Line up and light three candles.   Place about a foot away and six inches apart.   Try to blow out the center candle without disturbing the others.

7. Fasten a rubber tube to a nasal olive inserted in one nostril.   Insert

---

[2] Young, E. H., *Overcoming Cleft Palate Speech*, Minneapolis, Hill-Young School, 1928, page 32.

tube in glass of water. Blow through a soda straw immersed in another glass of water. Hold the free nostril closed and try to blow bubbles with the soda straw without causing any bubbles in the other glass.

8. Place a cold mirror under the nostrils and pant through the mouth without causing any clouding of the mirror.

9. Use whistles, peashooters, pinwheels, horns, harmonicas, and other musical instruments or toys to provide motivation.

10. Puff cheeks and let the air suddenly escape so as to move a strip of confetti held before the mouth.

In all of the above exercises, care must be taken to prevent the nostrils from contracting. This can be accomplished by having the student watch himself in the mirror as he does the task or by using a double-ringed nostril dilator. As soon as the student has learned to do the exercises successfully, he should try to get the same outflow of air through a wider mouth opening. Many cleft-palate cases can learn excellent mouth exhalation through a narrow opening but have more difficulty when the jaw is dropped and the lips are parted. We have found that a large, narrow-necked funnel, padded with sponge rubber, used with a wooden tooth-prop will permit the practice of the above exercises with a wide mouth opening. A small card, held horizontally beneath the nose, from the far edge of which is suspended a feather, is another useful device for teaching mouth breathing for speech.

Increasing mobility of articulatory structures. It is also necessary to give a good deal of tongue, jaw, and lip exercise to the majority of cleft-palate cases who have had operations after the speech habits were formed. Many of these individuals seldom employ these articulatory structures in a well-co-ordinated manner. Instead, they use the tongue to fill space and to block the air passage, causing it to be extremely inactive and sluggish. Lists of these exercises will be found in almost any of the references. Whenever possible, the tongue exercises should be performed during exhalation, either silently or when producing a whispered "ah."

Correction of defective consonant and vowel sounds. In teaching the child to apply to speech his newly gained control of the palate and his new habit of exhaling through the mouth, most of the same techniques used in treating the articulatory cases are employed. Ear training is essential, and the teacher should learn to imitate the student's nasal substitutions for the plosive and fricative sounds, so that discrimination will be easier. At intervals throughout the ear-training period, the student should be required to make the sounds in his old incorrect manner, alternately holding and releasing his nose. In that way, enough variation will be produced to make his errors very vivid. Much work before a mirror, and, in some instances, candid photography, will help to identify the substitutes.

Each period of speech training should begin with a series of "warming-up" exercises, designed to free the tongue and to encourage the student to use an active velum in directing the air stream through the mouth opening. The vowels should be taught first, although perfection in terms of nonnasality is seldom reached. A breathy type of vowel phonation, with some type of nasal check, such as a cold mirror held beneath the nostrils, is usually taught. The vowels should occasionally be given excessive nasality to clarify the contrast. Most clinicians begin with whispered vowels and work gradually up through short intensity stages to normal vocalization.

The first consonants to be taught are the *h*, *wh*, *p*, and *t*. At first they should always be performed in conjunction with the blowing exercises and whispered vowels. The labials can often be taught by modifying the exercise using puffing of the cheeks. The next consonants usually taught are the *w*, *b*, and *d*. In teaching these, the student should select the vowel which is most free from nasality and phonate it breathily as the consonant is attempted, thus producing syllables such as *oooooob* or *ooooood*. The tube from the nostril to a glass of water will help to check any nasal air puff that might still occur.

After these consonants have been mastered, reviewed, strengthened, and used in a few familiar words, the *k* and *g* sounds may be attempted. These are usually rather difficult to teach, and some form of phonetic placement is often required. When the necessity for an oral puff is emphasized, and the sudden lowering of the back part of the tongue is clearly demonstrated, most cleft-palate cases acquire the sounds. Much care is needed to differentiate the true *k* sound from that of the glottal catch, and the ear training should be very thorough. Occasionally a modification of the *ng* (ŋ) sound will produce a good *g*, especially when a series composed of alternate *ng* and *ah* sounds is phonated.

The fricatives and the sibilants tend to cause particular trouble. This may best be overcome by using a very broad, loose fricative at first, one in which no tight constriction of the air channel occurs. The *f*, *v*, *s*, *z*, and other similar sounds may seem rather breathy and sloppy, but they may be gradually modified after the basic idea of expelling air through a narrow or sharp mouth aperture is gained. Often, a series of periods devoted to whistling through the teeth or through narrowed lips seem to hasten the acquisition of these fricative sounds. The nasalized fricatives tend to be made by constricted nostrils, and this must be carefully watched. It is wise to use one of the sounds which the student can make successfully in combination with a more difficult one, since the palate will remain raised for the latter if a quick transition is made. Every agency should be employed to make the student mouth-conscious when speaking.

We have emphasized the type of work necessary in treating the older child or adult, since these individuals are those most frequently met by most speech correctionists. The children whose operations were early and successful usually acquire good speech before they go to school. About all they need is some rather careful teaching of the various speech sounds, similar to that sketched in the chapter on delayed speech, and the exercises for strengthening the palatal musculature.

We have mentioned that profound personality problems often accompany the cleft-palate child's speech defect. Indeed, these problems sometimes prevent the teacher from helping the child with his speech. The peculiar speech, the nose twitchings, and the occasional harelip cause many social penalties and call for a great deal of mental hygiene before any kind of treatment can be instituted. There are also some cases who reach the surgeon or speech correctionist too late, and it is better to teach these individuals an unemotional acceptance of their handicap than to attempt to improve their speech. Much depends upon the individual's intelligence, motivation, and patience. Many months are usually needed for treatment, but success is not uncommon.

ILLUSTRATIVE EXERCISES FOR CLEFT-PALATE SPEECH

Cleft-palate speech presents two major problems: (1) to decrease or eliminate nasality in phonation, and (2) to correct the defective consonant sounds, many of which are omitted or distorted by their partial emission through the nose.

The following exercises are designed (1) to direct vocalized air through the mouth opening instead of the nostrils; (2) to strengthen the soft palate and quicken its action; (3) to teach the case to recognize defective sounds and to learn their correct production; (4) to strengthen the tongue and make it more mobile; (5) to produce the vowels with less nasality; and (6) to eliminate unsightly contraction of the nostrils.

Have cases observe their own and each others' mouths in a mirror, and point out the place where the air leak occurs. Call the velum the back door to the nose, and tell them that we must learn to squirt the air out through the mouth when we talk. Tell them to blow through the mouth and wiggle their tongues at the same time. Then test to determine which vowels (prolonged or sung) are the best and which are the worst.

Tell them that one of the most important things in correcting their speech is to learn to blow air through the mouth and that many of our exercises will be of this sort. Have them blow the corks as far as possible. Then hold some tissue paper against the wall by blowing. Then hang a paper mustache from beneath their noses and blow it until it comes off.

Get them to hear their own errors on some of the vowels and some of the consonants, and explain why they made these errors. Do some alternation between m and b and n and d in nonsense syllables. Say some sentences in breathy (mouth-breathing) speech. Have no m or n in these sentences. Imitate the denasal adenoidal speech of a person with a cold. Contrast nasal and denasal vowels. Practice powerful mouth explosions on the p, b, t, d, k, and g sounds.

Work in front of mirror to see if we can cut out that nose squeezing. Breathing: Inhale, count to one, repeat, count to two, and so on, until they count as far as they can. Then, later, try while holding nose.

Have them practice vowels in isolation, holding nostrils open, after listening to you make them with and without nasality, telling you which is right. Then say the vowels with P in the initial position, then medial. Check with mirror for nasality.

Say words to each other from different sides of the room in a stage whisper.

Give each a glass of water and a straw. Let them be the wind and blow waves, making a cold shivery sound as they blow.

Have them use a mirror and try to raise and lower the soft palate, while observing it.

Alternate between nasal and good sound and denasal and good sound. Give children squares of paper. Tell them to throw a square of paper in the wastebasket for every bad sound, but put finger to mouth for the good sound. This is for ear training. Have children listen to "clinician," who uses vowels and p, b, t, g, k consonants.

Tongue exercises: Touch roof of mouth in front, middle, and back saying la. Repeat 5 times. Hum Yankee Doodle, making tongue clicks in time to music.

Blowing exercises: Using a paper ball, play football, starting with lips forming M then exploding to B. Keep score.

Tongue exercise: Make a roll with the tongue by bringing the sides up and down and together when the tongue is protruded. Do it in front of the mirror again and again to the time of the metronome.

Inhale deeply and exhale entirely through the mouth. After several trials, vocalize faintly during exhalation. Whistle as you stretch your arms wide at your sides. Make the whistle last until your arms are straight out at side. Pant in short breaths as you return hands to meet in front of you. Repeat, saying *ho-ho-ho-ho-* quickly and forcibly. Get them in conversation and try to find some good and bad words.

Have them practice *ng*—as for exercise of the palate. Try to get the vowels as free of nasality as possible. Have them open their mouths very wide on the *a*. Read them a story from one of the speech books and nasalize a word here and there. Have them raise their hands each time. The first one to raise his hand gets a jelly bean.

Have them repeat the syllable *ho-ho-ho-* very quickly and forcibly. Have them pronounce the nonsense words *appah, appay, appon,* and so on, holding the consonant for a second then letting it explode quickly. You can also use *b, t, d,* and *k,* this way. A mirror held below the nose, or a cardboard with a feather on it, will help to show how much air is being allowed to escape.

Have them take turns saying different vowel sounds while holding their noses and while not holding their noses. The listening child closes his eyes and sees if he can tell whether the nose is held or not. You talk to them through the mike, alternating between nasal and nonnasal sounds.

Practice with the *M* and *B* combinations on the beginning, the end, and in both positions in the same one-syllable words.

Tongue exercise: Use the tongue click with many different mouth shapes and positions.

Alternate snorting through the nose with blowing through the mouth (on both exhalation and inhalation) in silence, then on the following whispered vowels: *ah, ee, a, eh, oo, oh.* Repeat, but use phonation. Record those that go bad on the mouth breathing.

Have one child blow the *mouth organ,* while the other attempts to whistle the same note. Do several exercises of this sort. Exchange tasks.

Begin in silence, then progress through a soft to a loud whisper, then through soft to loud shouting phonation, the following words: *pipe; tote; gag; cake; bob; church; judge; dead.* Get the cases to progress as far up the ladder as possible before they become nasal.

Have them imitate a person who has a bad cold in the head. Give them a model, and the sentence to say: "I hab a bad cobe in duh headuh."

Using a cold mirror held under the nose, have the child prolong the following sounds and observe whether the mirror gets clouded with nasal air. Ask them to try to keep it clear and to breathe out of the mouth: *ah . . rrrr . . . vvvvv . . . lee-lee-lee, oooooo, ssssss, zzzzzz, ffffff, sh.*

Then try some of the plosive sounds: *puh-puh-puh, tuh-tuh-tuh, kuh-kuh-kuh;* then some voiced plosives: *buh-buh-buh, duh-duh-duh, guh-guh-guh, juh-juh-juh.* Record which ones give some nasal air. If the mirror is too warm it will not cloud, and in this instance, put a small feather on the mirror and see if it is moved. It would probably be well to do this anyway so that the case can see it. If two children are there, give one a score card with these sounds to check nasal errors.

Use the spirometer and record scores of three trials. Be sure to provide for an adequate rest period of at least a minute between each trial. Have them *exhale* first, then deeply *inhale*, then blow. Do this for three trials with nose held, and then without being held. If no spirometer is available, blow a balloon.

Using the *blowing tube* with the end in a glass of water, have the children make the water bubble as they pronounce words beginning with *p, t, b, d, ch,* and *j*. Have the children practice donkey breathing on the vowels which begin each of the words of this sentence: "Alice Oman is all alone." Try to get them to do mouth breathing.

Blow a paper ball representing a horse to see which horse won. (Saying *m, m.* . . . . Pretend to blow a trombone soft and loud, using vowel sounds.

Talk and blow through various sizes of tubes, starting with smaller ones up to bigger ones.

Other exercises are: Cool off burned tongue with *oo* sound. Repeat *ah* in a whisper many times *ah-ng, ah-ng*. Use mirror and bit of Kleenex to watch air come out of nose and mouth. Blow up cheeks, then let air out of "tire" for *S*. Cover eyes and sound word using vocal phonics.

References

1. Backus, O. L., *Speech in Education*, New York, Longmans, Green, 1943, pages 173–180.
Gives a description of the disorder, speech involvements, causes, surgical repair, mouth-breathing exercises, articulation therapy, reduction of assimilation nasality, and socialization.

2. Beatty, H. G., "Etiology of Cleft Palate and Hare Lip," *Journal of Speech Disorders*, 1936, Vol. 1, pages 13–20.
A detailed description of the embryological development of normal and cleft palates and harelips.

3. Berry, M. F. and Eisenson, J., *The Defective in Speech*, New York, F. S. Crofts, 1942, pages 284–304.
A good summary of the literature, both speech and medical. Describes causes, nature, and varieties of cleft lips and palates. Advises mouth-breathing exercises first, then alternate mouth and nasal emission, then exaggerated jaw and lip activity in articulation, teaching the plosives first. Treatment of one case is outlined.

4. Blair, V. P., "Cleft Palate—Its Surgery," *Journal of Speech Disorders*, 1937, Vol. 2, pages 195–198.
A brief description of the surgical aims and methods used in repairing palatal clefts.

5. Browne, D., "The Closure of the Naso-pharynx," *Speech* (London), 1936, Vol. 2, pages 15–20.
Describes the action of the muscles that close the nasopharynx.

6. Brown, J. B., "Elongation of the Cleft Palate to Gain Better Naso-pharyngeal Closure," *Proceedings of the American Speech Correction Association*, 1939, Vol. 9, pages 21–25.
Describes the operation. "Speech training is considered as important as in any other type of palate closure."

7. Brown, S. F. and Oliver, D., "A Qualitative Study of the Organic Mechanism Abnormalities Associated with Cleft Palate," *Journal of Speech Disorders*, 1940, Vol. 5, pages 265–270.
Many other organic abnormalities were found to be associated with cleft palates and these are considered to have an important effect on speech.

8. Cobb, L. H. and Lierle, D., "An Analysis of the Speech Difficulties of 56 Cleft Palate and Harelip Cases," *Archives of Speech*, 1936, Vol. 1, pages 217–230.
A phonetic analysis of the speech difficulties of these cases. All of them showed excess nasality on the vowels, but the amount of nasality was not proportional to the amount of cleft. Plosive and fricative sounds were the most difficult, and delayed speech was common. A bibliography is given.

9. Dorrance, G. M., "Congenital Insufficiency of the Palate," *Archives of Surgery*, 1930, Vol. 21, pages 185–248.
Many cases with no cleft but with too short a palate have cleft-palate speech. Many of these can be helped by surgery.

10. Dorrance, G. M., "The Push-Back Operation in Cleft Palate Surgery," *Annals of Surgery*, 1935, Vol. 101, No. 1, pages 445–460.
A description of the operation with its advantages for speech.

11. Eckelmann, D. and Baldridge, P., "Speech Training for the Child with a Cleft Palate," *Journal of Speech Disorders*, 1945, Vol. 10, pages 137–148.
An excellent description of actual procedures used for cleft-palate children.

12. Fitz-Gibbon, J., "Cleft Palate," *Proceedings of the American Speech Correction Association*, 1934, Vol. 4, pages 52–55.
A description of obturators and their use when surgical operation fails or cannot be employed. Nostril openers are also described.

13. Gaines, F. P., "Frequency and Effect of Hearing Loss in Cleft Palate Cases," *Journal of Speech Disorders*, 1940, Vol. 5, pages 141–145.
A slightly greater hearing loss in cleft-palate cases.

14. Harkins, C. S., "Rehabilitation of the Cleft Palate Child," *Journal of the Exceptional Child*, 1943, Vol. 9, pages 98–106.
A very clear and nontechnical description of modern surgical techniques. Discusses obturators and other prosthetic devices. Stresses speech correction.

15. Harrington, R., "A Study of the Mechanism of Velopharyngeal Closure," *Journal of Speech Disorders*, 1944, Vol. 9, pages 325–345.
A thoroughgoing description of the muscle action of the soft palate. It shows some pictures of the palate in a patient whose cheek was opened to show it clearly.

16. Henderson, F., "The Incidence of Cleft Palate Speech in Hawaii," *Journal of Speech Disorders*, 1940, Vol. 5, pages 285–287.
Much greater incidence there than on the mainland.

17. Huber, M., "Speech Re-education Following Cleft Palate Reconstruction," *Canadian Medical Association Journal*, 1942, Vol. 46, pages 325–326.
Describes the advantages and methods of speech therapy.

18. Huber, M. W. and Kopp, A. E., *The Practice of Speech Correction in the Medical Clinic*, Boston, Expression Co., 1942.
Cleft lip and cleft palate are described carefully and vividly with fine pictorial illustrations. The speech-correction methods are briefly outlined.

19. Kantner, C. E., "Four Devices Used in the Treatment of Rhinolalia Aperta," *Journal of Speech Disorders*, 1937, Vol. 2, pages 73–76.
The author describes the use of balloons to create back pressure, manometric flames to show nasal discharge of air, and two other devices used in the treatment or diagnosis of cleft-palate speech or excess nasality.

20. Kenyon, E., "A Suggestion for Coöperation in an Effort To Lessen the Degree of Nasality in Cleft Palate Patients," *Proceedings of the American Speech Correction Association*, 1938, Vol. 8, pages 84–86.
An abstract describing the results of cleft-palate operations in terms of residual nasality.

21. Kenyon, E., "The Speech Complications Involved in Certain Types of Inadequate Palate, Especially Congenital Short Palate," *Annals of Otology, Rhinology, and Laryngology*, September, 1925, pages 1–14.
Voice, articulatory, and stammering disturbances result from congenitally short palates. These palates are due to insufficiency of the hard palate and may be hereditary. Training the superior constrictors of the nasopharynx may help in closing the gap, and remedial speech work may improve the general effectiveness.

22. Koepp-Baker, H., "Some Anatomic and Physiologic Considerations in Uraniscolalia," *Proceedings of the American Speech Correction Association*, 1936, Vol. 6, pages 181–196.
A clear description of the anatomical structure of the cleft and the normal soft palate, together with a discussion of the older and newer types of surgery used in repair.

23. Koepp-Baker, H., *Handbook of Clinical Speech*, Ann Arbor, Edwards Brothers, 1937, Vol. 2, pages 321–341.
A description of the nature of cleft palate and its surgical and speech-corrective treatment, written for the adult cleft-palate case. Chapter 16 includes tongue, lip, and palatal exercises and general principles of treatment.

24. Moser, H. M., "Diagnostic and Clinical Procedures in Rhinolalia," *Journal of Speech Disorders*, 1942, Vol. 7, pages 1–4.
Mentions twelve methods which will aid in strengthening the soft palate and directing the air through the mouth rather than the nose.

25. Oldfield, M. C., *Speech Training for Cases of Cleft Palate*, London, H. K. Lewis and Co., 1938.
A pamphlet valuable for its photographs of cleft palates. An account of the formation of the various speech sounds is also included.

26. Perlowski, F., "Massage of the Palate," *Proceedings of the American Speech Correction Association*, 1932, Vol. 2, pages 70–73.
A description of massage techniques and the results obtained by using them.

27. Ritchie, H. P., "Congenital Clefts of the Face and Jaws; 350 Cases on Which Operation Was Performed," *Archives of Surgery*, 1934, Vol. 28, pages 617–634.
Mentions that over 9 per cent of the cases have a family history of cleft palate. Describes different types of cleft palates and lips.

28. Seth, G. and Guthrie, D., *Speech in Childhood*, London, Oxford University Press, 1935, pages 163–174.
The authors discuss action of the soft palate, causes of nasal speech, rhinolalia clausa, rhinolalia aperta, surgical treatment of cleft palate, the effect of adenoids on speech, prognosis for cleft palate, breathing and blowing exercises, and exercises for the lips, tongue, palate, and practice of the consonants.

29. Shohara, H. H., "Speech Rehabilitation in a Case of Post-operated Cleft Palate Speech and Malocclusion," *Journal of Speech Disorders*, 1942, Vol. 7, pages 381–388.
Palatograms are used to show the development of acceptable speech.

30. Shultz, L. W., "The Care of Cleft Lip and Cleft Palate in Babies," *Illinois Medical Journal*, 1944, Vol. 86, pages 138–159.
Gives the causes, operative techniques, and post-operative treatment. Declares that 80 per cent of unoperated cases have inferiority complexes.

31. Van Thal, J. H., "Some Psychological Factors in the Treatment of Cleft Palate Speech," *Speech* (London), 1936, Vol. 2, pages 7–10.
Much psychotherapy needed with these cases.

32. Voelker, C. H., "Therapeutic Technique for Staphylolalia," *Archives of Otolaryngology*, 1935, Vol. 21, pages 94–96.
Term refers to cleft palate or inactive velum. Advocates use of glottal catch for *k* and *g* sounds and exaggerated production of the other consonants.

33. Ward, W. K., "Re-Educating Cleft Palate Speech," *The Practitioner*, 1929, Vol. 123, pages 148–152.
Gives an excellent series of exercises for oral emission of breath and voice.

34. Wells, C., "A Speech Training Center for Cleft Palate Children," *Quarterly Journal of Speech*, 1945, Vol. 31, pages 68–72.
Describes the functioning of such a center and the speech therapy used there.

35. Wells, C., "Improving the Speech of the Cleft Palate Child," *Journal of Speech Disorders*, 1945, Vol. 10, pages 162–169.
An excellent description of methods.

36. West, R., Kennedy, L., and Carr, A., *The Rehabilitation of Speech*, New York, Harper, 1937, pages 65–86, 268–275.
A description of the nature and treatment of cleft palate and cleft lip from the speech-correction point of view. Prognosis is discussed. Velar exercises and methods for eliminating the characteristic substitution of the glottal catch are given in the latter pages.

37. Young, E. H., *Overcoming Cleft Palate Speech*, Minneapolis, Hill-Young School, 1928.
A short text which includes many suggestions for the treatment of children with cleft palates. The phonetic placement method for teaching the speech sounds is emphasized.

XIII

The Problem of Bilingualism and Foreign Dialect

Since the United States is still the melting pot of the world, a country where large numbers of its citizens converse in other tongues and where many children still enter its schools without speaking a word of its language, the problem of bilingualism and foreign dialect will always be encountered by the speech correctionist. Research studies indicate that bilingual children are handicapped in the verbal intelligence tests, in reading, and in most of the other school subjects. Adults whose speech betrays their foreign origin or social environment are commonly handicapped in a majority of the ordinary occupations. These individuals require skilled treatment if they are to eliminate their speech difference and handicap.

Aims of treatment. This treatment must accomplish the following things: (1) the student must acquire the words and idioms of a basic English vocabulary, first in terms of comprehension, and second in terms of use; (2) he must learn those English speech sounds which never occur in his native language; (2) he must learn to produce and discriminate between those speech sounds which are common both in his native language and also in English, but which vary in duration, in diphthongization, in nasality, and in other relatively inconspicuous ways; (4) he must learn to hear and produce the characteristic patterns of stress and accent which distinguish the old language from the new; (5) he must learn to hear and produce the characteristic patterns of melody, inflection, and intonation which differ in the two languages· (6) he must learn to recognize the sound substitutions, omissions, and additions which contribute to the foreign quality of his speech; (7) he must learn the forms of sentence structure which differ in the two languages; and, finally, (8) he must learn to think in English.

Difficulties experienced by the non-English-speaking individual. It is obvious that the treatment of this individual is not an easy one. Moreover, the task is complicated by many other factors. The spelling of English words is far from phonetic. If the individual has learned his reading and writing skills in some foreign language, he tends to use the foreign sounds whenever he reads or writes, since the associations between vocal and printed or written symbols have already been formed. Many of the sounds used in both languages appear in English words in positions which are unfamiliar. If the individual lives in a home or environment where little or no English is spoken, or where his associates prize their foreign traditions, much difficulty will inevitably occur.

When the non-English-speaking child enters school, he presents a problem which few school systems have been able to solve successfully. In some of the larger industrial cities, special classes are provided for teaching the English language to both children and adults. Many of these special classes, and especially that which can give instruction to small groups within narrow age ranges, are very successful. In too many school systems, the "Americanization" course is so hurried and overcrowded that little is done besides teaching a basic vocabulary of mispronounced words, and, in the majority of schools, all new non-English-speaking students, regardless of age, are compelled to enter the first grade or opportunity room. Since the teachers are not trained in the teaching of speech, they frequently do little to help. The consequent maladjustment is eloquently expressed in the article by De-Vargas, given in the list of references at the end of this chapter.

Treatment of the young non-English-speaking child. When a non-English-speaking child first comes to school, he should be given a few days to orient himself. If any other student can speak his language, the teacher should inform the child through this interpreter that he should watch the other children and do what they do. He should be told that he will not be asked to talk for a little while, and that if he wants to know the name of anything he should attract the teacher's attention and point to it. If possible, the teacher should learn a few of the foreign words and phrases, so that she can say the child's name and "yes" and "no," can give such directions as "Come," "Find," and "See," and can ask such questions as "What is this?" These familiar words and phrases will eliminate the overwhelming insecurity which usually greets the foreign child upon entering school. For several weeks, the child should not be asked to make any attempts to say English words, but every opportunity should be provided for increasing his comprehension. Pantomime, pointing, and the use of pictures, when preceded by the speaking of his names by the teacher or some other student, often build up this comprehension to a surprising degree. Some teachers designate one of the other pupils to act as a talking dictionary several times a day and to name anything the foreign child dramatizes or to which he points. Such a program will invariably result in spontaneous speech attempts and in imitation. The other children often carry out similar procedures on the playground, and most of the language is acquired through play activity. The teacher should try to have a five- or ten-minute period each day in which she attempts to get the child to hear and produce those speech sounds which the foreign language does not possess or which it uses in a slightly different way. These sounds should be identified with noises made by animals or machines and should be practiced independently of any true speech.

As soon as the child begins to use English speech spontaneously, the teacher can begin to build vocabulary. She should not be too critical of pronunciation at first, but after the child has used the new word five or six times, she should point out the errors in contrast with the correct sounds, using the phonic training mentioned in the preceding paragraph to enable him to correct himself. Each new word should be presented in many different contexts and should be reviewed frequently. In order to prevent too narrow associations, each should be used as soon as possible with other contrasting words, such as opposites or different actions. Sentence words should be the first to be acquired, and some other child may demonstrate their meanings by his actions as the teacher repeats the new word. Pictures of children carrying out commands or directions are also useful. Often, the foreign child seems to make rapid progress by imitating the activity of the other members of a group of children as they respond to the teacher's spoken commands. Articles, prepositions, and abstract words should be introduced much later, and many of them can best be learned through indirect methods. Thus, the foreign child learns the words *on* and *under* by following directions to put objects on or under a given table. The teacher must always remember to use as simple directions as possible, employing one-word sentences and pantomime in the early stages so as not to confuse the child with too many words. She must also realize that the child thinks in the other language and must mentally translate everything said to him, a process which, in the young child, necessitates patient waiting for a response.

Although the average child has a vocabulary of approximately two thousand words before beginning reading, no such amount need be required of the foreign child. In fact, after a small basic vocabulary of fifty or one hundred words has been acquired, the foreign child should be given reading as part of his speech training. The words included in modern elementary readers are probably as basic to language acquisition as any. Pronunciation of the difficult words found in reading should be handled apart from the reading situation if the reading skills are not to be affected. The words that the foreign child mispronounces in oral reading should be noted and corrected later. As soon as some reading skill has been gained, the words of the foreign child's new vocabulary should be reviewed over and over, and incorporated into little stories. He should be encouraged to tell these before the group, and social approval should be given for each little triumph. We doubt that phonetic symbols are of much use in training the young non-English-speaking child; they merely increase the already heavy burden which school places upon him. We feel that any child of ten years or less, if given the proper preliminary help, will acquire normal English speech from his fellow students. Once the process of correct speaking is initiated, imitation seems to take care of even the stress and inflection aspects of the problem, providing that environmental factors do not interfere. The teacher should help the child keep a notebook of his most frequent errors; this can be passed along from teacher to teacher as he progresses through the grades.

The speech problem of the adult with foreign speech or accent. In treating the adult whose speech is marked by foreign accent or who has no English speech, more difficulty will be experienced and more strenuous techniques will be needed. It is usually wise to teach him the use of the phonetic alphabet, the rules of accent and stress, and the methods for following speech melodies and inflections according to some arbitrary system of scoring. One of the most useful texts for teaching phonetic transcription to foreigners is that by Barrows, given in the references at the end of this chapter. In teaching phonetics to non-English-speaking individuals, much care is needed to get acceptable English sounds associated with the symbols. For this reason, phonetics should follow training in the production and discrimination of the individual English speech sounds.

Vocabulary. If the student has very little vocabulary, it is usually wise to give him the most common and useful words. Ogden's *Basic English* provides an excellent vehicle for vocabulary building. The word lists by Thorndike or by Buckingham and Dolch will insure economy of effort, since each word is listed according to frequency of use. The study by Hughes gives a list of 660 words used in teaching Spanish-speaking children their first English vocabulary. Whatever word list is used, the teacher and student will need to supplement it with words that are peculiarly useful in the latter's immediate environment. As far as possible, the words should be taught vocally rather than by reading or writing. Phonograph recordings can serve as sound dictionaries, if phonetic transcripts are provided with the records. This method has proved very useful.

Each student finds it helpful to make his own vocabulary recording. After learning a series of words and how to transcribe them phonetically, he and the teacher pronounce them alternately into the microphone of a recording device, pausing for a second after each word. When the record is played back, the student can hear his own pronunciation, then the teacher's, and then is given time to pronounce it again before the next word is spoken. A series of these records, frequently replayed, is a very effective therapeutic device. Foreign-language-speaking students also make special recordings of words they are most likely to mispronounce, saying them both correctly and incorrectly. These dictionaries of error, when replayed daily, soon eradicate the mistakes. The students also are urged to keep notebooks in which they note all usage of familiar words which seems to violate the meanings previously taught.

Errors in producing the English vowels and consonants. No great difficulty will be experienced in teaching the foreign-language individual how to produce sounds that do not occur in his native language. They may be taught by the same methods outlined in the chapter on the treatment of articulatory defects. Probably the greatest obstacle lies in the average teacher's unfamiliarity with the student's language. Fortunately, the omissions, additions, distortions, and substitutions of sounds commonly made by each nationality are to be found in most of the standard textbooks in speech correction.

Generally speaking, there are few consistent substitutions characteristic of the individuals of any one nationality who are attempting to learn English. Some omit the sound entirely; others use some native speech sound similar to the English one; still others give the symbol the foreign equivalent and use the latter in pronunciation. A keen ear can soon detect what the errors are.

It is usually difficult to teach the foreign-language adult to dis-

AMERICAN SOUNDS ABSENT FROM OR "DISTORTED" IN EUROPEAN LANGUAGES *

Vowels and Diphthongs

	[ɪ]	[æ]	[ɔ]	[ʊ]	[ʌ]	[ə]	[oʊ]	[aʊ]	[eɪ]	[aɪ]	[ɔɪ]	[ju]
French	A†	A		A	A		D†	A	D	A	A	A
Italian	A	A		A	A	A	D		D			A
Spanish	A	A		A	A	A						A
Portuguese	A	A		A	A							A
Rumanian		A				A	D	A	D	A	A	A
Greek	A	A		A	A	A		A	A		A	A
German		A			A		D		D			A
Swedish	A	A	A	A	A		D					A
Norwegian	A	A			A		D	D				A
Danish	A			A	A		D		D	D		A
Russian	A	A		A	A	A	A	A				
Polish	A	A		A	A	A	A		D			
Czech	A	A		A	A	A		A				
Finnish				A	A						A	
Hungarian		A	A		A	A	D		D			A

The vowels [i], [ɛ], [a] and [u] are present in all.

Consonants

	[ŋ]	[r]	[l]	[θ]	[ð]	[z]	[ʃ]	[ʒ]	[h]	[ʍ]	[w]	[tʃ]	[dʒ]
French	A	D	D	A	A				A	A	A	A	A
Italian		D	D	A	A				A		A		
Spanish	A	D	D		A		A	A	A	A	A		
Portuguese		D	D	A	A				A	A		A	A
Rumanian	A	D	D	A	A				A	A			
Greek	A	D	D				A	A	A	A	A	A	A
German	D	D	D	A	A				A	A		A	
Swedish	A	D	D	A	A	A		A		A	A		A
Norwegian		D	D	A	A	A		A		A	A	A	A
Danish		D	D					A		A	A	A	A
Russian	A	D		A	A				A	A	A		A
Polish	A	D		A	A				A	A	A		
Czech	A	D	D	A	A					A	A		A
Finnish	A	D	D	A	A	A	A	A		A	A	A	A
Hungarian	A	D	D	A	A					A	A		

The consonants [m], [n], [p], [t], [k], [f], [v], [s] and [j] are present in all; [b], [d], and [g] are present in all except Greek.

---

* Sipin, L., "A Comparative Analysis of the Phonetic Systems of Certain Modern European Languages, with Applications to the Correction of Foreign Dialects," M. A. Thesis, State University of Iowa.

† "A" signifies absent; "D" signifies distorted.

tinguish those characteristics of duration, diphthongization, nasality, and force which differ in the old and new languages. Phonetic training will help him to recognize the natural tendencies in American speech to prolong and to diphthongize the vowels. English vowels are not pure vowels, but are diphthongs or triphthongs. Americans ordinarily use very little lip or jaw movement in articulating their vowels or consonants, and when the foreigner's stop consonants are too plosive or too energetic, they contribute to the foreign accent. Many foreign languages use trilled *r* sounds and produce the *l* with a retracted tongue. Others, notably the French, nasalize many of their vowels and voiced continuant sounds. All of these differences reflect themselves in foreign accent and must be eliminated if the individual is to lose his speech peculiarity. This may be done through discrimination and ear training similar to that used for the voice and articulatory cases. The errors must be brought up to consciousness, the old habits broken, and new habits substituted for them. The use of narrow phonetic transcription, which employs symbols indicative of vowel duration, tongue position, and nasalization, is often effective. Matching techniques, contrast of correct and incorrect sound sequences, practice in drawling and prolonging vowels, reading prescored material, and many other methods are useful in carrying out these aims.

Stress. Foreign-language speakers habitually use those stress patterns and accents which are characteristic of the old language, and often find themselves hopelessly confused by the tremendous variety of syllabic accents found in English. It is usually wise to teach the student two or three rules and then ask him to collect and record exceptions in his notebook. The rules which we have found most useful are:

1. In English, we tend to alternate stressed and unstressed syllables.
2. Words of three or more syllables are accented on the first syllable except when it is a prefix.
3. Compound words are accented on the first syllable.

Melody. Probably the most difficult of all characteristics of foreign speech to eradicate is the old melody pattern of the sentence. Each language has its own system of inflection patterns, and, since they are not usually recorded by symbols, they are relatively unconscious and hence difficult to eliminate. The Swedish individual tends to end his declarative sentences with an upward inflection. If he is to free his English of peculiarity, he must recognize this tendency, reject it, and substitute the down glide which is normal to the new language. Three rules are useful in teaching the principles of English intonation:

1. When you ask a question without using a specific interrogative word such as *what* or *when*, use a rising inflection on the last word.
2. When you finish a thought, use a falling inflection on the last word.
3. For unfinished thoughts, as found in dependent clauses or unfinished commands or statements, use a rising inflection on the word before the pause.

It is difficult to hear inflection patterns unless some motor performance is used to identify and record them. Many systems have been devised for this purpose. Klinghardt's system is clearly described in the reference by Koepp-Baker. Another is described in that by Bender and Kleinfeld.

Phonograph recordings are invaluable for this part of the work, and the student should imitate the instructor through a wide range of inflection variations. Phonograph records can be used as models for inflection transcription, and after the technique has been mastered the student can be given his own record to analyze in similar fashion. When the student can hear, analyze, or record the inflections of others, and can read from transcriptions of inflections, he has progressed a long way toward the solution of his problem.

Sentence structure. Errors in sentence structure are usually eliminated through two methods. First, the grammar of both the old and new languages is studied intensively, and all instances of contrast are noted and discussed with the instructor. Other examples of each variant word order are collected. It often helps to practice the English word order in the foreign language, since this seems to vivify the experience. Secondly, the student collects and frequently reviews all phrases and sentences which he considers odd or idiomatic. After checking with the teacher, the student enters speech situations appropriate to the employment of the sentences concerned.

Thinking in English. Enabling the student to think in English may seem an almost hopeless task at times, but, after the preliminary steps have been mastered, penalties can be placed upon translation, and through such devices as oral reading and rapid speech the student actually manages to make the shift. At first, this training in English thinking should be given in very small doses and only under the guidance of the instructor, since much verbal and mental confusion can result from this type of speech conflict.   If the thinking in English is carried out entirely in one situation, it tends to produce no such conflict, and later on a gradual spread to other situations occurs.   Acquiring perfect English after one is an adult is no easy task, but with patience and intelligent direction it can be accomplished.

References

1. Angus, W., "The Turk's Characteristic Difficulties in Learning English Pronunciation," *Quarterly Journal of Speech*, 1937, Vol. 23, pages 238–243.
An excellent illustration of the necessity of comparing the speech sounds of the former language with those of English in planning the treatment for foreign speech.

2. Barker, J. L., "Correcting the Mechanism Causing Most Foreign Brogue," *Journal of Speech Disorders*, 1936, Vol. 1, pages 3–12.
Points out that breath interruptions, phrasing, intonation patterns, and other phenomena are very important in teaching the foreigner English.

3. Barker, J. L., "Dynamic Versus Static Phonetics," *Journal of Speech Disorders*, 1940, Vol. 5, pages 153–183.
Phonetic placement is a poor method for teaching English speech sounds to French- or Italian-speaking peoples because the transitional movements and sounds are so different in these languages.

4. Barrows, S. T., *An Introduction to the Phonetic Alphabet* (revised edition), Boston, Expression Co., 1938.
A manual of graded lessons in the acquisition of the skills needed in phonetic transcription.

5. Bender, J. F. and Kleinfeld, V. M., *Principles and Practices of Speech Correction*, New York, Pitman Publishing Corporation, 1938, pages 113–115.
This part of the text describes the use of arrow symbols in the transcription of inflections.

6. Borden, R. C. and Busse, A. C., *Speech Correction*, New York, F. S. Crofts and Co., 1929, pages 160–207.
This chapter includes a description of the errors made by foreign-speaking individuals and the various methods for their correction.   Rules are given for clearing up some of the confusions due to the peculiarities of English spelling.

7. Buckingham, B. R. and Dolch, E. W., *A Combined Word List*, Boston, Ginn and Co., 1936.
A compilation of the 19,000 most frequently used words in English.   The rankings of each word as assigned by various authors of other word lists are given.

8. Coale, W. and Smith, M. E., *Successful Practices in the Teaching of English to Bilingual Children in Hawaii*, U. S. Department of the Interior, Office of Education, Bulletin No. 14, Washington, D. C., 1937.

Anecdotes from teachers who were successful in teaching English to foreign-speaking children, including Orientals. Kindergarten speech training needed.

9. David, B. J., "Teaching Speech to Refugees," *Quarterly Journal of Speech*, 1943, Vol. 29, pages 483–484.
Must not concentrate on English articulation, inflection, and articulation alone but on cultural patterns.

10. De Banke, C., "Speech Training in South Africa," *Quarterly Journal of Speech*, 1933, Vol. 19, pages 77–78.
All governmental employees must be bilingual, and training in English is required in all schools. Describes the governmental training program.

11. DeVargas, D., "Teaching 'Mexicans' an English Vocabulary," *Elementary English Review*, 1937, Vol. 14, page 31.
A brief description of the reasons for failure in teaching children of Mexican background to speak English. Some suggestions to prevent this failure are cited.

12. Gisolfi, A. M., "Italo-American," *The Commonweal*, 1939, Vol. 30, pages 311–313.
Explains and illustrates the errors of Italian dialect.

13. Howatt, G., "The Non-English Speaking Child," *Journal of the National Educational Association*, 1938, Vol. 27, pages 75–76.
Qualifications of teachers of these children, in terms of speech. Also discusses Americanization.

14. Hughes, M. H., *Teaching a Standard English Vocabulary*, Bulletin of the State Board of Education, Santa Fe, New Mexico, 1930.
A list of 660 words designed to serve as a basal vocabulary to be taught to Spanish-speaking children prior to their entrance into the first grade.

15. Jameson, R. D., "Basic English and Children," *School and Society*, 1939, Vol. 49, pages 84–87.
The advantages of teaching Basic English as a core vocabulary.

16. Koepp-Baker, H., *Handbook of Clinical Speech*, Ann Arbor, Edwards Brothers, 1937, Vol. 2, pages 293–321.
Designed for the use of the foreign speaker himself. The causes of foreign accent, the peculiarities of English pronunciation, the laws governing stress and accent, a list of the most common substitutions, additions, and omissions for each language, and a description of Klinghardt's system for transcribing inflection patterns are included.

17. Lynn, K., "Bilingualism in the Southwest," *Quarterly Journal of Speech*, 1945, Vol. 31, pages 175–180.
A good survey of the literature on speech for Spanish-speaking children. Articulation errors are analyzed in detail.

18. Mammem, E. W. and Sonkin, R., "A Study of Italian Accent," *Quarterly Journal of Speech*, 1936, Vol. 22, pages 1–10.
The errors of Italians who speak English are analyzed and explained. Three characteristic patterns of intonation are also illustrated.

19. Powers, F. F. and Hetzler, M., *Successful Methods of Teaching English to Bilingual Children in Seattle Public Schools*, U. S. Department of the

Interior, Office of Education, Bulletin No. 76, Washington, D. C., 1937. Chinese and Japanese children were given intensive training in articulation and pitch intonation.   Good annotated bibliography.

20. Stengel, E., "On Learning a New Language," *International Journal of Psycho-Analysis*, 1939, Vol. 20, pages 471–479.
A very interesting study of the emotional reactions of a person learning a new language.

21. Thomas, C. K., "Chinese Difficulties with English Pronunciation," *Journal of Speech Disorders*, 1939, Vol. 4, pages 255–259.
Describes the general difficulties experienced by Chinese learning English. The difficult sounds are the *s*, *n*, *ng*, *l*, and *r* sounds.

22. Tireman, L. S., Dixon, N., and Cornelius, V., "Vocabulary Acquisition of Spanish-Speaking Children," *Elementary English Review*, 1935, Vol. 12, pages 118–120.
A study of vocabulary gains during one year of teaching non-English-speaking first graders.   A basic vocabulary was chosen and taught, resulting at the end of the year in a median comprehension of 633 words and a median usage of 567 words.

23. Voelker, C. H., "The One Thousand Most Frequently Spoken Words," *Quarterly Journal of Speech*, 1942, Vol. 28, pages 189–197.
From other studies, the author compiled a word list, including the 100 most frequently used words, which would be useful as a core vocabulary for foreign-speaking individuals.

XIV

Cerebral Palsy (Spastic Paralysis)

This disorder is important in speech correction, not because of its frequency, but because of the severity of the associated speech defects. The cerebral-palsied child may have defective articulation of the lalling variety, but he also may show pronounced abnormality in voice and fluency. Since the speech correctionist is almost certain to meet some of these individuals and must help them gain effective communication, we shall discuss their problem briefly.

Diagnosis of cerebral palsy is, of course, the province of the physician, but the speech correctionist often meets cases who have never had the benefit of medical diagnosis. To undertake a program of speech rehabilitation without medical examination is not only hazardous but directly violates one of the ethics of the American Speech Correction Association. Some of these unfortunate children, because of their drooling, unintelligible speech and uncouth co-ordinations, are generally regarded as feeble-minded and treated as such. According to research, only about 30 per cent of cerebral-palsied children are feeble-minded, and the other 70 per cent may range all the way upward to genius level. The ordinary intelligence tests, involving speech or co-ordination, do not adequately measure the spastic's mental ability.

The majority of cerebral-palsy cases are caused by injury to the brain at birth. The trauma may be due to extreme pressures on the skull, causing abnormal moulding and cerebral damage. Strangulation by the cord or other causes of cyanosis or oxygen lack may produce destruction of brain tissue. Certain diseases with high fevers such as pneumonia or jaundice can also cause cerebral palsy. Many soldiers with gun-shot wounds in the head developed spastic or athetoid symptoms as well as aphasia.

Although the term *spastic paralysis* has come to be used as the popular designation for all types of cerebral-palsy cases, there seem to be four major varieties: the athetoids, the ataxic, the myasthenic, and the spastic. Usually more than one of these four symptom complexes are found in the same case. According to Phelps (14) the athetoid and spastic varieties make up more than 80 per cent of all cases.

Spasticity itself has been defined as the paralysis due to simultaneous contraction of antagonistic or reciprocal muscle groups accompanied by a definite degree of hypertension or hypertonicity. It is due to a lesion or injury to the pyramidal nerve tracts. The muscles overcontract; they pull too hard and too suddenly. Slight stimuli will set off major contractions. The spastic who tries to move his little finger may jerk not only the hand, but the arm or trunk as well. The spastic may have a characteristic manner of walking—the typical "scissors gait." The hands may be clenched and curled up along the wrists in their extreme contraction, or the whole arm may be drawn upward and backward behind the neck. The spastic tends to contract his chest muscles, thus enlarging the thoracic cavity during the act of speaking (10) and compelling him to compress the abdomen excessively in order to force out some air. He thus may be said to inhale with the thorax at the same time that he exhales with the abdomen. Great tension is thereby produced, which reflects itself in muscular abnormality all over the body. It also shows up in speech in the form of unnatural pauses and gasping and weak or aphonic voice. Many of the "breaks" in the spastic's speech are due to this form of faulty breathing.

Since it is difficult for the spastic to make gradual and smooth movements, the speech is often explosive and blurting. Often the extreme tension which characterizes spasticity will produce contacts so hard as to resemble or engender stuttering symptoms. The sounds involving complex co-ordinations are of course most usually defective, and the tonguetip sounds which make contact with the upper gum ridge are most difficult. Where there is some facial paralysis, the labial sounds are much more difficult than might be expected. In cases where there are both symptoms of spasticity and athetosis, the articulation is prone to be more distorted than if spasticity alone is present. The diadochokinetic rate of tongue-lifting is a pretty good indication of the number of articulation errors to be found in any one case.

Cerebral-palsy cases are also classified in terms of how much of the body is affected. If one limb is spastic or athetoid, the term *mono-*

plegia is used; if half the body (right or left) is affected, the word *hemi-plegia* designates the condition. *Diplegia* refers to involvement of both upper *or* lower limbs; *quadriplegia* to spasticity or athetosis in all four limbs. According to Heltman and Peacher (13) the greatest number of articulatory errors are shown in quadriplegia involving combined athetosis and spasticity, and the fewest errors are evidenced in spastic diplegia.

By *athetosis* we refer to the cerebral-palsy cases with marked tremors. In these the injury is to the extrapyramidal nerve tracts. Athetosis may be described as a series of involuntary contractions which affect one muscle after another. These contractions may be fast or slow, large or small. The head may swing around from side to side. The arm may shake rhythmically. The jaw and facial muscles may show a rhythmic contortion or repetitive grimaces. In some athetoids, these movements disappear in sleep or under the influence of alcohol. There seem to be two major types of athetoids, the non-tension type and the tension-athetoid, who is often mistaken for a true spastic. The tension athetoids are those who have tried to hold their trembling arms and legs still by using so much tension that it has become habitual. The latter may be distinguished from true spastics by moving their arms against their resistance. The tension-athetoid's arm tends to yield gradually; the spastic's releases with a jerk.

Athetoid speech often tends to become weak in volume. The final sounds of words and final words of phrases are often whispered. A marked tremulo is heard. Monotones are very common, and in the tension athetoids the habitual pitch is near the upper limit of the range. Falsetto voice qualities are not unusual. Another common voice quality is that of hoarseness, especially in the males. Like the true spastics, athetoids make many articulation errors, and the finer the co-ordinations involved in producing the sound, the more it is likely to be distorted. Tonguetip sounds are especially difficult. Breathing disturbances are common.

Intelligent cerebral-palsied individuals meet so many frustrations during their daily lives that they tend to build emotional handicaps as great as their physical disability. Fears develop about walking, talking, eating, going downstairs, carrying a tray, holding a pencil, and a hundred other daily activities. These often become so intense that they create more tensions and hence more spasticity or athetosis. Thus one girl so feared to lift a coffee cup to her lips that she could not do so without spilling and breaking it, yet she was able to etch delicate tracings on a copper dish.

Many of these children are so pampered and protected by their parents that they never have an opportunity to learn the skills required of them for social living. Their parents are constantly afraid that they will hurt themselves, but as one adult tension athetoid said, "My parents never let me try to ride a bicycle and now at last I've done it. Better to break your neck than your spirit." Many spastics come to a fatalistic attitude of passive acceptance of whatever blows, or kindness, or pity society may give them. Others put up a gallant battle and succeed in creating useful and satisfying lives for themselves.

Speech therapy. Very often the cerebral-palsied child is first presented as a case of delayed speech. These children often do not begin to talk until five or six, but many of them could learn earlier with proper parental teaching. In general, the same procedures used on other delayed-speech cases and in teaching the baby to talk are employed. Imitation must be taught. Sounds must come to have meaning and identity. Words must be taught in terms of their sound sequences and associations. Babbling games using puppets are especially effective in getting a young spastic child to talk. It is especially necessary that the child be praised for all vocalization, since he is likely to fall into a whispered or mere lip-moving type of speech. When possible, the first speech teaching should be done when the child is lying on his back in bed, since the thoracic muscles are not so likely to cause chest expansion as the abdomen is contracting during speech. Phonograph records with singing and speech games are very useful in stimulating these children.

In most cases of cerebral palsy the physiotherapist has done a great deal of work with the child before the speech correctionist is called in. Many of the activities used in physiotherapy can be made more interesting to the child if vocalization is used in conjunction with them. Thus one child whose very spastic left leg was being passively rotated in a whirlpool bath was taught to say "round and round; round and round" as the leg moved. He was unable to say these words at first under any other condition, but soon he had attained the ability to say them anywhere, and the distraction seemed to ease some of the spasticity. General relaxation of the whole body forms a large part of the treatment of the spastic and tension athetoid, and even these exercises may be combined with sighing or yawning on the various vowels. Relaxation of the articulatory or the throat muscles seems to be very difficult for these cases, and we often indirectly attain decreases in the tension of these structures by teaching the child to speak while chewing.

Rhythms of all kinds seem to provide especially favorable media for speech practice, if the rhythms are given at a speed which suits the particular case.   In following these rhythms it is not wise to combine speech with muscular movements, because of the nature of the disability.   Visual stimuli, such as the rhythmic swinging of a flashlight beam on a wall, are very effective in producing more fluent speech. Tonal stimuli of all kinds are also used.   Many cerebral-palsied children can utter polysyllabic words in unison with a recurrent melody whether they sing them or not.

In general, the spastic's articulation disorder is of the lalling type. Most of the sounds that require lifting of the tonguetip are defective. When the t, d, and n sounds are adequate, it will be observed that they are dentalized.   The tongue does not make contact with the upper gum ridge but with the back surface of the teeth.   Several of these cases were able to acquire good l and r sounds without any direct teaching.   Instead, we taught them to make the t, d, and n sounds against the upper gum ridge, and the tonguetip-lifting carried over into the l and r sounds immediately.

In most of these cases, the essential task is to free the tongue from its tendency to move only in conjunction with the lower jaw.   The old traditional tongue exercises have little value, but those that involve the emergence of a finer movement from a gross one (see the tongue exercises in Chapter VIII) are very useful.   Just as we have been able to teach spastics to pick up a pin by beginning with trunk, arm, and wrist movements, so we can finally teach him to move his tonguetip without closing his mouth.

Phonetic placement methods in the teaching of new sounds are seldom successful.   The auditory stimulation and modification of known sounds are much better.   Babbling practice has great value in making the new sounds habitual.   We have found that it is wise to make a set of phonograph records for each case, which provides them with material appropriate to their level and with which they can speak in unison when alone.

The voice disorders that characterize the cerebral-palsy cases are best treated through relaxation and breathing exercises.   In the latter, polygraphic recording of breathing is especially valuable. The child does not pay attention to his chest or abdomen as such but rather to the tracings that come from the polygraph pens. While counting or reciting from memory, he is told to try to produce tracings that resemble those on a chart in front of him. The model is of course a tracing of normal breathing during vocalization. Gradually he attains proficiency in this breath control, and the relief from tension and voice improvement is so marked that he carries the new breathing patterns into his other speech.

Many cerebral palsy cases inhale much more deeply for speech than for silent breathing. They often exhale most of this air prior to speech attempt or in the utterance of the first syllable, and then strain from that time onward. This practice may often be overcome by asking them to say a few words and then blow out a candle on the same breath. Having the child speak into a tube with a small nozzle fastened to a stand in front of a flame will also help him to learn proper breathing habits without ever becoming too conscious of the muscular movements involved.

The breaks in fluency which are so characteristic of the spastic are often eliminated by this training in breathing. But it is usually wise to teach these children a type of phrasing which will not place too much demand upon them for sustained utterance. The pauses must be much more frequent than those of the normal individual, and they should be slightly longer. Thus the sentence: "Practice about thirty words involving the *s* blends according to the following models" might be spoken as a single unit by an adult normal speaker, but the adult cerebral-palsy case should pause for a new breath at least three or four times during its course. If he trains himself to do so, his fluency will improve; since no untimely gasps for breath will occur, his voice will be less likely to rise in pitch or to be strained, and the final sounds of the words will be better articulated. Spastics frequently omit the puff of their final plosives and use lax vowels and continuent consonants because they run out of breath so easily.

Fluency may be improved also by giving the child training in making smooth transitions between vowels or consecutive consonants. Thus, he is asked to practice shifting gradually rather than suddenly from a prolonged *u* to a prolonged *e* sound. At first, breaks are likely to occur, but they can be greatly improved through practice, and the child's general speech reflects the improvement. The plosives often cause breaks in rhythm because the contacts are made too hard and consequently set up tremors.   We have had marked success in treating these errors with the same methods we use for the stutterer's hard contacts.   In one case, who always "stuck" on his *p*, *t*, and *k* sounds and showed breaks in his speech, we were able to solve the problem by simply asking him "to keep his mouth in motion" whenever he said a word beginning with these sounds.

It is, of course, necessary to supplement this speech therapy with a great deal of psychotherapy, especially in adult cerebral-palsied individuals.   They must be taught an objective attitude toward their disorder.   They must whittle down the emotional fraction of their total handicap.   They must increase their assets in every way.   As fear and shame diminish, the tensions will decrease.   In many cases, greater improvement in speech and muscular co-ordination will come from psychotherapy than from the speech therapy itself.

References

1. Anonymous, "We, the Spastics," *Journal of Speech Disorders*, 1939, Vol. 4, pages 291–294.
Describes the sensitivities of the spastic, the penalties he receives, and his post-spasm reactions.
2. Carlson, E. R., *Born That Way*, New York, Day, 1941.
Autobiography of a spastic who became an authority on the subject of cerebral palsy.   Written in popular style and contains many useful ideas for therapy and mental hygiene.
3. Carlson, E. R., "Infantile Cerebral Palsy; Its Treatment by Selective Inhibition of Sensory Stimuli," *Annals of Internal Medicine*, 1937, Vol. 11, pages 324–344.
One of the best descriptions of the psychology of the spastic.
4. Carlson, E. R., "The Training of the Birth Injured," *Physiotherapy Review*, May, 1932.
Educational and muscle training described.   The sequence of treatment.
5. Carrell, R. L., "Speech Training in the Child Crippled by Spastic Paralysis," *Journal of Speech Disorders*, 1937, Vol. 2, 155–158.
Speech therapy based upon relaxation.
6. Fagan, H. R., "Methods of Treatment for Spastic Speech," *Journal of Speech Disorders*, 1939, Vol. 4, pages 25–32.
Describes general course of treatment, with several case studies.
7. Fischel, M. K., *"The Spastic Child,"* St. Louis, C. V. Mosby, 1934.
An excellent account of how parents can treat their spastic children.   Many illustrations of good mental hygiene and speech and muscle therapy are given.
8. Fröschels, E., "A Contribution to the Pathology and Therapy of Dysarthria Due to Certain Cerebral Lesions," *Journal of Speech Disorders*, 1943, Vol. 8, pages 301–320.

Summarizes observations of cerebral-palsied speech in terms of breathing, voice, and articulation. Treatment should not be phonetic but should consist of jaw-shaking, pushing, and chewing while speaking.

9. Girard, M., *The Home Treatment of Spastic Paralysis*, Philadelphia, Lippincott, 1937.
A simply written book with many illustrations. Designed for parents of cerebral-palsied children.

10. Hull, H. C., "A Study of the Respiration of Fourteen Spastic Paralysis Cases During Silence and Speech," *Journal of Speech Disorders*, 1940, Vol. 5, pages 275–276.
Breathing is very disordered, and opposition between thorax and abdomen during speech is very common. Abdominal contraction is compensatory.

11. Lord, E. E., *Children Handicapped by Cerebral Palsy*, New York, Commonwealth Fund, 1937.
The intelligence and psychology of the cerebral-palsied child is thoroughly treated. Mental hygiene is stressed.

12. Palmer, M. F., "Similarities of the Effects of Environmental Pressures on Cerebral Palsy and Stuttering," *Journal of Speech Disorders*, 1938, Vol. 8, pages 155–160.
The effect of fear, excitement and confusion on the precipitation of the symptoms of cerebral palsy.

13. Peacher, G. M. and Heltman, H. J., "Misarticulation and Diadokokinesis in the Spastic Paralytic," *Journal of Speech Disorders*, 1943, Vol. 8, pages 137–145.
Recommends diadokokinetic training. Sonants are faster than surds. Many of the articulation errors may be due to the sluggishness of articulation.

14. Phelps, W. M., "The Differential Characteristics of Spasticity and Athetosis in Relation to Therapeutic Measures," *New York State Medical Journal*, 1941, Vol. 41, pages 827–831.
One of the best clarifications of the differences between the two major varieties of cerebral palsy and their treatment.

15. Pusitz, M. E., "Speech Correction in Cerebral Palsies," *Journal of Speech Disorders*, 1939, Vol. 4, pages 205–218.
The nature of cerebral palsy is explained, and treatment based on relaxation is outlined.

16. Robbins, S. D., "Dysarthria and Its Treatment," *Journal of Speech Disorders*, 1940, Vol. 5, pages 113–120.
Advocates same type of treatment for all dysarthrias: slow speech, relaxation, sighing, mouth play, muscle training, voice training, and articulation and rhythm control.

17. Rogers, G. G. and Thomas, L. C., *New Pathways for Children with Cerebral Palsy*, New York, Macmillan, 1935.
Experiences of spastic children in a camp school are described.

18. Rutherford, B., "A Comparative Study of Loudness, Pitch, Rate, Rhythm and Quality of the Speech of Children Handicapped by Cerebral Palsy," *Journal of Speech Disorders*, 1944, Vol. 9, pages 263–273.

Breathing very important in producing abnormal speech.   Differences in speech of spastics and athetoids.   No characteristic "spastic speech."

19. Rutherford, B. R., "Frequency of Articulation Substitution in Children Handicapped by Cerebral Palsy," *Journal of Speech Disorders*, 1939, Vol. 4, pages 285–287.
The nature of the articulatory errors is analyzed.

20. Rutherford, B. R., "The Therapeutic Value of Cerebral Dominance in Treatment of the Speech of Spastics," *Journal of Speech Disorders*, 1937, Vol. 2, pages 111–115.
Case histories of some spastic stutterers who benefited from this type of treatment.

21. Rutherford, B. R., "The Use of Negative Practice in Speech Therapy with Children Handicapped by Cerebral Palsy, Athetoid Type," *Journal of Speech Disorders*, 1940, Vol. 5, pages 259–264.
Many of the undesirable contortions of athetoids are habits and may be removed by therapy.   Many examples are given.

XV

Hearing Problems

The speech correctionist meets many individuals with defective hearing in the course of his daily work. Some of them have not learned to talk; others exhibit disorders of voice or articulation; still others have linguistic or social adjustment problems. In many of the smaller school systems the speech correctionist is called upon to teach elementary lip reading if her training in this specialized field enables her to do so. In any speech-correction activity, there will be frequent necessity for referral of children with hearing problems to the proper agencies. It is with these facts in mind that we provide a chapter on the problems of hearing.

Individuals with hearing losses may be placed in one of three groups; they are either *deaf, deafened,* or *hard of hearing.* The deaf, by one definition, are those who have no hearing for purpose of communication. Although there may be some slight amount of hearing present, it is not enough to allow these people to acquire speech through the normal channels, even with the use of modern hearing aids. A second manner of defining the deaf is in terms of the time their handicap occurred. The deaf person is one who was born with little or no hearing or acquired the loss before the normal developmental period of speech occurred. This last definition has value because it distinguishes the deaf from the deafened—those who had previously possessed normal hearing sufficient for speech acquisition but who have lost it.

Although, in the past, few deaf or deafened children were encountered by the public-school teacher or speech correctionist, since these children were educated in institutions or special rooms, a trend toward association with other children may be clearly discerned. Deaf and deafened individuals are being sent to day schools and to institutions for higher learning for certain classes or for vocational instruction. There is a growing belief that association with normally hearing per-

413

sons can be mutually beneficial.   The segregation of the handicapped is becoming obsolete.

The Deaf

What does the classroom teacher need to know about these people and what can she do to help them?   The deaf individual comes into a regular classroom with his inability to hear, his faulty speech, his abnormal voice quality, his language deficiency, and his inability to understand perfectly through speech or lip reading what is being said. This appears to be a discouraging list of liabilities, and some teachers, after being exposed for a few days to the difficulties of instructing a person of this description, give up and conclude that the person is "just not intelligent enough" or that he must be abnormal in some other ways.   Although much research remains to be done in clarifying the picture of the deaf, we know that they are not, as a group, mentally subnormal.   Results by authorities in the field show that, as compared with the hearing child, a deaf child is about 10 points below in I.Q. on performance and nonlanguage tests.   These results, of course, refer to the average child.   There are many bright and some very bright deaf children.   Fifty per cent of deaf children probably have an I.Q. of 90 and above.   By and large the intelligence is of the concrete rather than the abstract kind.   Because tests of abstract intelligence are based upon language, they are quite useless with the deaf.   The general results with intelligence tests show us, however, that we cannot always base the lack of progress of a deaf person upon mental deficiency.

In terms of educational achievement we find the deaf to be three or four years retarded, and this retardation is probably due to language deficiencies.   Children who become deaf after six years of age do much better than those congenitally disabled.   In motor or mechanical ability, the deaf are equal to or superior to the hearing individual. Although the deaf appear to have a difficult problem of social adjustment, there do not appear to be any distinctive personality problems of this group.   Teachers are no more likely to have a behavior problem with a deaf than with a hearing student.

It is interesting to note that at least one study has reported that "the deaf blame their difficulties more on the attitudes of the hearing than on the sense defect itself."   Many of them feel they are capable, but that there is definite unwillingness on the part of the hearing person to give them a chance. People will not trouble to include the deaf person in what is going on, and more often than not they give only perfunctory answers to questions. It is within this area that the classroom teacher can perform her most valuable service for these people. Give them opportunities to recite. It is often possible to phrase a question that can be answered with just a brief sentence of three or four words. Even giving them a chance to answer a question that requires but a single word will help to offset the feeling that being deaf means being ignored. Another helping device is reading, one of the most valuable compensations for the handicap of deafness. If properly guided, special reading assignments may mean the difference between the student being able to keep up with the class or his falling hopelessly behind. He will often run into difficulty in his reading because of his limited vocabulary and language handicap, but an interested teacher can aid here by serving as a sort of dictionary. The deaf often lose interest in the regular dictionary because of the abstractness of many of the definitions or the necessity to look up several words used in the definition; or they become confused by the multiple definitions. The teacher can provide an extremely worthwhile service by having the pupil write down words he does not understand and then helping him with the definitions.

The deaf admittedly need help with their social adjustment, and such help can best be given in the school under the guidance of some interested teacher. Normal-hearing children always seem to be interested in a project on how we hear, and in lip reading or the handicap of deafness. Each classroom has certain students who will go out of their way to help in a situation of this sort. One teacher we know arranged with all but three members of the class to have them invite the deaf boy in the room to their homes for an evening sometime during the year. The mutual social adjustment resulting from these contacts was not measurable, but by the end of the year, the deaf boy was an accepted and well-liked member, not only of the schoolroom, but of the community as well. The children soon discovered that he could do card tricks, and no party was even planned without including an invitation to him. This is just one example of what can be done if teachers will react to deafness in an objective, constructive manner and will at least make an attempt to help and understand these people who in the past have been so badly handled or injured.

The speech correctionist's role. In addition to helping the deaf solve their problems of social adjustment and providing the classroom teacher with some of the information she needs, there are many things the speech correctionist can do. Haycock (4) says, "It is commonly observed that the speech of deaf-born pupils becomes less intelligible as they advance from the lower to the higher classes in school." One of the major reasons for this situation is that as they progress in school less time is spent in lip reading and speech training and more on vocational activities. Moreover, the demands for speech grow more intense at this time, and frustration and communication failure more frequent. Hence, when the deaf child is ready to leave school or to go into a regular classroom for all or part of his class work, his speech is often unintelligible.

When the speech correctionist endeavors to help a deaf child with his speech, her aim is to concentrate on speech intelligibility rather than normal speech. As in other aspects of speech correction, the training deals with articulation, voice, and rhythm.

With regard to articulation, Hudgins (5) found that errors involving the voiced-unvoiced distinction, compound consonants or blends, and the failure of the releasing consonants were not only the most frequent of the error categories but also the most important relative to speech intelligibility. Vowel substitution and malarticulation of diphthongs were the most important of the vowel error types. Comparison of the relative importance of speech rhythm for intelligibility reveals that this factor is as important as correct consonant articulation, and that rhythm and consonants are more important than correct vowel production. Sentences spoken rhythmically have a four-to-one chance of being understood over those spoken with incorrect rhythm. Hudgins states that "speech rhythm is a specific form of rhythm" and that it does not mean the learning of complicated musical rhythms. It refers rather to work with accent, grouping, and phrasing of syllables.

Voice quality is another problem that adds to the abnormality of most deaf individuals' speech. However, this author feels that more importance should be attached to corrective work on consonants, vowels, and rhythm. The aim should be toward speech that will enable the person to communicate adequately. It is more important that the deaf person be able to answer questions so that they will be understood than it is for him to develop better voice quality.

Many of the same techniques used in regular articulation work can be used with the deaf. The sound should be taught in isolation first, then much time should be spent in strengthening the new sound before it is placed in familiar words. An exception here is that the ear training used with normal people will be replaced by kinesthetic and tactile sensations. Much time must also be spent in saying isolated familiar words containing the new sound before it is used in sentences or conversation. Speech correctionists working with the type of case for which this material is presented will find the most common missing sounds to be the s, j (d$\mathrecal{z}$), r, l, and ng(η).

The deaf student should be helped to distinguish between voiced and unvoiced sounds. The sonant stops b, d, and g are the most frequently misarticulated in this respect, and some lessons should contain exercises aimed at enabling the student to distinguish between these voiced sounds and their voiceless counterparts.

Some time should also be spent in palatal exercises. Examples of these may be found in the chapter on cleft-palate speech. The emphasis with the deaf should be on teaching them to recognize and distinguish between nasal and nonnasal sounds as they are combined with various vowels.

The significance of rhythm to intelligibility has already been mentioned. It is a complicated factor and one that has been somewhat neglected in working with the deaf. It refers to the groupings of movements about a main component that is said to be accented. Fortunately rhythm does not depend on sound alone, and there does not appear to be anything about the rhythms of speech that is impossible for deaf students to learn. Acquiring a more adequate speech rhythm involves syllable rate, word accent, and proper groupings of syllables about the accent in the formation of breath groups. It is important to remember that it is the syllable rather than the individual sounds that carry the rhythm. Some excellent methods for syllabification, accent, and phrasing are found in a manual by Fairbanks. [1]

One last suggestion for work with these people is in regard to vocabulary and language. It has been said before that time spent on speech and language becomes disproportionate to time spent on other subjects as the deaf child progresses in school. Some deaf adults in one clinic had very little conception of verb tenses, plurals of words, correct articles, and so on. One example is of a case wanting to say "How large a fish have you ever caught? " Instead he said, "How big fish did you caught? " A few brief excerpts from an autobiog-

---

[1] Fairbanks, G., *Practical Voice Practice*, New York, Harper, 1944.

raphy show many more confusions: ". . . I begin to learned to talk . . . and then when I was in the nine grade and I went to Davis Tech and I like it . . . I never been spoke in the class room . . . I was silent and my voice was shut and I watched the teacher's lip read everytime." The person who wrote the autobiography was eighteen years old at the time and had been in a good oral school for the deaf since the age of four.

Many of these people speak unintelligibly because they are trying to imitate verbally what they see in print or what they lip-read. They will attempt almost any word, regardless of number of syllables, with the result that hardly anyone can understand them. Our language is so unphonetic that even normal hearing people often have confusions. In some instances, the written symbol may represent as many as four different sounds. It is no wonder the deaf have trouble. In some words the *c* may be pronounced as *s*, in others as *k*; sometimes the sound *j* (d$_3$) is represented by the letter *j*, sometimes by *dge*; then again they may meet words like *soldier* or *vigil*. Attempting to acquire a speaking vocabulary equal to that of the normal person is an almost impossible task for the average deaf person.

Fortunately such an attempt is no longer necessary. It is now possible for the deaf to learn to use a limited vocabulary that will enable them to communicate with no loss of meaning. This system of condensed language is known as Basic English. It consists fundamentally of 850 words with which it is possible to express oneself adequately in the English language. It is the best device we have yet encountered for giving deaf adults communicable speech with a minimum of polysyllabic words. C. K. Ogden and I. A. Richards have written a number of books that can serve as teaching aids. These include a dictionary that defines about 20,000 words in terms that the average deaf adult can readily understand. There is also a series of films available from the March of Time. The advantages of Basic English for the deaf are: (1) it is a means of giving them adequate verbal communication with a minimum of confusing terms and definitions; (2) it contains only a few words of more than three syllables; (3) once the student has mastered the 850 words he can talk anywhere, anytime, and has no further absolute need to increase his vocabulary; (4) language concepts are acquired along with speech; (5) only a few basic rules need to be learned and these take care of the great majority of changes and exceptions.

The speaking vocabulary does not have to be confined to Basic

English. The deaf student can continue to add new words as long as he wishes. However, with a speaking knowledge of just the Basic English, he will be able to express himself without having to struggle with the many polysyllabic synonyms which we have in our language. The teacher may feel that this learning of a separate vocabulary for speech will handicap the deaf individual for lip reading. It is well known, however, that one's vocabulary for reading and comprehension is always greater than the vocabulary for speech. Our experience has not shown us that the deaf differ in this respect, and we have not yet worked with any who became more limited in lip-reading ability because of using Basic English.

In the last analysis, the final criterion for work with the speech of the deaf must be intelligibility. Any device or exercise aimed at making it more possible for other people to understand the deaf person will no doubt be a good one, and well-trained and interested speech correctionists will be able to modify many of the techniques used with the normal hearing articulation and voice cases to fit the needs of the deaf.

The Deafened

The deafened, those who lose their hearing after having acquired speech in the normal way, form our second group of acoustically handicapped people. With the ever-increasing improvements in hearing aids, the number of persons in this class is fortunately decreasing each year. There will always be some, however, whose loss is too severe or of a type that does not respond to electrical amplification. The job for the speech correctionist is to help these people to preserve the elements of speech that provide intelligibility. It is essential that the deafened individual begin corrective work as soon as possible after the loss has occurred. It is far easier to retain speech habits than to establish them after the speech has deteriorated. With proper care and a good attitude on the part of the deafened person, there need be but little effect on the speech of those who become suddenly deaf after the age of ten.

One of the first symptoms to become apparent is that certain defects present before the hearing loss become exaggerated. For example, a slight lisp often becomes worse or nasality will be highly exaggerated. Sometimes the subject loses almost complete control of the velar action, resulting in nasalization of practically all of the vowels and many of the consonants. There are many individual differences in the sequential pattern of deterioration, but usually the more difficult phonemes such as *ch* (tʃ), *j*(dʒ), *zh*(ʒ), and some of the voiced fricatives (z, v) deteriorate first. Many times the voice quality shows the most obvious abnormality. It may become weak or monotonous. In some cases it becomes very harsh with peculiar forms of inflection, for long vowels often become shortened and lose the more delicate qualities.

In working with the deafened, the speech correctionist's major goal should be to help substitute kinesthetic cues for the old auditory ones. Especially is this true for the consonants. It is also possible to associate some secondary kinesthetic cue with volume to enable the deafened person to know when he is speaking loudly enough. We once worked with a case who was able to build up a conditioned response by using his clenched fist as a signal for different levels of loudness. If a situation required rather loud phonation, he simply held his fist tightly closed and he was able to make himself understood over the loudness level of an average office (about forty decibels).

The deafened individual should be encouraged to read profusely and to talk a great deal. He should begin lip-reading instruction immediately and should try to become adept as soon as possible. Fortunately, unless there are psychological barriers of resentment or sensitiveness, skill in lip reading is comparatively easy for the deafened person to acquire. He should have explained to him, however, that no lip reader, no matter how skilled, is able to get everything from all people's lips, and that there will be some few individuals who will be impossible to understand. The deafened probably suffer greater shock because of the suddenness of their handicap and are more likely to resist accepting the fact that they now lack one of the most important senses. If the resulting malattitudes are fostered by poor parental behavior or exaggerated shows of pity and concern by classmates or teachers, the subject is likely to become neurotic and to avoid the contacts and aids that are so necessary for his future happiness and security. Public-school speech correctionists, with their training and experience with other handicapped individuals, certainly have something in the way of advice, guidance, and help with speech skills to offer those who suddenly become deafened. Especially when the deafened person is a veteran should the speech correctionists take pains to offer their services. Most of these war casualties have received excellent training in the military hospitals, but they frequently need some interested and understanding individual to help with the problems which arise daily for those who have suddenly lost their hearing.

The Hard of Hearing

In contrast to the treatment of the deaf or deafened, the public schools have assumed the responsibility for the education of the hard of hearing for many years. Yet most of the audiometric surveys are disclosing that there are many hard-of-hearing children whose disabilities are unsuspected and who have always competed at a disadvantage. The speech correctionist often discovers these children in the course of her work, since they frequently manifest articulatory defects.

Although group hearing tests and audiometric surveys are fortunately becoming more popular, they have reached only a small percentage of the school population. It is hoped that more and more school systems will be able to take advantage of these modern devices for ascertaining auditory acuity. Until routine hearing checks become a regular feature of all school programs, there are other characteristic symptoms of hearing loss that the classroom teacher is in a position to observe and that will in many cases enable her to identify hearing loss. These characteristic marks of hearing loss are: (1) voice becoming very loud or very soft; (2) verbal direction ignored consistently; (3) apparent and repeated confusions in understanding teacher and other pupils; (4) frequent requests for repetition of questions; (5) close observation of the face of teacher; (6) consistently turning the head to one side when paying attention to speaker. There are other symptoms which may possibly indicate hearing loss. If a child shows the following behavior, check hearing: spells of dizziness; head noises; inattentiveness or misunderstanding of instructions; good performance on tests of book material and poor performance on lecture material; frequent colds with ear discharge; sudden changes in attitudes such as aggressive, shouting behavior or pronounced withdrawal, which occur after severe illness; excessive fatigue during class recitation.

The speech correctionist in her daily contacts with other teachers can often suggest procedures which will make the lot of the hard-of-hearing child much easier. She can suggest that the child be seated to his best advantage and permitted to turn around to hear the other children or to change his position to achieve better lighting conditions for lip reading. She can help to prevent the tendency toward segregation and social maladjustment. She can tell the classroom teacher to avoid the exaggerated mouth movements or whispered stimulation they so often inflict on the hard-of-hearing child in their efforts to help him understand. She can tell the classroom teacher that when the child asks for a repetition of what was said, the sentence should be stated in another way. Simple repetitions of the same material in a loud impatient voice often confuse the child or provoke resentment. She can point out how often the teacher talks to these children with head down or averted, or with a book or hands in front of the face. Finally, she can arrange to have the child examined by an otologist or given lip reading by a teacher trained in such methods. Competent physicians can be located through the Volta Bureau, Washington, D.C., or through the local medical association. There are usually societies for the hard of hearing within reach which may be contacted for other help.

In schools or communities where audiometers are available, it is of course advisable to have audiograms made of all children suspected of hearing loss. The otologist is pre-eminently qualified to do this. Many salesmen of hearing aids will make audiograms, but cases in which hearing losses are found should be referred to the otologist. Many people trained to use an audiometer do not have the knowledge, equipment, or legal right to make a thorough diagnosis of ear trouble.

The audiogram. The audiogram is a chart showing how loud certain tones have to be before the subject can hear them. The speech correctionist should know how to interpret them. The audiometer is an instrument which is able to stimulate the ear with tones of various strength. Usually eight different tones are used to cover the range of frequencies required by speech hearing. They range from 64 double vibrations per second (two octaves below the normal pitch of the average woman's voice) to 8,192 double vibrations per second. Each successive tone used for stimulation is double the frequency of its predecessor. The tone is increased in intensity until the person can hear it. This increase in loudness is measured in units called *decibels*. The speech correctionist is not interested in averages of hearing loss as much as he is in the frequencies at which the person has the greatest hearing loss. This is due to the fact that speech sounds vary in frequency and loudness. The following sounds have very important high-frequency (3200–8000 d.v.) characteristics: *sh*(ʃ), *ch*(tʃ), *s, z, v, f,* and the two *th* sounds (θ) ($\eth$).   A hearing loss in this range, if it were great enough, would tend to create difficulty in the perception or production of these sounds.   A severe hearing loss in the middle frequencies (400–3200 d.v.) would affect the *r, l, w, y* (j), *m, n,* and *ng* (η) sounds.   Low-frequency hearing loss is rather rare but is likely to produce confusions between cognate sounds such as the *s-z, f-v, k-g,* and other pairs.

We have indicated that the degree of hearing loss is important. The curve drawn across the audiogram, known as the hearing curve, indicates the loss for the varying frequencies.   In a normal-hearing person, it will stay within ten or fifteen decibels of the zero mark (2). An audiogram that shows a hearing loss of twenty decibels for more than three tones is usually indicatory of a slight handicap.   Children of more than ten years who test this way will not be likely to suffer in the classroom or need special education.   They do need periodic checks to watch for further loss.

If the audiogram shows a hearing loss of more than twenty-five decibels for more than three tones, the subject is likely to have a definite handicap.   Children with such hearing losses will understand strong, definite speech that is loud enough.   They will also give a fair response if spoken to in a normal tone, but they will have to guess from context since they will not hear all sounds equally well.   They will do poorly if the teacher has turned around or if they are placed in the back of the room.

Children whose tonal acuity falls below forty decibels for more than two tones are severely handicapped as a general rule.   They are likely to have defective speech as well as difficulty in comprehending speech.   They require much help over an extended period if they are to profit from speech correction.

Fortunately, the modern development of hearing aids has made the problem of speech correction for the hard of hearing much easier. Some of these children have been known to speak a given word correctly as soon as the hearing aid was used.   It is usually necessary to teach the speech sounds while the child uses his aid, but to strengthen them and habituate them with the hearing aid removed.   The reason for this is that kinesthetic and tactual cues are especially useful for these individuals.   The moto-kinesthetic method (see Chapter VIII) has been very successful with hard-of-hearing children, especially when supplemented by ear training via hearing aid.   The general procedures used with the hard-of-hearing child in correcting his speech defect are pretty much the same as those used for children with good hearing. The important difference is that the speech correctionist must know enough about hearing problems to adapt her techniques to fit the difference. With a good hearing aid, and by using as many other nonhearing devices as possible (mirrors, charts, demonstration of mouth-and-tongue positions, tactual cues to indicate movements, kinesthetic cues such as hand clenching or eyebrow raising with which to associate intensity or pitch changes), new sounds can be taught and old ones preserved. In severe hearing losses acquired later than the preschool years, the preservation of good speech is almost as important as the teaching of lip reading. Vowels tend to become lax and consonants slurred. Often the speech correctionist can fix these slipping sounds by strongly associating them with kinesthesia or tactual cues. Drills in pairs of words arranged so as to accentuate contrasts between words most frequently confused can aid in preventing speech deterioration.

References

1. Allshouse, V., "Speech Correction in Army Rehabilitation Program," *Journal of Speech Disorders*, 1945, Vol. 10, pages 106–108.
Describes the adjustment problems of the deafened, speech-correction methods, and procedures for preventing speech deterioration.

2. Berry, M. F. and Eisenson, J., *The Defective in Speech*, New York, F. S. Crofts, 1942, pages 321–339.
Discusses speech and hearing, types of hearing loss and speech involvements, intelligence, educational achievement and personality development, and treatment.

3. Fest, T. B., "Hearing Aids: Recent Developments," *Journal of Speech Disorders*, 1944, Vol. 9, pages 135–146.
Discusses types of hearing aids, service and costs, dependability, and problems experienced in fitting and using them.

4. Haycock, G. S., *The Teaching of Speech*, London, Hill and Ainsworth, 1937, page 302.

5. Hudgins, C. V. and Numbers, F. C., "An Investigation of the Intelligibility of the Speech of the Deaf," *Genetic Psychology Monographs*, 1942, Vol. 25, pages 289–392.

6. Hughson, W., Ciocco, A., Witting, E. G., and Lawrence, P. S., "An Analysis of Speech Characteristics in Deafened Children with Observations on Training Methods," *Child Development*, 1942, Vol. 22, pages 387–412.
Children trained while using hearing aids showed much greater speech improvement than hard-of-hearing children trained through other methods.

7. Irwin, R. B., "Teaching a Deaf Child to Talk," *Journal of Speech Disorders*, 1944, Vol. 9, pages 131–134.

A brief discussion of methods, including emotional release, visual aids, and the use of kinesthetic and tactual devices.

8. Kerriage, P. M. T., "The Effect of Hearing on Speech," *Journal of Physiology*, 1936, Vol. 87.
Describes speech defects due to deafness or hearing loss.

9. Larr, A., "A County Speech and Hearing Conservation Program," *Journal of Speech Disorders*, 1944, Vol. 9, pages 147–151.
Describes the speech and hearing survey, teacher and community education.

10. Niemoeller, A. F., *Complete Guide for the Deafened*, New York, Harvest House, 1940.
General discussion of hearing problems, anatomy and physiology of the ear, types of deafness, causes of impaired hearing, hearing tests, and re-education policies.

11. Numbers, C. H., "The Training of Residual Hearing," *Journal of Exceptional Children*, 1940, Vol. 6, pages 167–171.
Describes the intelligent use of hearing aids.

12. Osborn, C. D., "Medical Follow-up of Hearing Tests," *Journal of Speech Disorders*, 1945, Vol. 10, pages 261–273.
Data to show that hearing tests should be followed by medical treatment.

13. Peterson, G. E., "The Pure Tone Screen Test of Hearing," *Journal of Speech Disorders*, 1944, Vol. 9, pages 114–121.
Describes procedures in testing public-school children.

14. Pintner, R., "An Adjustment Test with Normal and Hard of Hearing Children," *Journal of Genetic Psychology*, 1940, Vol. 56, pages 367–381.
No marked differences in personality between the two groups.

15. Pintner, R., Eisenson, J., and Stanton, M., *The Psychology of the Physically Handicapped*, New York, F. S. Crofts, 1941.
Probably the best survey of the field of problems of the hard of hearing that can be found in condensed form.

16. Sutherland, D. A. and Miller, M., "Rehabilitating the Hard of Hearing Child," *The Child*, 1944, Vol. 4, pages 51–66.
A good description of a well-planned campaign using every resource available to improve the lot of a group of hard-of-hearing children.

XVI

The Speech Correctionist and General Procedures in Treatment

This chapter is designed to deal with the nature of speech-correction work and the demands it makes upon those who do it, be they parents, classroom teachers, speech-correction teachers, or members of a speech-clinic staff. Speech correction is re-education, not merely removal of the defect.

Qualifications of the professional speech correctionist. Not only is personality built about differences in speech, but also profound emotional reaction patterns are often associated with these differences. Then, too, re-education frequently demands much of a child in the way of courage, persistence, and applied intelligence. All of these characteristics of the speech-correction situation make certain demands upon the speech correctionist in terms of professional attitudes, academic preparation, personal qualifications, and skill in handling other people.

Speech correction, if it has not as yet attained a professional status, is so steadily achieving one that it behooves all workers in the field to conduct themselves according to a strict code of ethics, to join the American Speech Correction Association, and to keep abreast of the research which is contributing greatly to our knowledge of causes and techniques. The speech correctionist must recognize the delimitation of his field from that of the physician, the psychiatrist, and the orthodontist. He must be prepared to prove his worthiness of their respect and to seek their services whenever necessary.

Principles of professional conduct. Certain principles of professional conduct should be stated. They are: (1) Treat each case as a unique individual, seeking every possible opportunity to increase your knowledge and understanding of him as a person. (2) Refuse to respond emotionally to the speech defective's behavior. Treatment

426

must always be intelligent and purposive.   (3) Respect and guard carefully all confidential information.   The patient must have perfect confidence in the speech correctionist's intellectual honesty.   (4) Draw the line against undue familiarity.   Avoid physical contact with the patient.   Do not confide in him.   Do not show surprise, disapproval, mirth, or annoyance unless you use the expressions for a definite clinical purpose.   Refuse to engage in argument or controversy. Conduct yourself so as to increase his respect.   (5) Do not practice under false pretenses.   Posing always contributes to one's insecurity, and in the intimate relationship which exists in speech correction, poses will soon be detected.   (6) Plan your conferences and remedial work.   No patient must be permitted to know discouragement because of the teacher's refusal to do her part.   If the teacher accepts a case, she accepts the responsibility for doing her utmost.   If she contents herself with anything less than her best, she had better do something else. Human handicaps are not to be played with.   (7) Maintain a consistent program of self-improvement.   (8) Give no promises or guarantees of probable results to the patient or to anyone else.   (9) Accept only justifiable remuneration and avoid any taint of exploitation. (10) Treat other workers in the field with respect.

Preparation of speech correctionist. The academic preparation needed by the professional speech-correction teacher is wide and varied.   Of the sciences, biology, physiology, anatomy, the physics of sound, biochemistry, general, educational, and abnormal psychology, mental testing, and sociology are the most useful. Foreign languages are valuable, since many foreign-speaking children are referred to the speech-correction teacher.   Public-speaking courses provide training for the many talks which the special teachers are called upon to make. Courses in elementary education and the teaching of reading contribute greatly to the solution of the problem of teacher co-operation. Mental- and physical-hygiene courses are of obvious value.   Courses in history, literature, and the arts provide a broad background which is always useful in easing human contacts and providing discussion topics.   Physical education provides a background for the necessary special orthopedic knowledge required in treating the spastic child and in improving general health.   Courses in statistics aid in the evaluation and performance of research.   In addition to these general courses, the speech-correction teacher should have thorough training in phonetics, basic voice and speech science, and, finally, in courses in speech correction which cover a thorough survey of the field, diagnosis, examination techniques, and remedial methods, and which provide a great deal of supervised practice in all of these divisions.

To some people speech-correction work is very distasteful, and there seem to be certain personal qualifications which make all the difference between success and failure. In general, the nervous, impatient, high-strung individual does not make a good speech correctionist. Neither does the person who falls into routine, stereotyped methods and remains there contentedly. Successful teachers of speech correction possess the majority of the following traits to a high degree: a sense of humor, patience, curiosity, social poise, ingenuity in inventing and adapting techniques, professional enthusiasm, a sensitive and discriminating hearing, interest in the personalities of others, industriousness, objective attitude toward their own insecurities, calmness, ability to recognize subterfuge and mental mechanisms, and self-respect. Few people, of course, are born so virtuous as the above list of traits might imply, but speech correction puts such a premium upon such characteristics that those who do not possess them acquire them as soon as possible. All speech-correction teachers should make a systematic attempt to improve themselves in all of these directions.

Implied in many of the above traits is a skill which is so important that it merits special discussion—the ability to influence, motivate, understand, and control other people. All of us possess some of this ability, but there are few who could not profit from a course of self-training specifically designed to increase it. Such a course would include training in: (1) seeing the other person's point of view; (2) personal adjustment with recognition of one's own mental mechanisms and inadequate reaction patterns; (3) self-discipline; (4) carrying out a long-range program of self-improvement; (5) the study and prediction of human behavior; and (6) controlled experimentation in the field of human relations.

While it is manifestly impossible to give in detail the content of such a course of training without fitting it to the needs of some specific individual, some illustrative assignments may be helpful to a student preparing himself in speech correction.

The beginner in the field of speech correction should make an effort to experience the speech defective's handicap. He should assume a severe stutter, or a lisp, or cleft palate speech, and enter a few common speech situations. He should stop people on the street and inquire as to the location of certain buildings, using pronounced symptoms of the various speech disorders and noting his own reactions and those of the people to whom he speaks.   He should make an attempt to adopt the objective attitude, remaining calm and intelligent in the face of bad audience reactions.   He should attempt to make the audience feel more at ease by commenting on his handicap and explaining that he is attempting to get rid of it.

Besides the above methods, he can understand the speech defectives' points of view by reading their autobiographies, by associating with them socially, and by writing descriptions (from the speech defectives' points of view) of situations which are perfectly normal to him.   The student preparing himself to do speech correction can train himself in the recognition of his own inadequate reactions to insecurity by holding truth-sessions with his fellow students, in which each member presents the picture of his own personality assets and liabilities, then leaves the room while the other members discuss him, returning to be presented with the composite picture as provided by the discussion.   He then verbally accepts or rejects the criticisms and the group co-operates in outlining a campaign of improvement.   It is also well to have the student give a verbal and thorough autobiography before some similar congenial group.   A month's diary of inadequate behavior reactions or situations in which the student was insecure is effective.   Each student should finally present a paper or lecture on the various mental mechanisms, with illustrations of each from his own or his associates' behavior.

Speech correction in the public schools.   Speech-correction work is carried out in most schools by the special speech-correction teacher, the elementary classroom teacher, the high-school teacher of speech or English, or an unusually interested principal or superintendent. Without training, many of the latter individuals make woeful mistakes and soon become discouraged.   With some training or supervision, however, they do much to eliminate and prevent speech handicaps.   The same things may be said about parental speech correction.

The most efficient work is done by the special speech-correction teacher.   Her training and freedom from other activities permit this efficiency.   When she first enters a school system which has not previously had speech-correction service, she should be given several months to survey the various schools and to examine the children who are in need of the help she can give.

Many school systems prefer to have the classroom teachers select the cases with whom the speech-correction teacher is to work.   This method is usually not advisable because many classroom teachers are unable to detect the child who skillfully hides his stuttering or pretends to be ignorant rather than attempt to recite. Again, many teachers resent any interruption to their daily schedule, and they either believe the fallacy that all children outgrow their disorder or they minimize its importance. The speech-correction teacher can usually make her survey of a class in the space of an hour and select the cases who should work with her. The classroom teacher should be notified in advance by the principal that the survey is to be carried out so that misunderstanding will not wreck all chance for co-operation. In making this survey, the speech-correction teacher should examine each child individually. A standard, brief articulation test, which includes reading, naming, and propositional speech, should be used. If the school system is so large that this survey would be an all-year task, the teacher should concentrate on three or four schools and confine her activities to them.

After this preliminary survey has been completed, the speech-correction teacher should re-examine the cases found. This second examination should be much more detailed and complete and should follow the type of examination sketched in former chapters. Home calls should be made or the parents should be invited to come to the speech-correction office so that additional information concerning the causes, home conditions, and co-operation may be procured.

It is unwise for the special speech-correction teacher to carry a load of more than one hundred cases. Even this number will necessitate seeing approximately ten cases each hour, since each child should be seen at least twice a week for a speech-correction period of approximately fifteen minutes. Increasing this load merely discourages the teacher, causes her work to become perfunctory, and insures almost certain failure in a large percentage of her cases.

Selection of cases. It is often difficult to keep the case load within the limit that has been recommended, but every effort should be made to do so. This involves selection. Interviews with many speech-correction teachers bring out the principles they follow in order to make this selection most effective. They declare that when selection must be carried out, the first to go are those children with very minor defects—those, for example, who use the vulgar *t* and *d* substitutions for the *th* sounds. Where only one or two sounds are defective and the child can make them correctly when he watches himself, the speech correctionist usually gives some information concerning treatment to the classroom teacher and to the child's parents and lets the child go.

If there still remain many more than the hundred with whom she must work, the speech correctionist eliminates those who have pronounced organic defects, such as adenoids in a case of denasal speech or a very malformed jaw in a child who lisps. These disorders can be corrected by surgical or by orthodontic treatment, and although much can be done by the speech correctionist to teach compensatory movements, the work demands much more time and care than she can afford. Exceptions to this principle, of course, will always exist. Generally speaking, the teacher should select cases who are most likely to profit from her help.

The speech correctionist likewise tries to eliminate those children who have such low intelligence as to make the short periods of treatment relatively useless. School administrators often oppose this, pointing out that the feeble-minded child needs the tool of speech even more than does the normal child; but even though this attitude be accepted, it seems inadvisable to do speech correction with such children unless it can be done thoroughly enough to ensure success. Much more time is needed for them, and the problem should really be handled by the opportunity-room teacher who has had training in speech correction.

If many children in excess of the proper case load still remain, the speech correctionist should confine her efforts to the grades above the kindergarten, since many of the children in the preschool years have not matured sufficiently to acquire certain of the speech sounds. Speech-improvement work should be carried out at these lower levels, but it can be done by the kindergarten teacher.

If still more selection is necessary, the teacher should choose from this group those who show great need and at the same time exhibit good possibilities of improvement. Pronounced emotional conflicts may be referred to the school psychologist or psychiatrist. In any event, the speech correctionist should not wreck her chances of success by taking an immense load of cases. Proper selection according to logical principles will solve this problem.

Organization of speech correction in the public schools. Having selected her cases, the speech-correction teacher's next task is to arrange her appointments. Since there are several sources of difficulty inherent in getting a schedule which interferes as little as possible with the classroom teacher's work, the following suggestions are offered.

Classify the cases according to school, grade, type of defect, and probable teaching difficulty. Get the daily schedules of each classroom teacher. Confer with the classroom teacher to determine which periods she would prefer to have her speech-defective children miss. Be sure to avoid the nap, recess, milk-feeding, and writing periods. Do not schedule the period so that the child misses the activity in which he is most deficient. Try to schedule the youngest children for the early morning hours. When several children must come from the same room, try to arrange the scheduling so that they will miss consecutive periods and the disturbance will be minimized.

Although certain children must be taught individually, necessity will demand that approximately ten children must be met each teaching hour if each child is to be seen twice a week. Groups should seldom exceed five children, and in most school systems they average about three. The period should seldom be less than fifteen minutes in duration. The size of the group should vary according to the defects included, and in general it is wise not to use stutterers and articulatory cases in the same group. A larger number of articulatory cases can be handled in a single group than can those of any other type of defect. The younger the children, the larger the group may be. Approximately one fourth of all cases necessitate individual conferences.

Through the principal's office, the classroom teacher can be made to accept the responsibility for sending the child to the speech correctionist at the proper time. Often she writes the child's name and the appointment hour in one corner of the blackboard and insists that the child assume the duty of remembering. When the speech-correction teacher cannot keep her appointments, she usually notifies the principal's office so that the children will not wander aimlessly about the building.

Some school systems feel that the speech-correction work should be carried out in a central place, usually the special building which houses the spastic, deaf, and mentally handicapped children. The school busses bring the children to the speech-correction rooms, but this involves much waiting and waste of time. Another more important objection to such centralization is that, since the speech defective needs little special apparatus for retraining, the work can be done in the child's own school building, thus preventing him from feeling any more peculiar than necessary. Speech correction thereby becomes a subject similar to remedial reading or writing and carries few social penalties.   The first aid, nurse's room, library annex, principal's office, or any unused corner which is relatively quiet and free from interruption commonly serves as an adequate place.   The speech-correction teacher frequently carries a bag or two of toys, books, and other teaching materials.   A special room for speech correction would be preferable, of course, but the service does not need to wait for such space.

Experienced speech-correction teachers often find that one-half day each week should be set aside for office work, home calls, and interviews with classroom teachers.   A position of this sort in the public schools entails a great deal of such extra work and is usually considered by any administrator to justify this free period.   A series of mimeographed bulletins concerning the nature, causes, and treatment of the various speech defects should be sent out to the parents and teachers. Many speech-correction teachers find that an excellent way of getting classroom-teacher co-operation is to prepare a general outline of the speech-correction program for each child.   Copies of this are sent to the parent, principal, and the classroom teacher, and as each major achievement has been attained or a subgoal reached, the classroom teacher is notified.   This often results in an independent checking of the child's success in the classroom with a subsequent co-operation that otherwise might not have been forthcoming.

Whenever a child fails to keep an appointment due to illness or some other reason, the speech correctionist may use the opportunity to visit the classroom or to make some sort of written contact with the parent, thus showing her interest in the child.   The speech-correction teacher should keep abreast of the major projects going on in the classroom and use the latter to motivate or vary the corrective exercises and at the same time to help the child contribute to the regular classroom work.   After the proper rapport has been gained with the classroom teacher, the speech correctionist may occasionally offer to teach some subject such as reading or arithmetic, demonstrating how speech-correction work can be worked into the regular procedure without difficulty.   Although many antagonistic and un-co-operative attitudes on the part of classroom teachers are often experienced when speech correction is first begun, they soon disappear if the speech-correction teacher shows an interest in the child and a profound respect for her teaching associates.   If she appreciates the power the classroom teacher has to insure or negate her success, she will leave nothing undone in perfecting this relationship.   As soon as the work is well initiated, the speech correctionist should invite the principal or classroom teacher to visit one of the speech-correction periods.   The speech defective needs to practice his new skills under somewhat emotional conditions in order to insure complete success, and so no concern need be felt for his part.   Parents may also be encouraged to make these visits, which produce a respect and co-operation that can be achieved in no other way.   Needless to say, they also improve the speech-correction work.

Teachers of speech correction should also consider it a part of their duty to educate the general public as well as the school administration concerning their field.   They will be called upon frequently to address parent-teacher meetings, and they should use these opportunities to dispel some of the vast ignorance concerning the causes and treatment of the various speech disorders.

Speech correction and the classroom teacher.   Speech-correction teachers often inquire as to the amount of co-operation they can expect from the classroom teacher or parent.   The answer is, of course, that they can *expect* real co-operation from very few teachers or parents.   Some of the younger teachers, still vibrant with enthusiasm, and some of the older teachers, who have lost their early zest and wish to recapture it, will appreciate a new opportunity to help their students.   And there are the real teachers who constantly seek to improve themselves in the knowledge and skills necessary to their profession. Nevertheless, many classroom teachers do not welcome any new opportunity to help their students.   As one of them said, "We've got too much opportunity now.   We have almost more than we can stand. We have too many students and too little time.   Indeed, we are fortunate when we can do what we should to take care of our children as a group."   Any unbiased observer will recognize that this objection has evidence to support it.   However, if the speech-correction teacher is resourceful and tactful, she can usually convince the large majority of classroom teachers that the child with a speech defect can be helped in his regular subjects without adding appreciably to the teacher's burden.

The speech-correction teacher should be as definite as possible in her suggestions.   Thus, one speech-correction teacher who had been offered co-operation by the classroom teacher made the following suggestions:

In your store project, perhaps you can arrange to have Jimmy be the storekeeper.   I have taught him how to say the words "six," "seven," and "cents" without lisping, but he often forgets.   Perhaps if you will tell him that he must say those three words correctly or lose his turn behind the counter, it will help.

When you have your "telling" period, will you ask Sarah to tell about how we played radio this morning?   She is supposed to say "wadio" the first time and then wink at you.   After that she should use it correctly.

I understand you are teaching some phonics now.   Perhaps Bob can be given a chance to show a little superiority for a change by telling the other children about the *f* and *v* sounds.   I will prepare him for this recitation, if you are interested.

Would you mind letting Jimmy and Mary tell their story together tomorrow morning?   They have been practicing.   I suppose it's really a little play.   Concerns the making of soup.   It can probably fit into the story period without causing any bother.

John can name and find on the map and tell several things about several strange places that begin with the *k* sound.   Some day in Geography when you find a convenient moment, he can interest the class for several minutes.   Although this is the sound he fears most, I think he can handle the words without losing his control.

It is obvious from these examples that remedial speech work can really contribute to the interest of classroom activities and that the range of application is very wide.   Classwork is primarily useful in making the new speech habits permanent, in recognizing and canceling errors, and in preventing maladjustment.   When no speech-correction teacher is available and the classroom teacher must do all the remedial work, she should devote short five- or ten-minute periods during the recess or after school hours to the intensive and individual therapy needed in the beginning stages of treatment.   After the child has been taught his new sound, or a method for handling his stuttering, or a new way of phonating, the classroom may be used as a reinforcing agent.

Speech correction in the home.   Many of the same observations hold for parental co-operation.   The parents can seldom be used in the beginning steps of treatment.   They tend to be too hasty, even when they know what to do.   The history of past failure in speech teaching tends to handicap them, and too many attitudes inappropriate to the remedial situation are aroused by the parent-child relationship.   There are, of course, many parents to whom the above strictures do not apply, and some of them have done excellent remedial speech work, but unfortunately they are in the minority.

Again, when it is necessary that the parent do all the remedial work, it is wise to insist that the preliminary work be done in a special room, such as a bedroom or guest room. This will tend to identify the speech work as demanding different attitudes from those which ordinarily exist between parent and child. Speech periods should be short, well planned, and motivated. Having two ten-minute speech periods each day, always occurring at the same hours, will facilitate the work. If the parent possesses personality traits which tend to interfere with effective teaching, she should do her utmost to discard them the moment she enters the speech room. If she shows a new personality to the child, the latter will usually adjust to it and much advantage will be gained.

In the majority of cases, it is advisable to have some person other than the parent do the remedial work. If no speech correctionist is available for this purpose, a careful and detailed program of treatment should be outlined by some specialist in the field, and a good teacher persuaded or hired to do the work under his supervision. Frequent reports are necessary if this admittedly makeshift arrangement is the only one possible.

When a teacher trained in speech correction is engaged in the remedial activities, the parents must not delegate all the responsibility to her. Much home co-operation is needed if the treatment is to be efficient. This co-operation can be gained in several ways. Conferences between parents and the speech-correction teacher can clarify the lengthy program usually necessary. Special techniques can be explained, the subgoals outlined, and the amount of expected progress can be estimated. Such conferences also permit the teacher to supervise the homework. Beside these conferences, the teacher should send daily assignments home to the parent. These should be very short, easily understood, and easily carried out. Some actual examples of these assignments follow:

Robert has learned how to do the talking-and-writing technique of which I spoke at our last conference. However, he occasionally says a "th" when writing the "s" symbol. Would you mind helping him as he writes a page of this talking and writing? I'd like to have you encircle every "s" that he mispronounces, and stimulate him with five good clear "s" sounds, before he continues.

Will you please tie this picture of a child making the "f" sound to the door between the kitchen and the dining room, and remind Mary to make the sound every time she goes through?

Will you call one of the chairs in the house the "Make-no-face Chair" and see to it that, whenever your son sits in it and stutters with that facial contortion I pointed out to you in our last conference, he gets up immediately and walks around it, saying "Make no face, make no face, make no face"? If he stutters without the facial contortion, he should be praised even more than if he has no blocks at all, for you remember that at this stage of the treatment we are most interested in getting rid of that one bad symptom. Free speech can come later. And please see to it that he does some speaking from this chair at least three times tomorrow. I would appreciate a note from you describing what happens.

While most intelligent parents welcome these assignments and provide the best of co-operation, it is obvious that other parents could not and would not carry them out. In the latter instance, the problem must be solved at school, using such resources as are available.

Group versus individual techniques. Although, from a consideration of the amount of attention and time to be given, it is better to work with the child individually, nevertheless there are certain advantages to group work which should not be overlooked. The latter provides more natural speech situations; some children are strongly motivated by competition; and speech games are more attractive when carried on in a group.

Since the children within any one group usually possess similar defects, seldom number more than three or four, and fall within a narrow age range, it is possible to employ any of the techniques used in speech correction successfully. When the teacher must give individual attention to any member of the group, she calls the child to her side, and the other members act as an audience, as critics, or carry on some type of seat work.

Some of the more common types of group activities are: listening to the teacher's stories and acting the parts she describes; relaxing; manipulating the speech organs or reciting in unison; echo games; word pointing; identifying categories; imitation activities; guessing games; completion exercises; rhyming; picture naming or describing; answering simple riddles; selecting appropriate sounds or word from a group of words; and matching activities. Any competent teacher will be able to invent many others. Whenever possible, these activities should be linked to the temporary interests and to the projects being carried out in the classroom of the child. Thus, each of the various holidays may be made the theme of the speech-correction project, and the activity characteristic of each season can be modified to provide a motivated vehicle for speech work.

Some children do not respond to group work and progress much more rapidly when treated individually. With these children, the teacher should seek to effect a strong transference, getting the child to desire her approval more than anything else. Self-competition which will foster very rapid progress can be created on this basis. The teacher should study the child as thoroughly as possible and should adapt her techniques to his interests. When working with older children or adult speech defectives, the speech-assignment method is commonly employed. Since the speech correctionist can seldom spare more than half an hour each day for individual work with any one case, the conference is usually devoted to: (1) the student's report of his experience in carrying out the previous day's assignments; (2) a discussion and analysis of any difficulty that occurred, with suggestions for alternative methods or means of canceling the failures; (3) some supervised retraining; and (4) the formulation and explanation of the next day's assignments.

The criteria of a good assignment follow: (1) it is directed specifically toward the attainment of a goal which the speech defective understands; (2) it can be performed economically as regards time and effort; (3) it demands no more than the student can be expected to do; (4) it is not vague or general but direct, detailed, and clear; (5) it should permit some objective report. These individual assignments may employ some older friend, parent, or teacher to supervise or assist the child in fulfilling them. Usually the more difficult cases demand this individual type of treatment, but most teachers find it advisable to alternate some group activity with it.

Differences in the treatment of children and adults. In a preceding chapter the speech defective was discussed from the point of view of his developing personality. In later chapters concerning the methods for treating each of the major types of speech defects, modifications of those methods as they pertain to children or adults were described. Nevertheless, the student must be reminded that this text is primarily designed to sketch the principles and basic methods of speech correction and not their specific application. It is doubtful whether any text could possibly hope to describe the great variation of techniques needed in actual remedial work. Each individual must be treated according to his own peculiar characteristics. The submissive or aggressive, the younger or older, the dull or the bright child—each demands his own modifications. With these reservations in mind, it seems advisable to give some general principles in applying the methods of speech correction to children in the age range from four to ten years.

The teacher must provide the motivation in the majority of such cases.   Deferred rewards are seldom effective.   Concrete symbols of achievement must be used whenever possible, and the teacher must not be too critical.   Often the children must be praised for an attempt even though the result is far from satisfactory, for the teacher's praise can become a very important reward and motivation.   The teacher should praise success and ignore failure, unless the latter is relatively rare.   Whenever too much failure is occurring, vary the activity so that success occurs.   Use social approval such as can be gained from other children in the group, from the classmates or regular teacher, or from the parents.

Children can seldom be expected to react to subgoals unless the latter are made ends in themselves.   Abstractions of any kind should be avoided.   The child needs more help and direction and less logic. Many times any reason seems to be acceptable to him, providing it is simple enough to be understood.   Children often seem unable to retain or recall the things taught them from one speech period to another.   If the original impression was sufficiently vivid, this failure does not occur.   If the teacher prepares the child for the recall by recounting the activities of the preceding period or by giving a short review of them, the child is usually successful.

One very successful public-school teacher of speech correction writes as follows:

I always try to create the attitude that when the child comes to speech class, he comes to work, even though most of our activities approximate play.   We always speak of doing *speech work*.   Some of my fellow teachers do everything through games, but I believe I get better results my way.

The way I feel or act makes all the difference with little children.   If I'm interested, happy, and enthusiastic, I can get them to do anything. Their enthusiasm can easily be worked up.   I always try to watch their mood when they first come in, and either fit my activity to that, or else try to modify it.   I never make any detailed lesson plans ahead of time. They never work, and some of my best methods have been invented on the spur of the moment.   It's fatal to become stereotyped in your speech-correction work.   Children sense it immediately.   Although it is some trouble, I always make and keep individual notebooks for each child.   In this we collect our new sounds and words and record our achievements. This creates self-competition of the best type.   On the star page, they often ask me what each star was for, and this certainly seems to motivate them.

I find that I must watch fatigue and shift of attention closely. If I can prevent them during the first two weeks, I never have any further trouble with motivation. The children seldom need to know the reason for any activity; they merely need to share it.

I don't believe that we break old habits in young children. We always build new ones which displace the others. Thus I seldom use penalties of any kind or call attention to errors. Praise and social rewards for success seem more important.

Although I often can find wonderful rationalizations, I know deep in my heart that, whenever I have failed with a young child in getting rid of his defect, it is my fault, not his.

References

1. Ainsworth, S., "Suggestions for a Successful Speech Correction Program in Public Schools," *Quarterly Journal of Speech*, 1945, Vol. 31, pages 471–477.
Many excellent suggestions about public relations, co-operation from the classroom teacher, record keeping, and bulletins.

2. Backus, O. L., *Speech in Education*, New York, Longmans, Green, 1943, pages 89–113.
Relationships with the classroom teacher and parents to achieve better co-operation are sketched in detail.

3. Backus, O. L. and Dunn, H. M., "Experiments in the Synthesis of Clinical Methods into a Program of Rehabilitation," *Journal of Speech Disorders*, 1944, Vol. 9, pages 1–18.
Describes group activities in speech correction for different age groups.

4. Brown, F. M., "A State Auxiliary Program of Speech Correction," *Journal of Speech Disorders*, 1945, Vol. 10, pages 133–135.
Describes the working together of a central speech clinic and an itinerant clinic.

5. Chapman, M. E., "The Speech Clinician and the Classroom Teacher Co-operate in a Speech Correction Program," *Journal of Speech Disorders*, 1942, Vol. 7, pages 57–61.
Describes some bulletins used by the speech correctionist to get co-operation from the classroom teacher, and describes the duties of the speech-correction teacher.

6. Eckelman, D., "The Speech Correctionist Talks with the Classroom Teacher," *Elementary English Review*, 1945, Vol. 22, pages 157–162.
Describes speech improvement and speech correction procedures and gives a classification of speech disorders often found in the classroom.

7. Fishel, M. V., "What the Elementary Teachers Can and Cannot Do in Speech Correction," *Proceedings of the American Speech Correction Association*, 1936, Vol. 6, pages 89–94.
A collection of brief case studies of speech-defective cases in the Janesville, Wisconsin, school who were aided by elementary teachers after the correct

diagnosis had been made by a speech teacher and the therapy had been suggested by her.   These teachers were, in general, those who had had some voice or speech training, those with exceptional personalities, and those who co-operated with the special teacher in working on some of the more simple speech defects.   A plea is made for more adequate teacher training in speech.

8. Milisen, R., "Introducing Speech Correction into a New School System," *Journal of Speech Disorders*, 1939, Vol. 4, pages 241–245.
Outlines the problems often met in introducing speech-correction services for the first time.   Many practical suggestions are given.

9. Morris, D. W., "The Speech Survey," *Journal of Speech Disorders*, 1939, Vol. 4, pages 195–198.
Describes the best methods for making a survey of speech defects.

10. Mulgrave, D. I., *Speech for the Classroom Teacher* (revised edition), New York, Prentice-Hall, 1946.
The part which the classroom teacher may play in speech correction is discussed—her attitude, her co-operation with the special speech-correction teacher, and some general considerations and suggestions regarding remedial measures.

11. Raubicheck, L., "The Speech Training Laboratory, An Abstract," *Proceedings of the American Speech Correction Association*, 1936, Vol. 6, pages 127–129.
This brief article gives the advantages of laboratory practice in speech and voice problems, the types of groups handled there, and the four parts of each clinical period which the teacher has supervised.

12. Routh, R., "Remedial Speech Work in the Indiana State Teachers College Laboratory School," *Teachers College Journal*, March, 1937, Vol. 8, No. 4, pages 33–40.
A description of a speech-correction project in a demonstration school. Individual diagnosis, methods, and results of treatment are discussed.

13. Schuell, H., "Working with Speech Defectives in Public Schools," *Journal of Speech Disorders*, 1939, Vol. 4, pages 241–245.
Describes the problems of the speech correctionist in her everyday work, the types of cases, the variety of techniques, and the need for co-operation.

14. Wells, C. G., "Expanding State Speech Correction Services," *Journal of Speech Disorders*, 1945, Vol. 10, pages 123–128.
Various plans for providing speech-correction services on a state-wide basis are described and discussed.

15. Young, J. A., "A City and County Speech Re-education Program," *Journal of Speech Disorders*, 1942, Vol. 7, pages 51–56.
Describes how a speech-correction service was established in a county which could not afford it.

APPENDIX

The Case History

Administering the case history. While the parents or the case himself is usually the source of most of the information, it is generally necessary to interview other associates of the speech defective. Former teachers, the family doctor, welfare investigators, and neighbors or friends may be called upon. The speech defective is often asked to get the co-operation of his former associates in determining the early symptoms or reactions toward his speech defect. These individuals often provide more information than the parents. While the majority of questions should be made as pointed as possible, a few general questions appropriate to the material in each major section should be used. Questions should be phrased so that the influence of suggestion will not prejudice the answer. An exception to this rule, however, is found in the recommendation that delicate questions be asked so as to favor an affirmative answer. Answers should be recorded immediately, and the examiner should master a system of abbreviations or shorthand so that there will be no delay. He should always distinguish in the recording between the person's actual answers and his own interpretation of those answers. The examiner should perfect himself in the art of interrupting irrelevant vocal wanderings and bringing the parent back to the point in question. It is unwise to have the child present during questioning of the parent, and except when the relationship between parents is being studied, it is wiser to question only one at a time. The summary of important case-history findings should be written up as soon as possible.

The case histories given here are phrased in the form of direct questions. This policy was chosen because the text is intended for beginning students in speech correction, and experience has shown the author that such students require this guidance. It must be emphasized repeatedly that each question is merely the first of a series of supplemental queries when the answer indicates that vital information

may be forthcoming.   No examiner will ask all the questions, nor will
he confine himself to them alone.

The case histories which follow are of two types, general and special.   The general case history may be considered the device used to
procure a picture of the individual's background and physical, mental,
personality, and speech development.   A shorter form of this history
may be obtained by using only the starred items for exploration.
Demands upon the teacher's time and the overwhelming case load
frequently experienced in public-school work occasionally necessitate
this compromise, but the short case history is seldom used except for
certain simple types of articulatory or voice cases.   In addition to the
general case history, the appropriate special case history should be
used.   Even as the general case history is used for exploration of the
person having the speech defect, so the special case history is used to
tap the parent's fund of information concerning the causes, development, and consequences of the speech defect itself.

GENERAL CASE HISTORY

Person Interviewed.............................. Interviewer...........................
Name of Case........................... Date of Birth............... Sex...........
Address.................................... Telephone Number...............
Rapport..

1. Father
     *Name..
      Age (if dead, date and cause of death)...
      Handedness............... Education............... Occupation...............
      Religion.................... Health..................... Nationality..............
     *Type of speech defect, if any..
      Type of physical defect, if any...
      Nervous diseases.. Excesses (liquor,
      drugs, etc.)..
      Marital history (separation, divorce, previous marriage, etc.)
      ....
      ....
      Attitude toward child's defect...

2. Mother
     *Name..
      Age (if dead, date and cause of death)...
      Handedness............... Education............... Occupation ....
      Religion.................... Health..................... Nationality..............
     *Type of speech defect, if any..

GENERAL CASE HISTORY (*Continued*)

Type of physical defect, if any..

Nervous diseases..

Marital history..

Attitude toward child's defect...

3. **Other** relatives (Write number of people having the following disorders)

	Physical Defect	Speech Defect	Other Important Information
*Brothers			
*Sisters			
Mat. Grandmother			
Mat. Grandfather			
Mat. Aunts			
Mat. Uncles			
Pat. Grandmother			
Pat. Grandfather			
Pat. Aunts			
Pat. Uncles			
Other persons living in home			

BIRTH HISTORY

Give age of the mother at the beginning of the pregnancy............................

Age of the father.................... Number of months of pregnancy....................

Weight of child at birth.................... Length of body at birth....................

Prenatal Conditions

Give the approximate weight and height of the mother at the beginning
of this pregnancy..   ....

Was mother working during the pregnant period?..

If so, what kind of work?.. How soon did she
stop before the birth?..

How soon did she resume her activities after the birth?........................

What was the condition of the mother's health during pregnancy?
Good, fair, poor. Was mother able to eat regularly and retain the
food?..

Did mother have any severe shocks during pregnancy?............................

Injuries?..

Was mother examined by a physician before and during pregnancy?

....

Was the pelvis measured?..

BIRTH HISTORY (*Continued*)

What comments did the doctor make?..
Will you furnish us with the name and address of the physician?
Name...
Address...
                    Street   City   State

Birth and Postnatal Conditions

Number of hours of labor, including the time from the first pains until
   the expulsion of the afterbirth...
*At birth was the baby delivered feet first, head first, breech (hip) first,
   or by Caesarean operation?..
*Did delivery necessitate the use of instruments?..
*Were there any injuries?........................ If so, where?...
.... Did baby have difficulty initiating
breathing?........................... If so, how was breathing started?.............
.... How long was it before he started
breathing normally?............................ Did he cry as soon as he was
born?............... Was it loud?............... feeble?............... Did he nurse
as soon as he was placed at the breast or did he need to be coaxed?
.... How long did this condition last?..................................
Did he move around much the first two or three days or was he
still and quiet?... Was his pulse strong,
weak, slow, fast, normal?...
Was the soft spot on the top of the head soft and concave or hard
and bulging?...
Did the baby have convulsions?...................................... blueness of the
body, lips, or feet?... slow blood clotting
time?... slight bleeding about the nose and
mouth?... twitchings of the muscles of the
face?........................... Was he one of a pair of twins?...........................
If so, was he the strong or weak one?..
Did the head have an abnormal molding immediately after birth?
.... Was mother attended by a doctor, nurse,
midwife, others?...

DEVELOPMENTAL HISTORY

1. Was baby breast fed?........................... For how long?...........................
2. Why was he weaned?...
3. Was baby bottle fed?........................... For how long?...........................
4. Did the bottle milk agree with him?..

DEVELOPMENTAL HISTORY (*Continued*)

5. Were both fontanelles closed before child was 20 months old?
....

*6. Was the child's rate of growth seemingly normal?................................
If not, why not?..

*7. Give age in months at which the following took place:
First tooth............................ Full set of teeth...........................
Full set of second teeth... Creeping on all
fours........................... Sitting alone........................ Walking alone
.... Feeding self........................ Got voluntary control
of bowels... Got voluntary control of
bladder............................ Using spoon............................ Using any
object as tool..
Do you have any other information with regard to the child's
development?..

*8. The following is a list of common childhood diseases. Please give
age of child when disease occurred, whether it was serious or mild,
whether the child had a high fever, and any noticeable effects which
followed it:
   Tonsilitis
   Whooping cough
   Pneumonia
   Scarlet fever
   Typhoid fever
   Tuberculosis
   Pleurisy
   Chicken pox
   Smallpox
   Influenza
   Diphtheria
   Measles
   Mumps
   St. Vitus dance
   Convulsions
   Rickets
   Enlarged glands
   Heart trouble
   Rheumatism
   Thyroid disturbances
   Nervous trouble
   Infantile paralysis
   Any others

9. Was child excessively spoiled and indulged because of his illness?
....

Developmental History (*Continued*)

*10. Has child ever been seriously injured?　State nature, age at injury, and effects..

11. Was the child: very active?...................; fairly active?...................; very inactive?............................

12. Would you say that the child was slow, average, or rapid in his general development up to three years of age?............................

Present Physical Condition of Child

*1. What is the child's weight........................... and height........................... at present time?

*2. Does the child have any physical deformities?........................... What are they?...........................

3. Has the child had a physical examination lately?........................... What were the main findings of his examination?........................... Who was the physician?...........................

4. Is there any abnormality in the following:
  a. Size of tongue...........................
  b. Protrusion of upper or lower jaws...........................
  c. Arrangement of teeth...........................
  d. Palate...........................
  e. Nasal passages...........................

5. Has he ever had tonsils and adenoids removed?........................... Tongue-tie clipped?...........................

6. Does the child have any defect in hearing?........................... Seeing?...........................

7. Is the child usually in good health at the present time?...........................

*8. Is he: very energetic?...................; fairly energetic?...................; not very energetic?...........................

Co-ordination

Check the following items according to whether the child shows inferior, average, or superior skill:

Gracefulness	Dancing	Skipping	Jumping
Throwing	Catching	Kicking	Sewing
Cutting	Drawing	Writing	

Mental and Educational Development

1. Has the child ever had a mental or intelligence test?........................... What was the name of the test used?...........................

2. What was the I.Q. obtained, or general ranking?...........................

*3. If the child is in school, in what grade is he at present?...........................

*4. Are his marks above average, average, or below average?...........................

DEVELOPMENTAL HISTORY (*Continued*)

*5. Has the child ever failed a grade?............................... Has he ever
skipped a grade?........................ Which one?.................

*6. What are the highest marks the child has ever received?..................
.... In what subjects?...

*7. What are the poorest marks the child has ever received?..................
.... In what subjects?............................:

8. Is the child frequently tardy?........................ Why?.................

9. Does the child play truant?..

10. Has the child been absent from school very often?..................
If so, for what reason?.................................

11. Has the child been punished by his teacher?.............................
Why?...

*12. Does the child like school?............................ If not, why not?

....

13. Which of his teachers does the child like most?...........................

....

14. Teacher's name.................................... School...................

15. What other schools has the child attended?...........................
When?...

Handedness

1. Have the child's hands ever been bandaged, tied up, or restrained
in any way?............................ For what reason and how long?

....

2. At what age did he show a definite tendency to favor one hand
while eating?.................... Which hand?.................... Up to
that age, did the child use either or both hands indiscriminately?

....

*3. Did anyone ever try to influence his handedness in order to change
him from left to right or vice versa?.............................
How?...

4. What is the attitude of the father toward left-handedness?.............

....

5. What is the attitude of the mother toward left-handedness?.............

....

6. Did any injuries or illnesses ever change his handedness?..................

....

*7. Has child ever written backward?......................................

*8. Are there any activities which he can do better or as well with the
usually nonpreferred hand?.................... What are
they?...

Play

1. Give names and ages of the three children with whom the child
plays most often...

DEVELOPMENTAL HISTORY (*Continued*)

*2. Is the child the follower or the leader?.................................... .

 3. Do they tease the child?..

 4. Do they fight with him?..

 5. Do they get along with him?.......................... Do any of them have speech defects?..

 6. What games does he prefer to play?..................................

 7. What toys does he prefer?..

*8. Does he play alone as well as he does with other children?.............

....

 9. Does he prefer to play alone?..

*10. Which parent does the child prefer?.................................. Why?

....

*11. Which playmate does the child prefer?............................... Why?

....

 12. Who took care of the child when the mother was absent?...............

....

Language Development

*1. How many months old was the child when he began to say single words?...; simple sentences and phrases?...

 2. What were the first single words spoken?..............................

 3. Give any other examples of the child's early speech with the approximate dates for each..

....

 4. What method was used in teaching the child to talk?.................

....

  a. Who did most of it?..

 *b. Do you feel that the child was overstimulated or understimulated with respect to speech?.................................

  c. Did he understand what was said to him before he had learned to talk?..

 *d. Did anyone talk baby talk to child?............................ Who?..

  e. Did anyone use double-talking to child?........................ Who?.. (Double-talking is like this: We-we-will-will-go-go.)

  f. Were the child's wants usually anticipated before he could communicate the need?..

  g. Did the child gesture much in attempting to communicate?

....

  h. Do you think that the child's present vocabulary is superior, average, or inferior to other children his age?.................

  i. Did the child often surprise you by using large words?.........

....

DEVELOPMENTAL HISTORY (*Continued*)

j. Did the child habitually mispronounce certain words?............

Give samples..................

5. Were there any sounds that he could not say?...............
   Which?..................

*6. Did the child ever lisp?....................... Describe.................

*7. Was the child taught to speak pieces?...................... Was he often called upon to perform before strangers or friends of the family?..................
   What was his usual attitude toward such demands?..................

8. Has there ever been any tongue-tie?.......................... Cleft palate?...................... Harelip?..................

9. Was there any marked articulatory defect?..................

10. Describe the rate, intensity, and pitch of child's speech with respect to its being rapid-average-slow; loud-average-soft; high-average-low

*11. Did the child ever tend to say words backward ("got for" instead of "forgot," etc.)?.......................... Give examples:

*12. Was the child generally retarded in speech development?...............

13. Was the child very talkative, average, or rather silent and quiet?

14. Was any foreign language taught to the child or commonly spoken by his associates?..................

Home

1. In what type of community is the home located: rural, town, city?

2. Do the parents own or rent the home?..................

3. How many rooms in the house?..................

4. Check the following items in possession of the family: car; piano; radio; 100 or more books; daily newspaper; gas, oil, or electric kitchen stove.

*5. Check word which most nearly describes economic condition of family: very poor; poor; comfortable circumstances; well-to-do.

6. Check phrase which most nearly describes father's attitude with an "F," and phrase which describes mother's attitude with an "M."
   a. Has no cultural interests (seems to live only to work and eat)..................
   b. Has slight interest in other people's experiences, likes radio, likes magazine stores, does some social visiting..................

DEVELOPMENTAL HISTORY (*Continued*)

    c. Has a hobby in some creative field (music, pictures, cabinet-making, gardening, reading, etc.)...

    d. Takes a specialized interest in one of the arts: reads widely; is aware of other places and times; discriminating taste.

7. Is there family friction with regard to money matters, religion, or anything else?...................... Is child aware of it?......................
8. Are both parents usually at home in the evening?......................
9. Does the child have plenty of playthings or amusements?......................

10. Are the neighbors congenial?...................... Do the parents like the neighbors?......................
11. Do the parents play with the children?......................
12. Has the child ever lived in another town?......................
*13. Of what things is the father proudest?......................
*14. Of what things is the mother proudest?......................
*15. What things have made the father unhappy?......................
*16. What things have made the mother unhappy?......................
*17. Of what things is the child proudest?......................
*18. What things have made the child unhappy?......................

*Childhood Problems

Following is a list of common childhood problems. Indicate how often these problems occurred in this child by encircling the letter which most clearly describes it. O indicates that it occurs often, S indicates seldom, and N indicates never.

1. Nervousness	O S N	16. Tongue sucking	O S N
2. Sleeplessness	O S N	17. Hurting pets	O S N
3. Nightmares	O S N	18. Setting fires	O S N
4. Bed wetting	O S N	19. Constipation	O S N
5. Playing with sex		20. Thumb sucking	O S N
organs	O S N	21. Face twitching	O S N
6. Walking in sleep	O S N	22. Fainting	O S N
7. Shyness	O S N	23. Strong fears	O S N
8. Showing off	O S N	24. Strong hates	O S N
9. Refusal to obey	O S N	25. Queer food habits	O S N
10. Rudeness	O S N	26. Temper tantrums	O S N
11. Fighting	O S N	27. Whining	O S N
12. Jealousy	O S N	28. Stealing	O S N
13. Selfishness	O S N	29. Running away	O S N
14. Lying	O S N	30. Destructiveness	O S N
15. Smoking	O S N		

31. How did the child's associates (parents, etc.) react to these problems?..

DEVELOPMENTAL HISTORY (*Continued*)

32. How is the child usually disciplined and who does it?...................

33. What types of discipline are most effective?.....................
Least effective?...................

Adult Developmental History

Vocational
1. What opportunities did the case have for earning money as a child?
....

2. Did he have an adequate allowance?.....................
3. What positions have been held? Give salary, working conditions, length of time employed, reason for leaving.....................

Educational
1. Preferred subjects in secondary schools and college...................

2. Subjects disliked...................
3. Attitudes toward instructors...................
4. Extra-curricular activities...................
5. Scholastic record...................
6. Reasons for quitting school...................
7. Conflicts with school authorities...................

Sexual experiences (Indicate type, frequency, and attitudes toward activity)

Social
1. Favorite associates...................
2. Disliked associates...................
3. Recreational activities...................
4. Arrests, probations, commitments to institutions...................

SPECIAL CASE HISTORIES

Articulation Cases
1. Has the child ever had any other speech defect?...................

2. Was the child slow in learning to talk? In what way? Did he ever lose his speech entirely?...................

3. With which sounds did he seem to have most trouble?...................

4. Did he ever have a mouth injury?...................

Special Case Histories (*Continued*)

5. Was he ever tongue-tied?..

6. Has he had his tonsils and adenoids out? Did any speech defect result?..

7. Has the child ever had any other mouth or throat operation? ....

8. Did the child ever wear a brace on his teeth?..

9. What dental work has been done?..

10. Did the child have any accident to his first set of teeth?..

11. Was his first set of teeth malformed?..

12. Has the child's speech shown any improvement recently?..

13. With what sounds or words does the child have trouble?..

14. Does he have most trouble with these sounds at the beginning, middle, or end of words?..

15. Do you think the child's speech disorder may be due in part to:
    a. Being stimulated by baby talk?..

    b. Being stimulated by foreign or vulgar speech?..

    c. Lack of proper training by parents?..

    d. Negativism or refusal to conform to the speech standards of the parents?..

16. What else may have caused it?..

17. At what age did his speech difficulty begin?..

18. Has it ever entirely disappeared?..

19. What has been done to correct it?..

20. Can you give us any other information about his speech?..

21. How sensitive is the child about his defect?..

22. Is he scolded or teased about it?..

23. Can the child carry a tune? Is his hearing normal?..

Special Case Histories (*Continued*)

Voice Cases—General

1. Is the subject able to produce any voice at all? Has he ever lost his voice? Has he ever overstrained it?..

2. What differences appeared after puberty?..

3. Can the subject carry a tune alone? In unison?..

4. What throat diseases or injuries has he had?..

5. Is his voice like that of any other member of the family or any habitual companion?..

6. What do you think caused the disorder?..

7. Are there certain conditions or situations which make it worse? At what times is it most noticeable?..

8. Has the subject been under any prolonged emotional strain?............

9. Is the child sensitive about his voice?..

10. What has been done to correct his voice defect?..

11. Has the child habitually spoken through clenched teeth or out of the side of his mouth for any length of time?..

12. Does the child do a lot of whining? Screeching?..

13. Does the child seem to be much more tense than the average child?

14. Has the child ever talked in a monotone or used a peculiar pitch level?..

15. Does there seem to be any retardation in sexual development? ....

Nasality and Denasality

1. Has the child's voice always been nasal?..

2. Are there times when he speaks without nasality? When?............

3. What vowels does he nasalize most?..

4. What consonants?..

5. Have his adenoids and tonsils been removed? When, and how bad were they?..

  6. Has he ever had any injury to his nose or throat?...........................

  7. Do any others of the child's family or acquaintances speak in a nasal tone?...........................

  8. Has the pitch of the child's voice always been about as high as it is now?...........................

  9. Has the child been under any prolonged emotional tension or nervous strain?   Is there anyone else in the family who shows such a condition?...........................

10. Is the child aware of his peculiar voice quality?   Is he sensitive or ashamed about it?...........................

11. When he lowers his voice and relaxes, does he have as much nasality?

12. Has the child suffered much from head colds or catarrh?...........................

13. Has the child ever had an operation on his nose?...........................

14. Can the child gargle?...........................
15. Has the child ever had sinus trouble?...........................

Delayed-Speech Cases

  1. Is the child superior, average, or inferior mentally?...........................

  2. Is the child hard of hearing?...........................
  3. Has the child ever had any disease or trouble with his ears?...........................

  4. Are there any deaf people in the child's immediate family?...........................

  5. Has the child ever shown short periods of speech?...........................

  6. Did the child ever have more speech than he does now?...........................

  7. Has the child ever uttered words under strong emotion which he has never said since?...........................

  8. Has the child ever seemed to have periods when he could not understand other people's speech?...........................

  9. Were there any injuries to the mouth?...........................

10. Were there any bad shocks during speech?...........................

SPECIAL CASE HISTORIES (*Continued*)

11. Were there any serious illnesses during the first year?.....................

12. Were two languages spoken in the home?...

13. Has the child ever been punished for speaking or during speech?
....

14. Is the child a twin?...............
15. Did the parents overstimulate or understimulate the child?.............

16. What people did the child dislike during the first two years?...........
....

17. Is the child ambidextrous?..........................
18. Was the child jealous of any other person?...................................
....

19. Does the child use his silence as a way of getting more attention?
....

20. Has the child ever had any sudden fainting spells? Paralysis?
....

21. Is the child isolated too much?..
....

22. How do the parents try to teach him to talk?...............................
....

23. Are the child's wants usually anticipated and fulfilled before he
expresses them?..
....

24. What sort of speech standard do the parents insist upon?.............
....

25. What history of negativism is present?.......................................
....

26. Check: threats; severe punishment; speech conflicts; competition
for speech; impatience; attitudes of parents and other children.
....

Stuttering Cases

History of stuttering
1. Give approximate or exact date at which stuttering was first noticed.
....

2. Within the month immediately preceding the appearance of stuttering, did the child experience:
a. A severe fright?...............
b. A severe shock of any kind?.........................
....
c. Severe sickness with high fever?...............
d. Severe punishment?...

SPECIAL CASE HISTORIES (*Continued*)

    e. A great deal of excitement or emotional upset?...................

    f. A situation involving great need for immediate communication in which he was unable to say what he wanted to?

    g. A situation involving communication but without sufficient vocabulary to enable him to continue?...................

    h. A situation in which he tried but was unable to compete successfully for attention or speech?...................

    i. A change in social environment?...................

    j. Use of the nonpreferred hand?...................

    k. Peculiarities in sexual behavior?...................

    l. Thyroid disturbances?...................
    m. Any other?...................

3. Did any other defect occur at the same time that stuttering did?
....

4. Who first noticed the stuttering?...................

5. In what situation was it first noticed or commented upon? Under what circumstances did it occur?...................

6. Were the first signs of stuttering repetitions of the whole word (boy-boy-boy); or repetitions of the first letter (b-b-boy); or repetitions of the first syllable (ca-ca-cat); or complete blocks on the first letter (b...oy); or prolongations of the vowel (caaaaaaat)?

7. If repetitions, about how many times did they occur before the word came out?...................

    a. Were all signs of stuttering alike?...................

    b. Did the child stutter in several different ways?...................

    c. If so, in what ways did they differ from one another?...................

    d. Did the first blocks seem to be located in the tongue, lips, chest, diaphragm, or throat?...................

    e. About how long did each individual block (on one word) seem to last? (Imitate and time yourself.)...................

SPECIAL CASE HISTORIES (*Continued*)

    f. Did the child stutter easily or exert some force, much force, or terrible forcing at the time when you first noticed his stuttering?...

8. Were the words stuttered upon the words which began sentences, or were they scattered throughout the sentence?.....................................

9. Was the stuttering confined to one single word, or two or three words, or to no particular words?...

10. Were there any particular sounds with which he seemed at first to have more trouble? If so, what were they?.....................................

11. When stuttering first began, did the child ever avoid a speech situation because of his stuttering? Give examples, if any.....................

12. Did he pause noticeably before attempting a word?.............................

13. Did he ever repeat a word until he had said it without stuttering?

14. Did he ever prolong a word preceding the word stuttered upon?

15. Did he ever repeat a phrase several times before attempting the word upon which he stuttered?...

16. Having had trouble with a word in a sentence, did he ever repeat the whole sentence until it was said without any stuttering?...........

17. Did he ever obviously substitute another word for one with which he was having trouble?...

18. Having stuttered upon a word, did he increase the rate, pitch, or intensity of the other words which followed it?.....................................

19. At the time when stuttering was first noticed, did the child seem to be aware of the fact that he was speaking in a different manner?

20. Did he seem to be indifferent to his blocks?.....................................

21. Did he ever show surprise or bewilderment after he had had trouble on a word? If so, how did he show such reactions?.............................

22. Did the blocks at first seem to the stutterer to be unpleasant?

    a. Why do you think they were unpleasant, if they were?............

SPECIAL CASE HISTORIES (*Continued*)

b. Do you think he felt irritated with himself? Frustrated?

---

c. Did he ever show anger when anyone helped him with the word?

d. If not, what was his reaction?

---

e. Did he ever show any fear of stuttering?

---

f. If so, how did he show it?

---

g. Did he ever show any shame as a reaction to stuttering?

---

h. If so, how did he show it?

---

i. Did he ever show any flushing? Paleness? Eye-bulging? Heart-pounding? Gasping? Sweating? Peculiar body movement as a reaction to his stuttering?

---

23. Did the child ever seem conscious of his stuttering in any way at first? If so, amplify your answer. After having a lot of trouble on a word, did he ever:
    a. Suddenly stop trying?
    b. Suddenly leave the speech situation?

    ---

    c. Shout the word? Cry? Hit someone? Smash something? Spit upon somebody? Hide his face? Laugh? Do something else?

    ---

    d. Seem to be a little more careful with his speech in attempting words on which he had difficulty? How? By lowering voice? By slowing down? By ceasing other bodily activity for the moment? By looking straight ahead of him for the moment? By shifting his gaze away from the listener? Any other way?

    ---

24. What attempts have been made to treat the child for his stuttering?

---

25. At the time when stuttering was first noticed, were there any situations in which he seemed to have more trouble? If so, what were they?

26. Were there any people to whom he stuttered more often? Who?

---

27. Were there any topics of conversation with which he had more trouble?

28. Did he seem to have more trouble when narrating something?

---

29. When asking questions?..

30. When answering questions?..

31. When interrupting?...

32. Did he ever stutter when overheard talking to himself?.............

33. Did he talk to children with less trouble than to adults?................

34. Did excitement seem to cause more stuttering?...............................

35. Did he talk to strangers with less trouble than to people he knew well?..

36. At the time when stuttering began, did fatigue, fear, illness, or pressing need for communication seem to cause more trouble?

37. Did he stutter more on words which were new to him and which he had not used or did not use often as yet?.....................................

38. Did he stutter more or stutter less on words which he had been using a long time—that is, "pet" words or stock phrases?..................

39. Did the child speak any languages besides English?   Which ones? Did he stutter more or less in these languages than in English?

40. When talking without stuttering, did he seem more active generally and more animated or lively—"more in the spirit of speaking"— than when stuttering?..

41. When saying something on the spur of the moment—blurting it out as though he had given no thought to what he was going to say— did he stutter more or less than when he seemed to decide what he was going to say before speaking?...

Development of stuttering

1. Since the stuttering first began, has there been any change in the stuttering symptoms?..

2. Did you notice a gradual increase in the number of repetitions per word stuttered upon?..

3. Did you notice a gradual increase in the number of times the stuttering occurred?...

4. Were there any instances in which the number of troublesome words and number of repetitions suddenly increased?..............................

SPECIAL CASE HISTORIES (*Continued*)

5. Were there any periods (week or month) when this seemed to have occurred?...

6. Can you give any explanation for these "bad" periods?........................

7. If possible, give their approximate dates and causes.............................

8. Did there seem to be any period of change from repetitions as the usual form of stuttering to complete blocks (b-b-boy to b...oy)?

9. Was there ever a time in which repetitions began to end in complete (though temporary) blocks (b b b...oy)?.................................

10. Was there ever any time when complete blocks were released in the form of repetitions (b.....b boy)?..

11. Has there been an increase in the length of time the complete block lasts? (Was it "b..oy" at first, and "b........oy" now?)....................
....

12. When the complete blocks first appeared, upon what sounds or words were they noticed?..

13. Did the child force when the complete blocks were first experienced or was there a mere holding of the posture until release came?

14. Did the amount of forcing increase as time passed?...........................

15. Did it seem to be localized in any particular part of the speech organs, at first: lips, tongue, jaws, throat, chest, entire body?

16. Did there seem to be any spreading of the forcing from one of the above speech organs to others? Explain...

17. Did the stutterer ever force on the repetitions of sound or syllable?

18. If the stutterer has any facial spasms or grimaces, give approximate date of their first occurrence, and describe their nature (how they look, what he does, etc.). Can you account for their appearance? Explain what you think caused them..
....

References

1. American Association of Social Workers, "Interviews," *Studies in Practice of Social Work*, 1931, No. 1.
This study considers the place of the interview in case work, involving both

psychological and sociological techniques. Types of interviews are discussed, and an outline for recording and analysis is given. Examples of both narrative and dialogue forms of interviews are given.

2. Hanks, L. M., "Prediction from Case Material to Personality Test Data," *Archives of Psychology*, 1936, Vol. 29, No. 207.
This author shows the reliability of the interview.

3. Kanner, L. and Lachman, S. E., "The Contribution of Physical Illness to the Development of Behavior Disorders in Children," *Mental Hygiene*, 1934, Vol. 17, pages 605–617.

Index